INTERNATIONAL SERIES OF MONOGRAPHS IN
EARTH SCIENCES

Editor: Dean Earl Ingerson

Department of Geology, University of Texas, Austin, Texas, U.S.A.

Volume 29

TRANSFORMATION OF PETROLEUM IN NATURE

TRANSFORMATION OF PETROLEUM IN NATURE

BY

P. F. ANDREEV, A. I. BOGOMOLOV
A. F. DOBRYANSKII, A. A. KARTSEV

TRANSLATION BY

ROBERT B. GAUL
Ventura, California

AND

BRUNO C. METZNER
Cranford, New York

TRANSLATION EDITED BY

E. BARGHOORN
Harvard University

AND

S. SILVERMAN
Chevron Research Co.,
La Habra, California

THE QUEEN'S AWARD
TO INDUSTRY 1966

PERGAMON PRESS

OXFORD · LONDON · EDINBURGH · NEW YORK
TORONTO · SYDNEY · PARIS · BRAUNSCHWEIG

Pergamon Press Ltd., Headington Hill Hall, Oxford
4 & 5 Fitzroy Square, London W. 1

Pergamon Press (Scotland) Ltd., 2 & 3 Teviot Place, Edinburgh 1

Pergamon Press Inc., 44–01 21st Street, Long Island City, New York 11101

Pergamon of Canada Ltd., 207 Queen's Quay West, Toronto 1

Pergamon Press (Aust.) Pty. Ltd., 19a Boundary Street, Rushcutters Bay,
N.S.W. 2011, Australia

Pergamon Press S.A.R.L., 24 rue des Écoles, Paris 5^e

Vieweg & Sohn GmbH, Burgplatz 1, Braunschweig

First English edition 1968

This translation is published on behalf
of the Geochemical Society and was made possible
by funds granted to the Society
by the National Science Foundation

Library of Congress Catalog Card No. 68–18516

08 012450 x

CONTENTS

TRANSLATION EDITOR'S PREFACE

THE APPEARANCE of this English edition of *Transformation of Petroleum in Nature* will be welcomed by petroleum geologists and geochemists as an important contribution to the literature of petroleum geochemistry. The content and scope of this volume are adequately covered by the prefacing remarks of Professor Dobryanskii, editor of the original version. Although the work is made up of contributions by four different authors, it does not suffer from lack of continuity or overall unanimity of purpose.

During the visit of the American delegation of petroleum geochemists to the USSR in October 1962, each of the authors was informed of the Geochemical Society's interest in preparing an English translation of the book for publication.When asked whether anything should be added to, deleted from, or otherwise modified in the existing version to bring it up to date, the authors indicated that nothing had arisen in the intervening four years to alter the basic concepts presented in the book. Bogomolov suggested that certain of his later papers [1, 2, 3, 4, 5, 6]† contained data that provide additional arguments and logical explanations for some of the proposed transformation processes, and Kartsev indicated that he preferred the general conclusions presented in his brief contribution [7] prepared for the 1962 international meeting on "Organic Processes in Geochemistry" to the summary statements in the sections he prepared for the present volume.

Although each of these later publications contains additional data that suggest specific reaction mechanisms and generally strengthen pre-existing evidence for certain preferred directions of petroleum transformation, they do not alter the general conclusions offered in the original version. Bogomolov's papers deal with the results of low temperature (150–250°C) conversions and possible reaction mechanisms involved in the alteration of specific organic compounds and certain hydrocarbon mixtures in the presence of clays. Oleic

† Numbers refer to references at end of Preface.

and stearic acids, for example, after a 10 hr exposure at 250°C, produce mixtures of paraffinic, naphthenic, and aromatic hydrocarbons in proportions characteristic of crude petroleums [4, 5]. Conversion of beeswax [6] under similar experimental conditions yields a broad molecular-weight range of paraffins (chiefly isoparaffins), high molecular-weight resins, but relatively insignificant amounts of aromatics and naphthenes. Cetane (n-hexadecane) subjected to similar conditions [1] also yields a mixture composed predominantly of paraffins and isoparaffins; aromatics are present in minor amounts and naphthenes are absent. Polycyclic naphthenic-aromatic hydrocarbon mixtures [2], separated from the 450–500°C fractions of two petroleums, when heated to 250° for 8 hr in the presence of activated clay (gumbrin) are converted to low molecular-weight paraffins, asphaltic-resinous materials, and new naphthenic–aromatic hybrid complexes in which aromatic rings predominate over naphthenic rings (aromatic–naphthenic complexes in the original mixture contained approximately equal proportions of naphthenic and aromatic rings). Catalytic conversion [3] at 150°C for 8 hr of a 500–550°C petroleum fraction, composed largely of high molecular-weight polycyclic naphthenes and minor amounts of isoparaffins, resulted in the formation of low molecular-weight hydrocarbons in the gasoline, kerosene, and light gas-oil boiling ranges along with tarry products with low hydrogen content and a high carbon content residue left on the clay.† For this experiment, results of conversion with both activated and unactivated clays were reported. Readers interested in Professor Kartsev's later views on the geochemical transformation of petroleum are referred to his 1962 summary article in an English volume [7].

Some of the terminology used in this volume may be unfamiliar because not all Russian terms have exact English equivalents. The meanings of most of these, however, will be evident to the serious reader; some of the more obscure terms are explained in footnotes. In several instances, obvious typographical errors in the Russian text were corrected. Wherever feasible, and especially in critical sections where direct translations resulted in awkward or unintelligible English versions, the original text was retranslated and then reworded to provide a coherent and intelligible exposition of what was judged to be the author's intended meaning of the passage. Be-

† An English translation of this paper is available in *J. Appl. Chem. USSR*, *33*, 1960, 2721–5.

cause of the frequency of such passages in certain parts of the book, editing of the translation proved to be a difficult and time-consuming task for me as well as for Professor Elso S. Barghoorn, who devoted considerable time and effort to improving the translation of the first three chapters, and also for Professor Earl Ingerson, who helped clarify some of the more obscure passages in the early parts of the book.

The product of these efforts offers to the world of English-speaking and -reading petroleum scientists a wealth of experimental data and a comprehensive statement of the thermodynamic principles governing petroleum transformations. And now that geochemical evidence is being cited more and more frequently in publications and enunciations dealing with origin, accumulation, and alteration of petroleum, it behoves every petroleum geologist and geochemist to be aware of the contents of this book.

Chevron Research Company
La Habra, California   S. R. SILVERMAN

REFERENCES

1. BOGOMOLOV, A. I. and KHOTYNTSEVA, L. I. Contact-catalytic conversions of cetane (Kontaktno-Kataliticheskie Prevrashcheniya Tsetana), in *Low-temperature Catalytic Conversion of Hydrocarbons (Nizkotemperaturnye Kataliticheskie Prevrashcheniya Uglevodorodov)*, Leningrad, 1962, pp. 54–62.
2. BOGOMOLOV, A. I. and PANINA, K. I. Low-temperature catalytic conversions of Naphthenic–aromatic mixtures from petroleum in connection with the problem of their genesis (Nizkotemperaturnye Kataliticheskie Prevrasheniya Smeshannykh Naftenovo–Aromaticheskikh Uglevodorodov Nefti v Svyazi s Voprosom ikh Genezisa), *ibid*, pp. 82–95.
3. BOGOMOLOV, A. I. and PANINA, K. I. Low-temperature catalytic conversions of high molecular-weight naphthenic hydrocarbons from petroleum in presence of natural clay (Nizkotemperaturnye Kataliticheskie Prevrashecheniya Vysokomolekulyarnykh Naftenovykh Uglevodorodov Nefti nad Prirodnoi Glinoi), *Zhur. Prikl. Khimii*, *33*, 1960, 2757–62.
4. BOGOMOLOV, A. I., KHOTYNTSEVA, L. I., and PANINA, K. I. Low-temperature catalytic conversions of organic compounds over clays (conversion of stearic acid), [Nizkotemperaturnye Kataliticheskie Prevrashcheniya Organicheskikh Soedinenii nad Glinami (Prevrashchenie StearinovoiKisloty)], *Trudy VNIGRI*, *Geokhimicheskii Sbornik*, No. 6, Issue 155, Gostoptekhizdat, Leningrad, 1960, pp. 163–93.
5. BOGOMOLOV, A. I. and PANINA, K. I. Low temperature conversions of organic compounds over clay II. Conversion of oleic acid (Nizkotemperaturnye Ka-

taliticheskie Prevrashcheniya Organicheskikh Soedinenii nad Glinoi III. Prevrashchenie Oleinovoi Kisloty), *Trudy VNIGRI, Geokhimicheskii Sbornik*, No. 7, Issue 174, Gostoptekhizdat, Leningrad, 1961, pp. 17–25.

6. BOGOMOLOV, A. I. and PANINA, K. I. Low-temperature conversions of organic compounds over clay III. Conversion of waxes (Nizkotemperaturnye Kataliticheskie Prevrascheniya Organicheskihk Soedinenii nad Glinoi III. Prevrashchenie Voskov), *ibid*, pp. 26–34.

7. KARTSEV, A. A. Geochemical transformation of petroleum, in *Advances in Organic Geochemistry*, Eds. U. Colombo and G. D. Hobson, MacMillan, New York, 1964, pp. 11–14.

FROM THE PUBLISHER
OF THE RUSSIAN EDITION

RECENT YEARS have been marked by an increased interest in the problem of petroleum formation, and especially in the closely related problems of the transformation of petroleum in nature. In spite of the significant advances which have been made in the knowledge of the geology and geochemistry of petroleum, many aspects of the complex processes involved in the formation and change of petroleum remain obscure. This explains the existence of divergent points of view.

An orderly discussion among authors having different opinions, when each one presents new facts and new arguments in support of his hypothesis and criticizes objectively the arguments of the adherents of other hypotheses, cannot fail to contribute to the advancement of science and thus to a more progressive development of geological exploration and prospecting for petroleum. The Leningrad State Printing House has therefore given the authors, who adhere to certain definite views, the opportunity to publish the present volume, although some of the basic positions supported in it are controversial.

Unfortunately, the authors have been unable to reach unanimity on all questions, although on the fundamental point—the dependency of the transformation of petroleum upon energy—a common point of view has indeed been found.

In summing up, it may be stated that, notwithstanding the fact that this work does not claim to provide a definitive solution to the problems treated, it is nevertheless of considerable value in that it points out possible ways for solving the interesting and important problem of the origin of petroleum and the changes occurring in it.

FROM THE EDITOR
OF THE RUSSIAN EDITION

DURING RECENT decades geologists and geochemists have more and more frequently noted a number of relationships between the properties of petroleum and the conditions under which it is found in the earth. Particularly evident is the connection between the age of petroleum and its chemical composition. This connection is detected not only in its group composition, but also in the composition of individual components, in the yield and properties of particular fractions, in the content of tar and wax, and in a number of physical properties. It may be stated that not a single property of petroleum is due to chance; that all its properties are related to each other, and, finally, that this can only be due to some basic principle which enables us to regard each kind of petroleum as a system in a state in which properties constantly change according to a definite plan as a result of definite energy relationships. Beginning with the earliest transformations of the original organic substance and continuing right up to its transformation into the end products—methane and carbon—all changes in petroleum follow the law of diminishing reserves of free energy of molecules. Approaching the problem in this manner enables us to reject at once a number of transformation factors which formerly were given much attention—in particular, the role played by natural external biological factors, the importance of high temperature, etc.

To explain the history of petroleum solely from the geological point of view without taking into account the chemistry of petroleum, or solely from the standpoint of chemical reactions apart from geological conditions, is to consider only one side of the phenomenon. Such an explanation obviously cannot help solve the problem of the origin of petroleum and its transformation in nature. Petroleum is formed and passes through its entire cycle of development with the constant interaction of geological and chemical factors, and although it is impossible at present to deduce the significance of these factors in each separate case, in no case can there be any doubt that petroleum is formed and is changed as a result of interaction with the surrounding medium. This is the fundamental assumption, although various specific factors of lesser importance may be involved such as sulfurization, petroleum oxidation, or biological action. The role of geochemistry is to identify the basic processes of change in those phenomena which, according to the law of probabilities, are the most likely to occur. It will no doubt be possible in the future to evaluate various supplementary factors which in many cases now obscure the general picture of petroleum transformation.

With regard to the problem of the origin of petroleum from preserved organic substances one may distinguish two aspects: one may consider the mechanism of chemical transformation itself—and naturally this is of greatest interest to chemists—but one may also consider the general direction of transformation, which indeed lies in the provinces of thermodynamics and geology. Although there can be no question about the organic origin of the source material of petroleum, the chemists have not yet established the mechanism of the transformation of this material into hydrocarbon mixtures, nor do experimental data shed sufficient light on this process or take into account probable geologic conditions. However, there is no question about the general thermodynamic direction of the process, and for the time being we should limit ourselves to this aspect of the problem of the origin of petroleum. Possibly, the chemical mechanism of the transformation of the original material will be understood when the experimenter finds out how to create conditions in the laboratory equivalent to those under which geologic processes operate.

This book does not set as its objective the solution of the problem of the origin of petroleum, because only a few general statements can be made in this direction. The objective of the book is to throw light on questions connected with the transformation of petroleum already formed as a system of mobile substances lacking the structural properties of the original source material.

The book is arranged according to a definite plan, which is intended to bring into harmony the geological and chemical interpretations of the entire question. This is a very difficult undertaking, and perhaps the collaboration of geologist and chemist can bring about a better solution. Unfortunately, there is still a rather large gap in the scientific background of specialists of both groups, which must necessarily be reflected in the varying scope of the problems to be solved and in bringing some of the particulars of the theme of petroleum transformation to one level.

The first chapters summarize and systematize the existing geological material on the question of the connection between the properties of petroleum and its geologic age, and, on the basis of broad statistical material, bring out the basic aspects of the natural phenomenon and explain the many observed deviations from this basic phenomenon. This part of the book is of interest to geologists and geochemists.

A considerable section of the book has been devoted to the thermodynamic transformation of hydrocarbons. The method of thermodynamic analysis employed by the authors allows them to evaluate the possibility, or even the probability, of many reactions which have been repeatedly proposed to explain the transformation of petroleum source material into hydrocarbon mixtures. The thermodynamic impossibility of some reactions has significance, particularly in those cases where the complete futility of developing various chemical systems is explained. Thereby the number of proposed chemical reactions is reduced, and at the same time other thermodynamically probable transformations are clearly outlined, which, in the products of reaction, lead to an aggregate of properties characteristic of petroleum. Many regularities in the composition of petroleum find a thermodynamic explanation and lose their fortuitous character.

Thermocatalytic reactions are one of the factors in petroleum transformation. One of the chapters of this book gives a short exposition of the historical development of the opinions held on the role of catalysts; experiments are described showing that the number of catalytically active substances is far greater than had hitherto been believed and that the activation of aluminosilicates only intensifies their action, but is not essential because of the vast intervals of geological time available. In this chapter the immense role played by a number of catalysts in connection with the transformable material is also elucidated.

The final chapters contain interesting experimental material on the transformation of various classes of hydrocarbons, oxygen- and sulfur-bearing compounds. To a considerable extent these chapters contain new and, in some cases, hitherto unpublished material.

The authors have undertaken to present not a collection of articles, but a monograph kept within one general plan. For this reason, the editing has been fraught with some difficulties.

The difficulty of composing this monograph on the geochemistry of petroleum was reflected in the fact that on some questions, even within the narrow selection of authors, it was not always possible to find a common viewpoint. This was true, for example, in regard to the oxidation of petroleum, the role of micro-organisms, and other lesser questions. Under these circumstances the authors simply stated that at the present time there is no common viewpoint regarding such questions.

The first and second chapters were written by A. A. Kartsev and the third and fourth, by P. F. Andreev. The first part of the fifth chapter was written by A. A. Kartsev and the second by P. F. Andreev. The sixth and seventh chapters are by A. I. Bogomolov. The eighth and ninth chapters were written by A. F. Dobryanskii.

CHAPTER I

GEOCHEMICAL TRANSFORMATION
OF PETROLEUM

THE PROBLEM of the geochemical transformation of petroleum is a part of the general problem of petroleum transformation. Besides this, the latter problem includes the questions of accumulation and transformation of the original petroleum-forming substances, the questions of the physico-geological mechanism of the differentiation of substances, and, in part, the questions of migration and the formation of oil pools.

Geochemical transformation of petroleum may be understood in two different senses. In the broad sense it includes all the natural chemical transformations occurring in the material remains of dead organisms† right up to the formation of petroleum, and, further, the processes of change in petroleum up through its complete disintegration and mineralization. Here petroleum should only be regarded as one of the stages in the transformation of living substance into methane, graphite, and similar end products.

In a narrower sense the geochemical transformation of petroleum is concerned with natural transformations occurring from the time that liquid petroleum is already formed until the time that it disintegrates into gases and solid substances. It is more correct here to speak of the transformation of petroleum components, since petroleum is not a single "mineral", but a whole family of compounds related to each other by gradual transitions. Geochemical transformation of petroleum in the narrow sense can be traced by comparing the compositions of sequences of petroleums from a series of producing formations. However, differences in the petroleums from various horizons in a deposit can also be inherited partially from earlier stages of transformations, so that it is practically impossible to separate the two concepts of the geochemical

† The authors hold to the theory of the organic origin of petroleum. For the mineral hypotheses, see below.

1 TP

transformation. The moment when the existence of "petroleum" begins remains uncertain, and this is one of the most obscure and debatable questions in the problem of petroleum formation.

The present book is mainly devoted to the geochemical transformation of petroleum in the narrow sense. Based on the study of the composition of petroleum and of the geological and geochemical conditions of its occurrence and keeping within the bounds of firmly established facts of chemistry and petroleum geology, it is possible for the present to elucidate only these processes. At the same time, an understanding of the "pre-petroleum" stage of transformations in petroleum-forming substances appears to be considerably less clear and the connection and continuity between the assumed petroleum-forming substances and petroleum is still far from obvious.

However, in order to present a complete picture, we give a brief survey in this chapter of the current status of the question of the incipient ("pre-petroleum") stages of the geochemical evolution of petroleum and their geological setting.

In the area of ("pre-petroleum") stages there are almost no established facts or universally recognized principles. This is equally true of the question of the geological setting in which the accumulation and transformation of petroleum-forming substances takes place. This situation is due primarily to the fact that the connection between the assumed petroleum-forming substances and petroleums is obscure, and different investigators assume different substances to be petroleum precursors.

We present below a brief consideration of the basic concepts concerning the problem of petroleum formation. In order to stay within the general scope of the present volume, attention is devoted principally to the geochemical aspect of these questions.

The following list of questions have evoked sharp differences of opinion:

A. The nature of the original petroleum-forming materials.
B. The circumstances under which the original petroleum-forming substances were accumulated.
C. Petroleum source rocks.
D. Factors and directions in the transformation of the original substances.
E. Time and mechanism of the migration of petroleum (or intermediate products) out of the source rocks.

F. Geochemical transformations of petroleum during the process of migration into the reservoir rocks.

We will consider these questions in the order indicated.

A. NATURE OF THE ORIGINAL PETROLEUM-FORMING MATERIALS

All theories concerning the nature of the original petroleum-forming substances may be assigned to one of two categories. On the one hand, the overwhelming majority of contemporary investigators believe in the organic (biogenic) origin of petroleum and, on the other hand, a few favor its inorganic (mineral) origin. The latter are sharply divided. Recognition of the inorganic genesis of petroleum compels an altogether different approach to other aspects of the problem. For this reason, we will consider these unique opinions at the outset, in order not to have to return to them later.

1. Mineral nature

Hypotheses of the inorganic origin of petroleum have been recently developed by N. A. Kudryavtsev [1, 2, 3] and P. N. Kropotkin [4, 5].

N. A. Kudryavtsev [3] advances the *magmatic* hypothesis of the origin of petroleum. According to this hypothesis, petroleum is formed in sedimentary rocks from the simplest hydrocarbons—methane, acetylene, and others† liberated from basic magma.

The chemical and geochemical aspects of the magmatic hypothesis have scarcely been developed. From the chemical point of view it appears impossible that methane should give rise to the most intricate complex hydrocarbon and non-hydrocarbon compounds that make up petroleum, under the conditions of a sedimentary cover at relatively low temperatures.

From the standpoint of the magmatic hypothesis, there is the inexplicable optical activity in petroleums and a peculiar regularity in the difference of its magnitude for different petroleums. N. A. Kudryavtsev assumes that the optical activity of petroleum either arises

† The presence of hydrocarbons other than methane in volcanic gases has not been established and is not very likely.

"under the influence of an asymmetrical lattice of the crystals of the inorganic substances" [3, p. 47], or is acquired as a result of the extraction of optically active organic substances by petroleum during its migration through sedimentary formations. However, both assumptions are in contradiction to the observed relationship between the optical activity of petroleum and the age of the sediments containing it. As is seen from the data of G. A. Amosov [6, 7], the amount of optical rotation in petroleum decreases at a regular rate with increasing age of the sediments containing it. This regularity is explained by the gradual destruction in the lithosphere of the optically active molecules inherited from the living substance. If the optically active substances in petroleums were derived from the rocks or had originated due to their influence, then there should be observed a reverse correlation: i.e. the older petroleums (those which have been in the rocks the longest) should be most enriched with optically active substances.†

The assumption that the secondary origin of the optical activity of petroleum is due to the influence of rocks is also contradicted by the very low activity, or complete absence of activity, in the petroleum clearly resulting from migration; e.g. the "white" petroleums of the Akchagyl stage of the Apsheron Peninsula and some other petroleums regarded as natural "filtrates". These petroleums, more than others, could have extracted optically active substances from rocks in the process of filtering through them, but the reverse is generally noted.

Again, the magmatic hypothesis may attempt to explain the optical activity of petroleum as being a result of the action of bacteria living in the rocks, as advocated by some authors. Generally speaking, the partial increase of the optical activity of some petroleums in this way appears possible. But when we attach decisive importance to this phenomenon we run into unsurmountable obstacles. In the first place, the above indicated relationship of the

† A. F. Dobryanskii[47] notes that for the most highly transformed petroleums the optical activity is the weakest, and, consequently, this property is lost during the process of change. Optical activity must be regarded as a fossil property which disappears in extremely "metamorphosed" petroleum. This is what establishes the connection between optical activity and the degree of petroleum transformation. This connection between the geological age of petroleum and its optical activity is probably statistical inasmuch as the older petroleums were encountered more frequently in company with those external factors which cause transformation. [Editors.]

optical activity of petroleums to age contradicts such an explanation —the older the petroleum, the more it should be enriched with secondary substances due to bacteria (as well as to the rocks). In reality, however, the reverse is observed. In the second place, the optical activity of petroleums at great depths (on the order of 3000 m) under clearly sterile conditions and, moreover, of petroleums having come there from still greater depths (from magmas), is still unexplained.

No less an obstacle to the magmatic hypothesis is the presence of nitrogen compounds in petroleums, as well as their nature and distribution. The explanation of the origin of complex organic bases and pyrrole ring compounds on the basis of Mendeleev's statements concerning the probable presence of nitrides in deep parts of the earth, seems, at least, a bit strange. Porphyrins are acknowledged even by Kudryavtsev to be substances of biogenic origin, and he explains their presence in petroleums as an extraction from sedimentary rocks (as do, moreover, a number of adherents to the organic theory of the origin of petroleum). However, such a point of view is inconsistent with many established facts. In the first place, the nitrogen content of petroleums (almost all the nitrogen goes to make up the complex compounds for which the possibility of inorganic synthesis is excluded) corresponds definitely with the type and composition of the petroleum, and indeed for this reason it is impossible to regard nitrogen compounds in petroleum as fortuitous admixtures. In the second place, in regard to porphyrins proper, it turns out (as was true in the case of optical activity) that the "white" petroleums, which are considered to be "filtrates" and therefore most likely to contain porphyrins extracted from the rocks, are devoid of them. So, the idea that porphyrins and other nitrogen compounds in petroleum are fortuitous extraneous admixtures must be rejected as unsound.

The important regularity is explained on the basis of data from a study by N. P. Kuznetsova. Taking into account the presence of porphyrins and simpler pyrrole compounds, she differentiates four types of petroleum [9].

These types are characterized in the following table (Table 1).

In interpreting these data one must take into account the fact that simple pyrrole compounds may be regarded as fragments of the more complex porphyrins. They are formed as a result of the disintegration of the latter. Bearing this in mind, it is easy to

TABLE 1

No. of type	Porphyrins	Simple pyrrole compounds	Representatives of type	Age and depth
1	+	+	Petroleums of Baku, Turkmenia, Sakaline	Cenozoic
2	−	+	Petroleums of Emba	Mesozoic <1 km depth
3	−	−	Light-colored petroleum of Southern Iskine	Mesozoic >1 km depth
4	+	−	Sulfurous petroleums of the Second Baku	Paleozoic

establish that with increase in age and depth porphyrins disappear by alteration to simple pyrrole compounds, and in the end even these fragments disappear. However, the appearance of porphyrins again in sulfurous Paleozoic petroleum is apparently caused by secondary processes associated with sulfurization of petroleum, and, moreover, the porphyrins in these petroleums are different from the others (vanadium porphyrins as distinct from nickel porphyrins [10]).†

Unfortunately, there are no corresponding data on non-sulfurous Paleozoic petroleums. It can be pointed out merely that porphyrins are absent in the sulfur-free Paleozoic petroleums of the Appalachian basin, which, consequently, belong either to type 2 or type 3.

Leaving aside sulfurous petroleums, the history of porphyrins in petroleum may be thought of as merely a gradual destruction of these substances, inherited from ancestral organisms. This story is identical in principle to that of the optical activity of substances and fully refutes the magmatic hypothesis.

From the standpoint of the magmatic hypothesis, the formation of petroleum deposits is possible only as a result of vertical migration. In a multi-horizon field vertical migration should, as a rule, leave traces in the form of a "migrational" sort of change in the properties of petroleums according to depth of occurrence. How-

† There are also present in type 4 some young sulfurous petroleums, which can possibly be explained by the disappearance of the simple pyrrole compounds existing there, with the biosynthetic formation of secondary porphyrins [10].

ever, in the great majority of oil fields the distribution of the properties of petroleums with depth is of a totally different nature and clearly refutes the assumption that all deposits were formed as a result of vertical migration.

From the standpoint of the magmatic hypothesis, it is exceedingly difficult to explain the origin of the petroleum deposited in the sedimentary cover of epi-Proterozoic platforms, where, between the basement and the cover, a discontinuity is observed corresponding to an extremely long period of time. And post-Proterozoic evidences of magma are not known in these areas. Petroleum that formed from Archean and Proterozoic magma would, in such cases, have completely disappeared long before the beginning of the Paleozoic sedimentary cycle and could not have formed later. In this connection N. A. Kudryavtsev himself presents the characteristic case of the Michigan basin, which, in reality, argues precisely against him. [This petroleum-bearing basin, which has Upper Paleozoic petroleum, is separated from the Paleozoic Appalachian geosyncline by the Cincinnati arch, which had already been formed in the early Paleozoic and consequently prevented further lateral migration of petroleum from the geosyncline to the platform. There are no indications of late Paleozoic magmatism within the confines of the basin.]

A number of other arguments against the magmatic hypothesis have been presented in articles by various authors.

A detailed criticism of the magmatic hypothesis was recently made by M. F. Dvali and P. F. Andreev [see *Proiskhozhdenie nefti (Origin of Petroleum)*, Gostoptekhizdat, 1955].

P. N. Kropotkin has advanced the emanation hypothesis of the inorganic origin of petroleum. He derives petroleum from hydrocarbons (methane?) which rise as a part of gaseous streams through deep fissures from the hard subcrustal substrata of the earth.

Kropotkin proposes a scheme in which light hydrocarbons are transformed into isoparaffins and naphthenes as the temperature drops from 300–350° to 90–150° during the upward movement of the hydrocarbons. This scheme, based on a distorted explanation of the data of Obryadchikov and Frost, is fantastic, since it contradicts the laws of chemical thermodynamics. At the same time, it fails to explain the origin of the observed composition of petroleum. Moreover, Kropotkin passes over in silence the inevitable initial stage of the given hypothetical evolution—the transformation of methane into more complex hydrocarbons—apparently aware of the extreme vulnerability of this link in his hypothesis.

All of the previously mentioned criticisms of the magmatic hypothesis are fully applicable to the emanation hypothesis, which is akin to it.

The hypothesis of the formation of petroleum from biogenic methane, advanced by I. I. Potapov is actually one of the mineral hypotheses. Inasmuch as methane can undoubtedly have an inorganic origin, this hypothesis differs from the mineral hypotheses only in form. So it is appropriate to discuss it in connection with the possibility of a mineral genesis of petroleum.

I. I. Potapov believes that petroleum is formed from methane as a result of the oxidation of the latter through the agency of sulfates dissolved in subterranean waters with the help of bacteria, radioactive emanations and silent electrical discharge. Geochemical evolution, according to Potapov, consists of gradual enrichment in increasingly complex compounds.

This scheme is no less fantastic than the preceding one. In the bacterial oxidation of methane only CO_2 and H_2O are formed. The radioactivity of sedimentary rocks is so small that to form large accumulations of liquid hydrocarbons from methane by its action requires an exceedingly long time. V. A. Sokolov, to whom Potapov refers, concluded, on the basis of calculations, that only a very small part of the petroleum hydrocarbons in young sedimentary rocks can be due to these processes [13, p. 277]. Moreover, the possibility that a whole complex of petroleum hydrocarbons can arise in this way is altogether unlikely. The role of electrical discharge is unquestionably small, if at all possible.

The methane hypothesis finds itself in irreconcilable contradiction with the previously mentioned data on optical activity and nitrogen-bearing substances in petroleum. The absence of intermediate products, which are essential in Potapov's scheme, and the existence of vast deposits of the lightest petroleums of saturated composition, are absolutely inexplicable on the basis of the methane hypothesis. From this standpoint, I. I. Potapov's hypothesis is even less tenable than the magmatic and emanation hypotheses, since, according to its assumptions, the whole process must go on in the sedimentary cover and at accessible depths, and consequently all of its stages must be revealed in the exploration for and recovery of petroleum accumulations.

I.I.Potapov attributes an important role to a geochemical type of water in the transformation of methane to petroleum, assuming that in the oxidation of methane the hard marine sulfate waters are transformed into alkaline waters considered by him to be completely reduced. This scheme does not withstand criticism either. Under the vague concept of "hard" waters are brought together waters of entirely different types—magnesium chloride sea water, sodium sulfate fresh water and calcium chloride brines. The last are sulfate-free. At the same time, Potapov considers the waters of the Apsheron Peninsula to be an oxidizing medium (calling them hard), whereas in reality they are more metamorphosed and reduced than alkaline waters and cannot possibly change into the latter under the influence of hydrocarbons.

2. Biogenic nature

In the light of what has been said above, there should be no doubt about the biogenic nature of petroleum-forming substances. But a different question is important in principle: Should the concept of biogenic nature be applied only to petroleum-forming substances, or should it be extended also to the petroleum itself? In other words, do petroleum hydrocarbons and other compounds entering into the composition of petroleum arise, beginning with the bodies of living organisms, or are they formed only as a result of the transformation of the material of dead organisms under the influence of inorganic factors? There are various opinions in this regard. The majority consider petroleum to be the product of complex chemical transformations of the substance of the original organisms. But there is an opposite point of view which is based on the fact that some hydrocarbons are present in the bodies of organisms and therefore reduces petroleum formation to the process of selecting these hydrocarbons. This *selection* hypothesis, which denies the geochemical evolution of petroleum before its accumulation in deposits, was advanced by certain anonymous American investigators in 1946 [14] and later developed by P. Smith [15, 16], V.A. Uspenskii, O.A. Radchenko [17, 18, 19], and partly by N.B. Vassoevich [18, 20].

P. Smith holds forthrightly to the idea that petroleum is formed from the hydrocarbons synthesized by living organisms [16]. V.A.

Uspenskii recognizes the possibility of some supplementary hydrocarbon formation outside of living organisms, but denies the importance of such processes.

The hypothesis of hydrocarbon selection patently contradicts certain known phenomena. In the first place, normal high molecular-weight alkane hydrocarbons are characteristic of organisms, while in petroleum the presence of a large number of isomers, including low molecular-weight compounds, is typical. In practice, the simplest hydrocarbons of all classes, which constitute on the average about 15–20% or more of petroleum (gasoline-ligroin fraction), are not known, and indeed cannot exist, in organisms. In the second place, the hydrocarbon-selection hypothesis does not explain the existence of such essential components of petroleum as tars, asphaltenes, nitrogen bases, and sulfur compounds (in low sulfur-content petroleums), which are not fortuitous admixtures, but are regularly associated with the hydrocarbon compounds of petroleum. In the third place, there is evidence that in contemporary sediments the amount of hydrocarbons increases absolutely with depth [21, 15, 22, 23], which indicates a considerable amount of new formation under these conditions.

Finally, the idea of the complete immutability of biogenic hydrocarbons during the entire course of their prolonged sojourn in the sedimentary strata, as well as the idea of the absence of processes for forming hydrocarbons from other substances under the influence of non-biogenic factors, are in contradiction with theoretical and experimental data. To acknowledge that petroleum hydrocarbons are the products of synthesis by living organisms is to deny to matter the capability of movement, change and development.

In contradistinction to the Smith–Uspenskii hypothesis, according to the opinion of the majority of contemporary investigators, petroleum substance was not created in a ready-made, or nearly ready-made, form by organisms, but rather is the result of complex geochemical transformations of the various constituents of living tissues. There is no unanimity on the question of what constituents of the living substance are the basis petroleum-forming material. It is, however, obvious that one must not attribute an exclusive importance to any single class of substances. The existence in petroleum of nitrogen compounds compels one to reserve some place in the composition of petroleum-forming substances for proteins and alkaloids, along with chlorophyll. The presence of sulfur in petroleum makes it impossible to deny the participation of sulfur-containing proteins. It is also impossible to neglect fats, or the substances related to them (lipids). There is an important principle involved in the question of the source of the cyclic constituents of petroleum, which constitute (without side chains), according to data of A. Sachanen, from 20 to 50% of the mass of ordinary petroleum [24]. Taking this fact into account, it is hardly possible to reject the idea of the participation in petroleum formation of vegetable oils and terpenes, as well as carbohydrates, which are the source of humic acids—the most abundant organic material contributed to the mass of sediments and rocks.†

To explain the relative role of individual classes of organic compounds in petroleum-forming material, there is need for detailed studies of the organic material in sediments and partially metamorphosed sediments or metasediments.

The role of individual groups of organisms in petroleum formation is determined by the relative importance of individual classes or groups of organic substances and the respective conditions under which this material was accumulated.

B. CONDITIONS UNDER WHICH THE ORIGINAL PETROLEUM-FORMING SUBSTANCES WERE ACCUMULATED

The question of lithologic facies or other physico-geographic conditions for the accumulation of petroleum-forming organic substances has several different aspects. Among the most important are: the nature of the basins in which the accumulation of petroleum-forming substances occurs (open, i.e. marine, or enclosed, i.e. lagoon-type), salinity of the waters in the basin, oxidation-reduction conditions in the water of the basin and in its sediments, and the lithologic type of sediments and the concentration of organic matter in them. On the whole, the question involves the entire breadth of the spectrum of petroleum-producing facies.

† These comments on the origin of the cyclic constituents of petroleum may lose their importance in principle if it is proved that chain molecules in the process of catalytic change can form cyclic systems. For example, A. I. Bogomolov showed that fatty acids during thermal catalysis with clays form large amounts of naphthenes. The possibility has also been shown experimentally of forming aromatic hydrocarbons from paraffin. [Editors.]

Opinions held on this question are highly varied, from the idea of the most limited conditions for the occurrence of petroleum-forming facies to the admission of the possibility of preserving petroleum-forming substances in virtually any subaqueous sedimentary complex.

Representing those adhering to the view of extreme specificity of petroleum-producing facies are V. B. Porfir'ev and his collaborators. In their opinion, petroleum-forming substances were accumulated in the form of a homogeneous organic deposit, which is possible, of course, only in aquatic basins of the closed, or semi-closed, type. These authors at the same time consider the presence of a "strictly anaerobic medium" necessary [25, 26, 27, 28, 29, 30]. The petroleum-producing sediments, in Porfir'ev's concept, are identical to the sedimentary facies giving rise to pure sapropel coals.

V. V. Veber is also inclined toward the lagoonal nature of petroleum-producing facies, although he does not attribute exclusive importance to lagoonal conditions, and admits a similar role for sulfate-reducing environments of the Black Sea type [22, 23].

I. O. Brod and N. A. Eremenko give strong support to the idea of a large areal distribution of petroleum-forming facies, considering that they are predominantly (but not exclusively) of a marine, and not of a lagoonal nature [31, 32].

The marine nature of petroleum-producing sediments as opposed to that of lagoonal nature is emphasized by American geologists in a symposium compiled in 1946 [33]. At the same time, a number of investigators, supported by certain facts, admit the accumulation of petroleum-producing material in the sediments of salty and brackish lakes (e.g. G. I. Teodorovich [34, 35]), and fresh-water lakes (e.g. I. O. Brod [36]).

The prerequisite of a reducing medium in the sediment is emphasized by many authors, although on the question of the dividing line between the oxidizing and the reducing medium, or on the sense of the term "reducing medium", there is no unanimity. In opposition to commonly accepted views, V. A. Sokolov considers that the reducing environment in sediments is immaterial, since petroleum can be formed even from organic matter completely resistant to oxidation [13, 37].

The notion that petroleum facies are extremely specific does not agree with the exceedingly wide distribution of petroleum types and leads to a number of highly improbable schemes. As a rule it becomes necessary to admit an exceedingly distant migration of petroleum, since petroleum-bearing beds generally do not contain carbonaceous or other suitable petroleum-forming facies.

V. V. Veber believes that in seas with normal gas content and composition, especially at considerable depth, organic material of terrestrial and planktonic origin is subjected to considerable oxidation before preservation and loses the capacity for further transformation in the direction of petroleum formation. He strengthens this assumption with extremely valuable factual data on the composition of "bitumens" in sediments [22]. However, although this fact is indeed important, the following considerations remain valid: first, petroleum can originate from constituents of organic matter in sediments, other than "bitumens"; second, even oxidized bitumens are capable of reductive transformation later; third, and finally, a low concentration of the petroleum forming substances may be compensated for by large volumes of sediments.

There is no valid basis for denying the possibility of the presence of petroleum-producing sediments under conditions existing in some lakes, including fresh-water lakes. The necessity of high salinity in a basin is not recognized by anyone except R. Fesha, who has proposed a scheme of petroleum formation based on analogy with the processes involved in making sauerkraut and salting cucumbers. It is apparent that such ideas must lead to the denial of petroleum-producing sediments in basins of normal salinity. Speaking of salinity, ocean water is much nearer to fresh water than the hypothetical brines of R. Fesha.

The role of the reducing medium both above and within the sediments can, for the time being, be appraised only under a scheme involving greater or lesser concentrations of petroleum-forming substances in the rocks. Almost all sedimentary rocks, including even subaerial loams, contain some quantity of organic matter. The impossibility in principle of forming petroleum hydrocarbons from every conceivable variety of preserved organic matter has not been proved. Humic substances, constituting the principal part of organic material in almost all sedimentary rocks, including even those formed under clearly oxidizing conditions, according to V. A. Sokolov, for example, are probably the principal source for the formation of petroleum.

We will now proceed to the question of petroleum source rocks.

C. PETROLEUM SOURCE ROCKS

As petroleum source rocks there have been proposed, on the one hand, rocks highly enriched with organic substance, and on the other, ordinary sedimentary rocks containing from a fraction of a percent to several percent of organic substances.

At the present time most investigators adhere to the second point of view.

Unique views are adhered to by V. B. Porfir'ev, I. V. Grinberg and V. F. Linetskii [25–30]. They deny in general the existence of petroleum source rocks, although they accept a low-ash sapropelite, which is fully spent in the process of petroleum formation even before its final lithification, as a source rock.

B. Hubbard [38] and some other authors [39] propose coals as petroleum source rocks. It is hard to reject completely the possibility of the generation of petroleum from the concentrated organic substances of coal-rich sediments, although some investigators indeed point out [53] that in a homogeneous organic mass there is an insufficiency of catalysts, and the absorptive forces are so great that they do not allow the hydrocarbons (except methane) to be liberated into the surrounding medium. It is an important fact that petroleum deposits are not found in most of the large coal basins.

The idea of the complete transformation of sapropelite into petroleum, advanced by V. B. Porfir'ev, requires also the admission of a high-temperature stage in the petroleum-transformation process. This runs into a number of objections in principle (see below).

All of this compels one to return to ordinary sedimentary rocks, i.e. clays, sandstones, and limestones. Clays are regarded by the overwhelming majority of investigators as the basic, perhaps the only, existing petroleum source rocks [18, 20, 32, 35, 40, and others]. However, a serious difficulty met with by this assumption is the poorly understood mechanism of the migration of petroleum from the clays into the reservoirs (see below). Moreover, in a number of regions where petroleum is present in carbonate rocks it is impossible to find clay beds which can be regarded as petroleum source rocks. This single fact indeed excludes the possibility of considering clays as the only type of petroleum source rock. The idea of such a universal role for clays has never had a definite or reasonable basis, and the mere existence of this concept only serves to illustrate the inertia and stagnation in ptheoretical etroleum geo-logy.

There are no definite criteria for distinguishing petroleum source clays from those which are not (leaving out subaerial formations). The criterion of high content of organic material has been largely discredited.

The possibility of the formation of petroleum in limestones is unchallenged. However, it is still unclear just which limestones (including dolomite) can produce petroleum and which cannot.

The majority of contemporary geologists exclude sandy siltstones from petroleum source rocks. However, such an idea, is in general based on misunderstanding. It is usually considered that in sandy sediments oxidizing conditions prevail, and organic matter oxidizes and does not accumulate. As proof, the fact is presented of a lower average content of organic matter in "sandstones" as compared with clays. But, in the first place, as is apparent from the foregoing discussion, a greater or lesser content of organic substances cannot serve as a criterion for calling rocks either petroleum source rocks or non-petroleum source rocks.

In the second place, many sandy siltstones contain not less, but even more, organic material than medium clays. These are usually poorly sorted sandy siltstones formed during rapid subsidence and rapid sedimentation. The Maikop "sandstones" of the Kirovabad petroleum region [41] may serve as an example of such rocks. According to data of D. V. Zhabrev, in the sequence of Tertiary deposits of Azerbaidzhan the fine-grained and clayey sandstones are not distinguishable from clays in their content of organic carbon [49]. It has been determined by the studies of V. V. Veber and his collaborators that in contemporary "sandy and silty sediments the organic content often reaches the same level that it does in clay sediments" [21, p. 346]. Moreover, it has been established by the same investigators that in the stage of early diagenesis, under certain conditions a part of the organic material is transferred to sandy sediments from the overlying oozes [22].

In the third place, insofar as we are discussing the quality of organic substance, we may point to the data of V. A. Uspenskii on the greater average content of "bitumen" in sandstones and siltstones as compared to clays [43]; to the data of A. I. Gorska on the greater average hydrocarbon content in "bitumens" of contemporary sandy sediments as compared to clay sediments (with approximately equal "bitumen" content) [21]; to the data of V. V. Veber on the greater reducing potential of bitumen in the sandy silt deposits of the contemporary and ancient Caspian is compared to clay deposits [21].† Analogous data on the greater reducing potential of bitumen in rocks possessing good reservoir properties are presented by P. F. Andreev and other authors for the Middle Miocene of the northeast Caucasus [44].

Thus the organic material in sandy silt sediments in rocks may be regarded, on the basis of their qualitative characteristics, as more likely to produce petroleum than the organic material in clays.

D. FACTORS AND DIRECTIONS IN THE TRANSFORMATION OF THE ORIGINAL SUBSTANCES

In taking predominantly oxygen-containing constituents of living substance as the original petroleum-forming substances, we must think of the geochemical aspect of petroleum formation as the process of loss by the petroleum-forming substance of oxygen atoms and other hetero atoms[+] with the relative retention of hydrogen.

As P. F. Andreev recently noted, the very sojourn of oxygen-containing substances of high energy potential in the oxygen-free medium of the sediment and rock should indeed lead to the spontaneous separation of hetero atoms from these substances, which is accompanied by a decrease of the store of free energy.

The following external factors have recently been recognized as assisting in the transformation of organic substances in sediments and rocks in the direction of petroleum formation: (1) temperature, (2) biochemical processes, (3) presence of mineral catalysts, and (4) radioactive emanations, and certain others. Temperature is recognized by many to be the basic factor in the chemical transformation of organic substances in rocks in the direction of petroleum, although the majority of investigators consider that the relatively low temperatures observed in petroleum-bearing beds, i.e. not higher than 100–150°C, are sufficient.

† The bitumen content of organic matter in these sediments is also greater (*Sb. Proiskhozhdenie nefti (Origin of Petroleum)*, Gostoptekhizdet, 1955, p. 273, Table 6).

+ "Hetero atoms" as used throughout this text refers to non-hydrocarbon atoms such as oxygen, sulfur, and nitrogen. [Trans. Ed.]

However, there are those who adhere to the idea of high-temperature petroleum formation. Thus V.B.Porfir'ev and I.V.Grinberg postulate that petroleum is formed (from non-lithified sapropelite of low-ash content) at a temperature of 300–500°, and it is precisely this temperature that causes the transformation of the original material, represented principally by fatty acids, into hydrocarbons, and the transformation of normal paraffins into iso-paraffins, alkenes, naphthenes, and aromatic hydrocarbons. These authors argue for their scheme basically on the idea that at lower temperatures hydrocarbons are not formed and if they are indeed formed in a dispersed state, then they cannot pass from the source rocks into the reservoirs. As a direct confirmation of the idea of high-temperature conditions for the genesis of petroleum, V.B.Porfir'ev and I.V.Grinberg point to the presence of phenols in petroleum.†

The high-temperature genesis of not all, but of many ("phreatic") petroleums is recognized by S.A.Kovalevskii [45]. A.N.Snarskii, conceiving of petroleum as a mixture of substances of various origins proposes high-temperature formation of certain petroleum constituents—the more complex aromatic hydrocarbons and the like [46].

The scheme of V.B.Porfir'ev and I.V.Grinberg is very vulnerable at several points. As has been pointed out above, it puts severe limits on the conditions under which petroleum formation occurs, making it necessary to assume extremely long migrations of petroleum both vertically and horizontally. The high-temperature hypotheses are similar in many respects to the mineral hypotheses.

Since the formation of hydrocarbons, including the aromatics, has been established even in recent sediments, an extremely important argument in favor of the necessity of high temperatures is eliminated. To be sure, it has not yet been established that the complex of hydrocarbons in modern sediments is identical to the complex of hydrocarbons in petroleum. However, that could hardly be the case. Furthermore, the mechanism of the movement of the petroleum substance from source rocks to the reservoirs is far from

† The authors manifestly overestimate the role of phenols in petroleum. Phenols are characteristic of extremely tarry petroleums, but even in these the phenol content does not exceed hundredths of a percent, and the impossibility of their formation as a result of secondary processes has not at all been proved. [Editors.]

clear. The existence of these obscure points contributes to the fact that the Porfir'ev–Grinberg scheme is still a debatable subject.

The ideas of A. N. Snarskii concerning the exotic high-temperature origin of aromatic hydrocarbons of petroleum must be definitely rejected as contradictory to firmly established facts concerning the regular relation of aromatic hydrocarbons to other constituents and to the general character of petroleum [47].

Champions of low-temperature petroleum formation base their ideas on the temperatures observed in petroleum-bearing sediments and on the presence in petroleum of thermally-unstable nitrogen compounds. In the opinion of most investigators, the temperature deficiency is compensated for by time. Thus V. A. Sokolov, proceeding from the kinetics of monomolecular disintegration of organic substances and extrapolating velocity constants to the region of low temperatures, arrives at the conclusion that "some humic substances" at temperatures below 50 °C can fully decompose during a period measurable in merely thousands of years, and among the products of disintegration there may be petroleum hydrocarbons and the like [13]. However, these deductions must be regarded only as tentative, inasmuch as they are based on simplified notions of the mechanism of thermal disintegration and do not take into account possible change in the thermodynamic direction of each process with change in temperature.

Recent genesis of hydrocarbons in contemporary sediments (see above) compels the assumption that the decomposition of organic substances is accelerated by some factors besides temperature. Biochemical processes, mineral catalysis, and radioactivity have been suggested.

Biochemical processes unquestionably play an important role in the early stage of the diagenesis of sediments. As regards the later stages, it does not seem possible that biochemical processes play a significant role. The statements that have been made (for example, by M. A. Messineva) concerning the influence of bacteria and their enzymes at all stages of the transformation of organic substances have not been substantiated by reliable factual material and reflect only the well-defined subjective positions of certain investigators.

It is pertinent that direct experiments have shown the inability of bacteria to form hydrocarbons (except methane) by the process of decarboxylation of fatty acids.

The importance of biochemical processes possibly consists in the primary processing of organic substances in sediments with the formation of labile groupings of molecules such as aldehydes, ketones, acids, and the like.

Mineral catalysis is a considerably more general and reliable factor. The majority of contemporary investigators attribute a fundamental role to aluminosilicate catalysis.

The role of catalysis consists in accelerating the course of thermodynamically probable chemical reactions (see below).

Aluminosilicate catalysts exist in sufficient quantity both in clays and in most sandy siltstones. In carbonate rocks the presence of sufficient quantities of aluminosilicate catalysts apparently cannot be expected in all cases. The idea of an insufficiency of catalysts in carbonate rocks and the consequences of it are treated by B. Brooks [48, 49, 50] and others.

Even those theorists who regard the catalytic properties of natural aluminosilicates with skepticism, e.g. V. A. Sokolov [13], are obliged to acknowledge the significant role of the mineral catalyst in petroleum formation. The basic objections to the catalytic activity of natural clays may be considered to be dispelled by recent experimental data.

Aluminosilicates may not be the only natural mineral catalysts in the processes of petroleum formation. P. F. Andreev, on the basis of the data from the studies of S. N. Danilov, points to the possibility of an important role of an acid–base–salt catalysis during diagenesis [51]. According to the ideas of P. F. Andreev, in the aqueous and reducing medium of benthic sediments the transformations of preserved organic substances by oxidation-reduction reactions are accelerated under the influence of catalytically active solutions of salts, acids, and bases (i.e. in waters expressed by compaction of the sediments).

The influence of acid–base–salt catalysis should not be excluded even for later stages of the geochemical evolution of petroleum. There it may be linked with the action of subterranean waters in reservoirs.

Radioactive emanations as a factor in the transformation of preserved organic matter into petroleum has attracted much attention. The possibility of forming hydrocarbons by the bombardment of fatty acids with α-particles, as is well known, has been proved experimentally. Based on these data and on the content of radioactive elements in sedimentary rocks a number of authors present calculations of the quantities of hydrocarbons that can be formed from dispersed organic substances under the action of radioactivity. Calculations presented by Ch. Sheppard, R. Birs and others confirm the possibility in principle of forming significant quantities of hydrocarbons by the action of this factor. However, the chemical mechanisms operating in these processes are poorly explained and it is not known whether this action would assure the formation of the hydrocarbon complex characteristic of petroleums.

The sojourn of the preserved organic matter in sediments and sedimentary rocks, as follows from the foregoing discussion, can lead to the transformation of a part of this material into hydrocarbons. The formation of hydrocarbons from oxygen-containing organic compounds is theoretically inevitable in a reducing medium.

However, if we disregard the concept of high-temperature transformation of low-ash sapropelite proposed by V. B. Porfir'ev and I. V. Grinberg, then only a very small part of the preserved organic material can be transformed into hydrocarbons and other substances of the petroleum complex. The hydrocarbon content of the dispersed organic material of sedimentary rocks is insignificant. According to data of A. I. Gorskaya the hydrocarbon content of the organic material in contemporary sediments amounts to about 0.1 % [21]. In organic material of Devonian clays, according to data of Yu. N. Petrova there is about 1 % of hydrocarbons [52]. In the organic material of the Miocene clays of the Northeastern Caucasus the content of hydrocarbons is of the order of 0.5 % [20]. These figures indicate, on the one hand, a relative increase in the role of hydrocarbons in dispersed organic matter with age (a very important fact, requiring, however, verification by much additional data). On the other hand, they indicate a very slight importance of hydrocarbons quantitatively. To be sure, one may speak of the migration of hydrocarbons to form petroleum deposits, and also of the transformation of non-hydrocarbon substances into hydrocarbons during the process of migration, but all these allowances can hardly change the orders of magnitude.

The major part of the dispersed organic material in rocks develops in the direction of carbonization; i.e. via the coal route. During the evolution of organic material in rocks there occurs a gradual loss of hydrogen, oxygen, and other hetero atoms. As P. F. Andreev and his collaborators [53] have pointed out, as the geological age increases, the oxidizable material in clays decreases; the escape of volatile materials decreases, and also, apparently, the concentration of methyl groups diminishes.

For the formation of petroleum it is apparently necessary to have separation of the complex of petroleum-forming substances proper from the remaining principal part of the organic constituents of the sedimentary bed and migration of these substances away from the source rocks.

E. TIME AND MECHANISM OF THE MIGRATION OF PETROLEUM FROM THE SOURCE ROCKS

General questions concerning the migration of petroleum and specific questions concerning the time and mechanism of its migration constitute the least understood parts of the problem of petroleum formation as a whole. If one does not adhere to the position of the total transformation of the original organic material into petroleum, then the complex of petroleum hydrocarbons and other compounds formed is basically in a dispersed state in the midst of the residual organic substance; the latter is destined to follow a course of carbonization. The separation of this complex, which is relatively mobile, from the residual organic matter, which is practically immobile is of great importance. Furthermore, since petroleum deposits are unquestionably allochthonous accumulations, the movement of petroleum from the place where it is generated to the places where it is concentrated is an important aspect of the formation process.

The problem of establishing the time during which this migration occurs is a complicated one. Studies of V. V. Veber and his collaborators, as pointed out above, have established that the movement of a part of the organic material (obviously, the most mobile part) from rich oozes, to non-carbonaceous sands occurs during the stage of early diagenesis [22]. From the physical point of view this process appears to be one of diffusion and capillary impregnation. The existence of this phenomenon is a fact of great importance.†
However, it has not yet been possible to regard this "protomigration" as migration of the petroleum proper from the source rocks, since the formation of the entire complex of compounds character-

† This importance is also stressed by I. A. Yurkevich [54].

istic of petroleum is hardly likely to occur at this stage. Neither do the petroleum-forming substances proper arise from and separate from the residual organic mass, since the migration involves too broad a range of compounds. Nevertheless, an obvious shift toward the enrichment of petroleum-forming compounds takes place.

The phenomenon under discussion takes place "at the earliest stage of diagenesis shortly after sedimentation" [22, p. 16]. It is possible that in the subsequent stages of diagenesis movements of organic substances also occur between layers of sediment, with the more mobile substances migrating preferentially. That such movements occur is proved by the greater bitumen content of organic material and by the greater reduction potential of bitumens in sandy silt sediments as compared to clays [22, 44]. Such differences cannot be developed during the earliest stages of diagenesis, since "bitumens" still play too unimportant a role in the composition of the shifting constituents. Besides, early movements occur only to sands distinctly poor in organic material. Apparently movements take place at the earlier stages principally as a result of the consolidation of clayey layers of sediments (oozes), and toward the relatively slightly consolidated layers of sandy siltstone. This movement must accompany a loss from the ooze of free or weakly combined water, which occurs, as is shown by data of Emery, Rittenberg and others, principally at depths as great as several hundred meters below the bottom of the basin.

Processes of petroleum formation undoubtedly continue also in those rocks into which the more mobile components of the organic substances of oozes move as a result of diagenetic protomigration.

There is good evidence that petroleum formation commonly takes place many millions of years after the formation of the rocks in which such deposits occur. Particularly significant in this regard are the deposits of light, gas-enriched petroleums trapped by stratigraphic disconformities. As examples we point to a number of deposits in the early Cenozoic of eastern Fergana [55] and in the Lower Carboniferous of the Dnieper-Donets depression. There is, however, no definite evidence to prove that these deposits are primary accumulations of petroleum and not formed as a result of the escape of petroleum from some other traps. Such escape, whether complete or partial, may occur as a result of change in tectonic or hydrogeological conditions, change in gas regime, or perhaps some other factors. It may be stated that many petroleum deposits are, without doubt, not diagenetic formations, but the same cannot be said for all petroleum deposits, wherever they existed.

In some way or other, in order to form deposits it is necessary for the petroleum to migrate from where it is generated, in dispersed form, to the traps. Depending on which rocks are the petroleum source, these movements, including migration proper, must be clearly differentiated.

If coal is the source rock, then migration of the petroleum substance is made exceedingly difficult as a consequence of the high absorptive capacity of the rock as a whole. As has been mentioned above, the possibility of the formation of petroleum hydrocarbons in coal beds is slight by reason of the absence of catalysts. The possibilities of coals being petroleum-producing rocks is necessarily small. But coals do generate methane, which forms under a far wider range of conditions, and is much less susceptible to absorption than are other petroleum hydrocarbons.

The migration of petroleum from clays is a very complicated and debatable question. This is one of the weakest aspects in the theory of the formation of petroleum from dispersed organic material. And not without reason have the adherents of the mineral hypotheses, as well as the adherents of the hypothesis of the total transformation of homogeneous organic layers into petroleum, directed their attacks precisely at this point.

Until recently the most popular idea has been the idea of the separation of petroleum from clays, along with water, which was squeezed out due to the solidification of the clays under the weight of the overlying beds. Actually, such migration at the diagenesis stage is entirely possible, and in some cases inevitable (see above). But as the lithification of the sediments proceeds, the possibility of migration strongly decreases. In clays the hydrocarbons and other petroleum-forming compounds are absorbed by the solid organic particles, while these in turn are surrounded by combined water, through which diffusion is extremely difficult. To migrate from where they are generated, petroleum-forming substances must be extracted from the remaining organic material, which is possible only as a result of solution and diffusion in the combined water. Moreover, the solidification of clays and the consequent expulsion of the combined water, according to data of a number of investigators [56, 57, and others], is distinctly retarded at depths no greater than a few hundred meters.

The migration of petroleum from lithified clays on a significant scale is highly problematical. The presence of completely petroleum-saturated sand lenses in clay beds (e.g. in the Cherokee series) indicates that saturation of sands by petroleum from clays undoubtedly takes place, but occurs most rapidly in the diagenesis stage. Apparently, migration can take place from lithified clays and clayey shales when there is strongly developed jointing. As is well known, commercial accumulations of petroleum are found in fractured clayey shales (e.g. the Monterey formation in California).

V. A. Uspenskii and N. B. Vassoevich have recently developed, on the basis of experimental data of M. A. Kapelyushnikov and his collaborators, the idea of the migration of petroleum from clays into reservoirs in the gaseous phase. According to this idea, under the influence of high pressure and gas saturation of the rocks (more precisely, of the water filling the pores of the rocks) the hydrocarbons are dissolved in gas, which, expanding further, transports them to the reservoir.

This point of view has been subject to the criticism of V. B. Porfir'ev and V. F. Linetskii [58, 59, 30]. Moreover, it must be pointed out that the experiments in M. A. Kapelyushnikov's laboratory were conducted under circumstances far from those obtaining in nature [60, 61]. Furthermore, there is no basis for assuming gas saturation of all the water in the rocks. V. A. Uspenskii proceeded from calculations on coal beds [62], which is wrong in principle. The generation of gases by homogeneous accumulations of organic matter is relatively far greater than by dispersed matter. The energy aspect of this idea has been developed by P. F. Andreev.

The solution of substances of the petroleum complex in gas, which in turn is dissolved in water without completely saturating the latter, is impossible. Partial solution of petroleum in gas can take place only when the gas is not in dispersed, but in concentrated form, i.e. in the form of a deposit (or as a supersaturated solution).

Moreover, there is a whole series of constituents of the petroleum complex (tars, asphaltenes, nitrogen complexes, and sulfur compounds) which cannot under any conditions dissolve in gas in any considerable amounts. This is confirmed also by the experiments in Kapelyushnikov's laboratory [60]. Petroleums which have actually gone through the gaseous phase (petroleums from "gas-condensate" fields) are almost entirely devoid of tarry substances and contain only insignificant oily fractions (for example, the "condensate" of the Lower Cretaceous deposits of the Shirvan area of Kuban contains less than 3% of heavy oil and the "condensate" of the lower Torton stage of the Uger field in western Ukraine, not over 7% of heavy oil). The composition of the huge majority of petroleums, containing significant amounts of tar and, on the average, of not less than 40% of heavy oils, indicates that they have not gone through the gaseous phase.

As Porfir'ev has correctly noted, if the gaseous phase had been in reality the initial phase of all petroleums, then "we would undoubtedly have encountered in nature immense accumulations of 'white petroleums', which, as a matter of fact, are extremely rare" [59, p. 321]. The accumulations of "condensates", found at great depths, cannot be compared at all in size with the deposits of ordinary petroleum and represent principally only remnants resulting from the destruction of the latter by the factors of metamorphism.

If limestones and dolomites are the source rocks, the question of migration is somewhat different. In the first place, it should be mentioned that in carbonate rocks, the bitumen content of organic material is considerably higher than in clays (according to Uspenskii's data, twice as high on the average [43]). According to this author, carbonate facies are less favorable for the accumulation of organic material and so there is less of it there in general, but it contains more of the stable parts, which is what "bitumens" are [63]. N. M. Strakhov has opposed this point of view [64]. Actually, the bitumen content in the organic material of highly organic carbonate rocks, is also considerably higher than it is in clays. For example, in the carbonate beds of the Devonian of the Ural–Volga region the bitumen content reaches 1% and higher, while in the Devonian clays it is generally less than 0.1% [52]. Obviously, in these cases one cannot link the high bitumen content of the organic material with the unfavorable conditions for the accumulation of this material.

A high, and, in many cases, a very high, content of "bitumen" in carbonate rocks is apparently accompanied by a more reduced character of the "bitumen" and a greater content of "heavy oil fraction" and hydrocarbons in the "bitumens" as compared to clays. This is indicated by the results of qualitative studies of the luminescent characteristics of extracts by V. G. Putsillo [65], V. A. Uspenskii [42, tables 9 and 10], P. F. Andreev [44], and Yu. N. Petrova [52]. All these data are evidence that at least in many carbonate rocks "bitumens" are enriched in hydrocarbons and, in composition, stand nearer to the complex of compounds characteristic of petroleum than do the "bitumens" in clays.

High content of the reduced and most mobile constituents in the organic material of carbonate rocks is a condition which no doubt assists in separating from the remaining organic mass those substances capable of migration.

Since carbonate rocks themselves are commonly reservoirs, migration of petroleum from the "source rocks" is not necessary here for the accumulation of petroleum. Migration need occur only from the sections where it is generated, which may be situated within the limits of the same bed as the deposit. In comparison with the case of petroleum generation in clays, the mechanism of migration and further movement in carbonates is considerably simpler.

The migration of petroleum from the localities of its generation should be thought of in connection with such characteristic phenomena as recrystallization, dolomitization, occurrence of secondary porosity, and jointing. The growth of crystals leads on the one hand to partial capture of organic substances by crystals and on the other, to the partial expulsion of the mobile constituents of the organic substances and decrease in the total adsorptive capacity of the rock. The formation of secondary cavities through dolomitization (and other processes) creates free space, into which the petroleum-forming substances migrate. Their separation from the residual organic matter of the rock is facilitated by their qualitative composition and relatively high concentration, and separation from the mineral granules is facilitated by the progressive decrease in the specific surface of the latter. The presence of petroleum and petroleum-like bitumens in cavities of carbonate rocks, as we know, is an extremely widespread phenomenon.

Of special importance for the migration of petroleum in carbonate rocks is the formation of joints, which here attain a scale unknown in clastic sediments. A network of joints permeating a thick bed of rocks must "gather" petroleum from separate cavities and even from dense portions of rock and result in the formation of oil accumulations.

In sandy siltstones migration of petroleum again occurs under special conditions. Attention should be directed first of all to resemblances to carbonate rocks, such as the collecting capacity in the source rocks themselves (here this capacity is still more highly developed than in the case of carbonate rocks, where it is not universally present) and, in comparison with clays, the high bitumen content of organic material. In neither case can one speak generally of the migration of petroleum from the "source rocks" in the proper sense (this is possible for carbonate rocks as a special case), but only of migration from where it is generated. But there is a distinction: in sandy siltstones there may be potential petroleum-forming substances syngenetic with the rock which have migrated into it during the diagenetic stage (see above). Along with the relative enrichment in mobile petroleum-forming constituents this signifies that these will be present here in an already somewhat isolated form and that the processes of the physico-geological differentiation of the mobile organic constituents from the rest has to some degree already taken place in the diagenetic stage. This phenomenon is very important, since it facilitates subsequent migration.

Under conditions of the already existing partial isolation and increased concentration of mobile organic substances and with a considerably reduced content of combined water, migration of petroleum from where it is generated in the sandy siltstones should occur relatively easily (compared to clays). The mobile substances either "float up" in the free water filling the pores of the rocks to the roof of the permeated bed and upward along the dip, or they are diffused through the water and accumulate relatively at the roof and floor of the bed, after which they also begin to move up dip by "floating up".

The processes of cementation also apparently have essential (positive) importance for the migration of petroleum in sandy siltstones. The influence of this factor has been studied by Waldschmidt [66].

A question of great interest is that of the chemical composition of the migrating substance. Is this substance "ready-made" petroleum or is it only "protopetroleum"?

The question of "protopetroleum" has been treated by V. B. Porfir'ev in a special article [30]. The superstitious apprehension which was at one time aroused by the term "protopetroleum", was, of course, absolutely senseless. The reasons for it had their root in altogether irrelevant circumstances. "Protopetroleum" would not have existed, if all the petroleum constituents had been generated in the organisms and, once they were preserved, had not undergone any changes. However, such an assumption does not correspond to the facts. For this reason there must be "protopetroleum" and the question consists merely in determining what it is. Based on what has been stated above, "protopetroleum", up to the moment when migration began, should be conceived of as a complex of compounds, mainly dispersed, among other organic constituents of the rocks. The chemical composition of this complex is obviously different at different stages and thus far it has not been possible to determine it with sufficient exactness.

In regard to the composition of "protopetroleum" at the stage when it was separated from the immobile organic mass, it can hardly have differed essentially from the state of "ready made" petroleum. It was already petroleum, but had not yet gathered into deposits. Chemical changes, of course, are observed even in the process of the migration and concentration of the dispersed petroleum. (A gradual loss of hetero elements together with tarry substances is probable.) There is no basis for asserting that the composition of petroleum as it migrates from the sections where it was generated should be identical in all cases. On the contrary, it is most likely that the petroleum type has to an important degree been already determined before its accumulation into deposits, since the large mass of the deposit is less subject to the action of the medium (catalysis and related processes).

F. GEOCHEMICAL TRANSFORMATIONS OF PETROLEUM DURING THE PROCESS OF MIGRATION INTO THE RESERVOIR ROCKS

Questions of the geochemical transformation of petroleum on the basis of a consideration of various circumstances and facts are explained in detail in later chapters of this volume. At this point we present only a brief explanation of the general status of these questions.

The general nature of the transformation of petroleum during migration and in reservoirs must be partly determined by its composition during migration from the source. Concerning this there are two fundamental views.

According to the first of them, which was developed mainly by V. A. Uspenskii [17, 19 and others], petroleum in the stage of its migration from its source and in the stage of concentration into deposits is a single phase (gaseous) system consisting principally of paraffinic hydrocarbons and, to a lesser extent, of naphthenic hydrocarbons, and later enriched (relatively?) by aromatic and naphthenic hydrocarbons, tars and other heavy constituents due to biochemical processes of oxidation.

According to the second view, which is developed in the present book, petroleum forms deposits in the liquid phase and already at this stage does not differ essentially from ordinary petroleum and contains a considerable amount of tars and other non-hydrocarbon compounds, as well as high molecular-weight aromatic and naphthenic compounds. One assumes the possibility of considerable differences in the composition of the petroleum migrating into the deposits at the different stages of subsidence and metamorphism of the containing sediments. The transformations of petroleum in the deposits are conceived of as a continuation of the processes of the initial stages of petroleum transformation, namely, a progressive conversion of petroleum towards a paraffinic composition, a disappearance of high molecular-weight compounds, and, finally, formation of methane and graphite as end products. The oxidation and sulfur enrichment of petroleum is regarded as a deviation from this basic course of evolution, which takes place under specific conditions.

The views of V. A. Uspenskii concerning the geochemical evolution of petroleum, are easily recognized as being closely linked with his concept of the process of petroleum formation as a selection of biogenic hydrocarbons and with his concept of the solution of the petroleum-forming constituents in gas as a requirement for their migration from the source rocks (clays). These concepts were examined above.

The following must be added to what has been said:

(1) The results of studies of the hydrocarbons dispersed in rocks show that these hydrocarbons are represented predominantly by naphthenes, aromatics, and solid paraffins. They contain, however, few liquid paraffinic hydrocarbons. The paraffinic chains, verified by spectroscopic analysis, evidently are attached to cyclic compounds [52]. For this reason it appears that there are no suitable conditions for the direct creation of petroleum of predominantly saturated composition during migration.

(2) The activity of bacteria universally present in petroleum

deposits, which is essential for the transformation of predominantly paraffinic petroleum into ordinary petroleum containing, on the average, more than 50% cyclic hydrocarbons, is more than doubtful. If this is assumed, then we would have to admit as a fact the "secondary generation" of petroleum, and consider it to be a two-stage biogenic product.

(3) There are no data to justify the assertion that the products of the biological treatment of hydrocarbons will also be hydrocarbons. Consequently, there is no evidence indicating that bacteria can alter the type of petroleum by creating new types of hydrocarbons, i.e. conversion of paraffins into naphthenic or aromatic hydrocarbons. On the contrary, existing data contradict such an assertion. V. A. Uspenskii attaches great importance in the alteration of petroleum to the selective destruction of paraffinic hydrocarbons by bacteria and to the resulting accumulation of cyclic compounds. However, with this reasoning, one must assume that on the average ordinary petroleum is "eaten up" by bacteria by a factor of one-half, or more. (In "the average petroleum of the world," according to Dobrianskii, paraffinic hydrocarbons make up only 30%, whereas in the "protopetroleum" of Uspenskii there must be at least 60%). Moreover, there is no explanation for the whole array of changes in chemical composition parallel to the "cyclicization" of petroleum: replacement of pentamethyl derivatives by hexamethyl derivatives, monocyclic and bicyclic naphthenes by polycyclic, normal paraffins by isoparaffins, and so forth.†

1. If the polycyclic and monocyclic naphthenes in petroleum which have undergone repeated biological action have a fossil (or residual) character, then obviously they are naphthenes liberated from identical fractions and should be identical. At the same time it is well known that in identical fractions the cyclic nature of naphthenes decreases concomitantly with the progressive paraffinization‡ of petroleum. From the chemical point of view this is an important observation and one cannot get around it. Thus a hypothesis has been advanced according to which naphthenes can be formed from paraffinic hydrocarbons through various intermediate stages, and perhaps even from non-hydrocarbons which somehow acquire a cyclic character. In chemistry such facts are unknown, at

† The following statements are A. F. Dobryanskii's.
‡ "Paraffinization" refers to the conversion of nonparaffinic hydrocarbons (or non-hydrocarbons) to paraffins. [Transl. Ed.]

least in the environment corresponding to that of a petroleum bed bearing a microflora. At the same time, the much higher cyclic character of various heavy and tarry petroleums, far removed from the paraffinic type, is an unquestioned fact. From the standpoint of chemistry and energy, the feasibility of the transition from naphthenic to paraffinic hydrocarbons is a more likely direction of transformation, and is opposite to that required by the Uspenskii hypothesis.

2. As a rule paraffinic petroleums are rich in gasoline, and naphthenic petroleums are poor in it. This fact is difficult, almost impossible, to explain within the framework of the hypothesis under consideration. Apparently, gasoline must be assumed to be already present in primary petroleum, i.e. in that part of the hydrocarbons which was somehow isolated from the young unconsolidated sediments. The total absence of gasoline in such formations is explained by the inadequacies of investigational procedures (volatilization, loss with the solvents, etc.). Here catagenesis comes to our assistance, since low molecular-weight paraffinic hydrocarbons are not subject to microbial destruction. However, this explanation, too, is unconvincing, because in this case we would have naphthenic petroleums rich in paraffinic gasoline, or, in any case, such petroleums would be known, and they do not exist in nature.

3. If cyclic petroleum is derived from paraffinic precursors as a residual product because of the disappearance of paraffins from the original hydrocarbons, in which paraffins are regarded as the predominant constituent, then we should expect the cyclic hydrocarbons in nature to be less in any case than the paraffinic hydrocarbons, whereas in nature just the reverse ratios are observed. This compels us to resort to the speculative conclusion that some of the paraffinic hydrocarbons were transformed into cyclic hydrocarbons, since it is obvious that accounts do not balance if we hold to the point of view of a merely residual character of the cyclic constituents.

The hypothesis fails to explain several regularities observed in petroleum, such as the constant association of light paraffinic hydrocarbons with the simplest benzene homologs, the increase in the content of benzene homologs with the increase in their molecular weight, the direct connection between the paraffin and gasoline contents of petroleum, etc.

All the facts and reasons presented are evidence against accepting the view that the geochemical evolution of petroleum consists basically of oxidizing transformations.

An explanation of the character of the geochemical evolution of petroleum is possible only on the basis of a many-sided approach to the problem. In the first place, we must have theoretical thermo-dynamic calculations; in the second place, laboratory experiments; and in the third place, an investigation of the relationship of the chemical composition of petroleum to geological and geochemical conditions. Materials dealing with these questions make up the subject matter of the following chapters. Questions concerning natural oxidation of petroleum are expounded separately in keeping with a decision of the authors, who regard these processes as a deviation from the fundamental direction of the geochemical evolution of petroleum.

BIBLIOGRAPHY

1. KUDRYAVTSEV, N.A. *Neft. Khoz.*, No. 9 (1951).
2. KUDRYAVTSEV, N.A. *Izv. AN SSSR, ser. geol.*, No. 4 (1955).
3. KUDRYAVTSEV, N.A. *Sb. Mat. disk. po probl. proiskh. i migr. nefti*, Izd. AN USSR, 1955.
4. KROPOTKIN, P.N. *Sb. Mat. disk. po probl. proiskh. i migr. nefti*, Izd. AN USSR, 1925.
5. KROPOTKIN, P.N. *Sov. geol.*, sb. 47 (1955).
6. AMOSOV, G.A. *Trudy VNIGRI*, No. 56, Lengostoptekhizdat, 1951.
7. AMOSOV, G.A. *Trudy VNIGRI*, No. 83, Lengostoptekhizdat, 1955.
8. EFENDIEV, F.M. and DZHAFAROV, M.A. *Izv. AN AzSSR*, No.10 (1951).
9. KUZNETSOVA, N.P. Issledovanie pirrolovykh soedinenii v bitominoznykh iskopaemykh (Studies of pyrrol compounds in bituminous minerals), *Trudy VNIGRI*, No.83, Lengostoptekhizdat, 1955.
10. RADCHENKO, O.A. and SHESHINA, L.S. *Trudy VNIGRI*, No.83, Lengostoptekhizdat, 1955.
11. POTAPOV, I.I. *Izv. AN AzSSR*, No. 6 (1951).
12. POTAPOV, I.I. *Sb. Mat. disk. po probl. proiskh. i migr. nefti*, Izd. AN USSR, 1955.
13. SOKOLOV, V.A. *Ocherki genezisa nefti (Notes on the Genesis of Petroleum)*, Gostoptekhizdat, 1948.
14. KNEBEL, G.M. *Bull. Am. Ass. Petr. Geol.* **30,** No.11 (1946).
15. SMITH, P.V. *Bull. Am. Ass. Petr. Geol.* **36,** No.2 (1952).
16. SMITH, P.V. *Bull. Am. Ass. Petr. Geol.* **38,** No.3 (1954).
17. USPENSKII, V.A. and RADCHENKO, O.A. *Neft. Khoz.*, No.8 (1954).
18. VASSOEVICH, N.B. and USPENSKII, V.A. Geologiya nefti (The geology of petroleum) in the book *Sputnik polevogo geologa-neftyanika (Handbook for the Field Geologist)*, vol.2, Lengostoptekhizdat, 1954.

19. USPENSKII, V.A. *Sb. Mat. disk po probl. proickh. i migr. nefti*, Izd. AN USSR, 1955.
20. VASSOEVICH, N.B. *Trudy VNIGRI*, No.83, Lengostoptekhizdat, 1955.
21. *Sb. Sovremennye analogi neftenosnykh fatsii (Contemporary Analogs of Petroleum Bearing Facies)*, Gostoptekhizdat, 1950.
22. VEBER, V.V. *Sb. Mat. disk. po probl. proiskh. i migr. nefti*, Izd. AN USSR, 1955.
23. VEBER, V.V. *Sov. geol.*, sb. 47 (1955).
24. SACHANEN, A.N. *The Chemical Constituents of Petroleum*, 1945.
25. PORFIR'EV, V.B. and GRINBERG, I.V. *Trudy L'vovsk. geol. ob-va, ser. geol.*, No. 1 (1948).
26. PORFIR'EV, V.B. and GRINBERG, I.V. *Trudy Nauchnogeol. soveshch. po neftu USSR*, Izd. AN USSR, 1949.
27. PORFIR'EV, V.B. and GRINBERG, I.V. *Nauchn. zap. L'vovsk. politekhn. in-ta, neft.*, Issue 16, No. 4 (1951).
28. PORFIR'EV, V.B. and LINETSKII, V.F. *Voprosy migratsii nefti (Questions Converning Petroleum Migration)*, Izd. Khar'k. un-ta, 1952.
29. PORFIR'EV, V.B. *Sb. Mat. disk. po probl. proiskh. i migr. nefti (Mathematical Discussions on the Problems of the Origin and Migration of Petroleum)*, Izd. AN USSR, 1955.
30. PORFIR'EV, V.B. *Izv. AN SSSR, ser. geol.*, No. 6 (1955).
31. BROD, I.O. and EREMENKO, N.A. *Neft. Khoz.*, No. 7 (1951).
32. BROD, I.O. and EREMENKO, N.A. *Osnovy geologii nefti i gaza (Fundamentals of Petroleum and Gas Geology)*, Izd. MGU, 1953.
33. COX, B.B. *Bull. Am. Ass. Petr. Geol.* **30**, No. 5 (1946).
34. TEODOROVICH, G.I. *Neft. Khoz.*, No. 12 (1952).
35. TEODOROVICH, G.I. *Neft. Khoz.*, No. 8 (1954).
36. BROD, I.O. and LEVINSON, V.G. *Proiskhozhdenie nefti i neftegazonakoplenie (Origin of Petroleum and Petroleum-gas Accumulation)*, Gostoptekhizdat, 1955.
37. SOKOLOV, V.A. *Sb. Pamyati akad. Gubkina*. Izd. AN SSSR, 1951.
38. HUBBARD, B. *Bull. Am. Ass. Petr. Geol.* **34**, No. 12 (1950).
39. ROBERTS, I. *Petrol Times*, 15/IX (1945).
40. VASSOEVICH, N.B. *Geol. Sbornik NITO VNIGRI*, No. 3(6), Lengostoptekhizdat, 1955.
41. KARTSEV, A.A. *DAN SSSR*, **65**, No. 3 (1949).
42. ZHABREV, D.V., IBADOVA, D.A. and KHUDOYAROV, I. *Izv. AN AzSSR*, No. 6 (1948).
43. USPENSKII, V.A., CHERNYSHEVA, A.S. and MANDRYKINA, YU.A. *Izv. AN SSSR, ser. geol.*, No. 5 (1949).
44. ANDREEV, P.F., POLYAKOVA, N.N. *et al. Trudy VNIGRI*, No. 83, Lengostoptekhizdat, 1955.
45. KOVALEVSKII, S.A. *Sb. Mat. disk po probl. proiskh. i migr. nefti*, Izd. AN USSR, 1955.
46. SNARSKII, A.N. *Sb. Mat. disk. po probl. proiskh. i migr. nefti*, Isd. AN USSR, 1955.
47. DOBRYANSKII, A.F. *Geokhimiya nefti (Geochemistry of Petroleum)*, Lengostoptekhizdat, 1948.
48. BROOKS, B.T. *Bull. Am. Ass. Petr. Geol.* **32**, No. 12 (1948).

49. BROOKS, B.T. *Bull. Am. Ass. Petr. Geol.* **33,** No. 9 (1940).
50. BROOKS, B.T. *Ind. Eng. Chem.* **44,** No. 11 (1952).
51. ANDREEV, P.F. *Trudy VNIGRI,* No. 92, Gostoptekhizdat, 1956.
52. PETROVA, YU.N., KARPOVA, P.P. and Kasatkina, N.F. *Trudy VNIGRI,* No. 82, Lengostoptekhizdat, 1955.
53. ANDREEV, P.F., IVANTSOVA, V.V., POLYAKOVA, N.N. and CHERNYSHEVA, A.S. *Trudy VNIGRI,* No. 83, Lengostoptekhizdat, 1955.
54. YURKEVICH, I.A. *Sov. geol.,* sb. 47 (1955).
55. KARTSEV, A.A. and Tabasaranskii, Z.A. *Sov. geol.,* sb. No. 57 (1957).
56. EMERY, K.O. and RITTENBERG, S.C. *Bull. Am. Ass. Petr. Geol.* **36,** No. 5 (1952).
57. DICKINSON, G. *Bull. Am. Ass. Petr. Geol.* **37,** No. 2 (1953).
58. LINETSKII, V.F. *Sb. Mat. disk. po probl. proiskh. i migr. nefti,* Izd. AN USSR, 1955.
59. PORFIR'EV, V.B. *Sb. Mat. disk. po probl. proiskh. i migr. nefti,* Isd. AN USSR, 1955.
60. KAPELYUSHNIKOV, M.A., ZHUZE, T.P. and ZAKS, S.L. *Izv. AN SSSR, tekhn. nauk,* No. 11 (1952).
61. KAPELYUSHNIKOV, M.A., ZHUZE, T.P. and USHAKOVA, G.S. *Trudy In-ta nefti AN SSSR,* vol. 3, Izd. AN SSSR, 1954.
62. USPENSKII, V.A. *Izv. An SSSR. ser. geol.* No. 6 (1954).
63. USPENSKII, V.A. and CHERNYSHEVA, A.S. *Trudy VNIGRI,* No. 57, Lengostoptekhizdat, 1951.
64. STRAKHOV, N.M. and RODIONOVA, K.F. *Byull. MOIP, ord. geol.* **29,** No. 2 (1954).
65. PUTSILLO, V.G. *Sb. Pamyati akad. Gubkina.* Izd. AN SSSR, 1951.
66. WALDSCHMIDT, W.A. *Bull. Am. Ass. Petr. Geol.* **25,** No. 10 (1941).

CHAPTER II

DEPENDENCE OF PETROLEUM PROPERTIES ON GEOLOGIC–GEOCHEMICAL CONDITIONS

PETROLEUM is found in the earth's interior under definite geologic–geochemical conditions which effect Vits properties and composition. The geologic–geochemical environment for the existence of petroleum in the earth's interior is determined, first, by temperature and pressure conditions which in turn depend on depths of deposition and tectonic processes and, second, by the properties of surrounding matter, i.e. the rock, water, gases, organisms. Under different conditions, and for known relationships with these, various processes occur, chemical (metamorphism and oxidation of petroleum), physical and physico-chemical (vaporization, adsorption, etc.), as a result of which the properties of petroleum are changed. The changes in petroleum occur in reservoirs (accumulations of petroleum) as well as outside of these, i.e. petroleum also undergoes change prior to its accumulation in reservoirs, along the routes of migration ("proto-petroleum").

The properties observed for petroleum making up accumulations are the result of the cumulative effect of various conversion processes occurring in petroliferous materials over its entire history, beginning with the stage of biogenic source material. Consequently, the observed properties of petroleum represent the product of extremely complex phenomena.

Nevertheless, a comparison of petroleum properties with the geologic–geochemical conditions of their occurrence must aid in bringing to light the basic factors which determine the composition and properties of petroleum as well as the basic directions of changes in these properties. The establishing of laws relating petroleum properties with conditions of its accumulation is the most important element in unravelling its history.

The basic results of investigations dealing with the relationship between properties of petroleum and geologic–geochemical conditions of its accumulation are presented below. The effects of the following basic factors are considered separately.

A. Age of the containing sediments.
B. Depth of strata.
C. Age and depth.
D. Differentiation within accumulations.
E. Facio-lithologic conditions.
F. Hydrogeologic conditions.
G. Tectonic conditions and migration processes.
H. Gases.
I. Basic laws.

The effects of temperature, pressure and microbiological factors are not considered separately since there is inadequate direct data on these parameters. At the same time these can be evaluated from other properties (temperature and pressure from depth of strata, microbiological conditions from hydrogeologic data). Age must express the duration of the activity for the basic alteration processes.

A. AGE OF THE CONTAINING SEDIMENTS

The relationship of petroleum properties to the age of the containing sediments was noted long ago. This question was examined in a general way from different points of view by H. Höfer [1], H. Hlauschek [2], V. A. Uspenskii [3] and others.

H. Höfer assumed that the difference between petroleums from different geologic systems occurs as a result of changes occurring in the earth's crust, basically consisting of the "paraffinization" of petroleums. H. Hlauschek, on the contrary, considered that petroleums do not undergo any changes in the earth's crust. According to Hlauschek, the difference in petroleums from sediments of different age is primary and is tied in with the evolution of organic life. According to V. A. Uspenskii, all of the differences between petroleums are acquired. In spite of the detailed characteristic properties of petroleums from different geologic systems mentioned in the work of V. A. Uspenskii and O. A. Radchenko [3], they offer no definite explanations for the differences among petroleums from different systems and groups.

Before speaking of the nature of the relationship between petroleum properties and the age of the containing sediments, it is necessary to establish the very existence of such a relationship and to determine its character. The main difficulty lies in the fact that it is not easy to determine the role of the age (in an exclusive sense) of containing sediments. If individual fields are examined, it is found that, as a rule, together with the increasing age of containing sediments, one also encounters an increase in the depth of the oil accumulations and other associated conditions, temperature, thickness of overburden, etc., which also affect petroleums in a similar manner. If, however, petroleums from different provinces are examined, another complication is encountered. In some instances older deposits can be correlated with deposits from relatively shallow depths, while in others, on the contrary, younger deposits will correlate with those from very great depths. There is also another obstacle in that the age of petroleum may, in general, bear no relationship to the age of the containing sediments. The difficulty in evaluating the effect of age on petroleum properties has already been pointed out by some investigators [4].

The indicated difficulties can only be partially overcome. The basic means for determining the actual relationship between petroleum properties and age of containing sediments consists of the examination of average values characterizing petroleums from different geologic systems and groups on a universal scale. It can be considered that in assaying a very large number of oil accumulations, the effects of local factors, depth of deposition, etc., which vary in their intensity for different accumulations, will be equalized and the effect of age difference will come to the fore. A statistical study of this kind was performed by V. A. Uspenskii and O. A. Radchenko [3]. On the basis of their published average values of petroleum specific gravities G. P. Tamrazyan computed weighted average values [5]. The data obtained by the indicated investigators are presented in Table 2.

If the petroleum characteristics shown in the tabulation are examined by groups (Paleozoic, Mesozoic, Cenozoic), a definite rule can be noted. From the Paleozoic through the Mesozoic, to the Cenozoic, there is an increase in specific gravity and sulfur content and a decrease in gasoline and wax contents of the petroleum. This character of petroleum changes had been indicated earlier.

In the work of N. B. Vassoevich and G. A. Amosov [6] a graph is

TABLE 2. *The average Characteristics of Petroleums according to Geologic Systems and Groups (according to V. A. Uspenskii, O. A. Radchenko and G. P. Tamrazyan)*

System or group	Sp.Gr. 1*	Sp.Gr. 2†	Sulfur (%)	Wax (%)	Yield (%) Gasoline	Yield (%) Kerosine
Cambrian ⎫ Silurian ⎭	0.840	0.847	0.32	4.9	22	17
Devonian	0.833	0.839	0.20	3.4	29	18
Mississippian	0.839	0.843	0.27	4.3	27	16
Permian	0.869	0.879	1.58	2.2	25	8
Triassic	0.884	0.854	0.22	4.1	10	18
Jurassic	0.856	0.861	0.56	3.3	22	15
Cretaceous	0.876	0.873	1.52	3.1	22	12
Tertiary	0.886	0.888	0.67	1.9	19	17
Paleozoic	0.842	0.848	0.45	4.1	26	15
Mesozoic	0.875	0.872	0.49	3.1	21	12
Cenozoic	0.886	0.888	0.67	1.9	19	17

* Average specific gravity.

† Weighted average specific gravity (weighted average values also given for % sulfur in the Mesozoics).

shown plotted from the values presented above and including also the data of G. A. Amosov on the optical activity of petroleums. As can be noted from the graph presented by the authors (Fig. 1.),

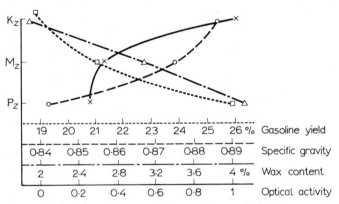

FIG. 1. The relationship between petroleum properties and age of containing sediments (from data of V. A. Uspenskii and O. A. Radchenko). Data on optical activity of petroleums (from G. A. Amosov [6]).

K_z = Cenozoic, M_z = Mesozoic, P_z = Paleozoic.

the optical activity of petroleums decreases with geologic age. According to N.B. Vassoevich and G.A. Amosov these laws are explained by "reduction processes" which they consider to be the principle factor in the catagenesis (metamorphism) of petroleum. From data on the statistical characteristics of the world's petroleums by groups, a rule is established for the relationship between petroleum composition and the age of containing sediments.

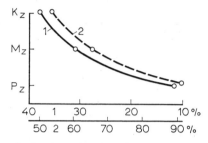

FIG. 2. Changes in the properties of the dominant type of petroleum as a function of the age of the oil-bearing rocks (according to the data of McNab *et al.* [7]). *1*—% of accumulations with specific gravities of <0.875 (at 15°C); *2*—% of accumulations containing >20% fractions yielded to 200°C.

For petroleums of the U.S.A. a similar relationship has been established by the work of J. McNab, P. Smith and R. Betts [7] (Fig. 2). These authors also explain the observed regularity as the result of change in petroleums under the influence of temperature and catalysis directed toward a reduction of specific gravity, i.e. the metamorphism of petroleums. This conclusion represents the only one possible in that the temperature and catalytic action of rocks are the only practical universal factors that can be deduced from a maximal generalization of the evidence. The action of all other factors is limited and not universal.

If we turn to Table 2 once more and examine the petroleums according to systems, we find that it is impossible to state a definite, universal rule through the geologic section of the earth. However, it is possible to note somewhat of a periodicity. This periodicity was first noted in the literature by G.P. Tamrazyan [5]. He noted that changes in the specific gravity of petroleums from the various systems correspond to the tectonic stages of the earth's development (the Caledonian, Hercynian, Alpinian). Indeed, from the

Devonian to the Permian, i.e. within the limits of the Hercynian geo-tectonic stage, and from the Triassic (based on weighted average values, and on average values from the Jurassic) to the Tertiary system, i.e. within the limits of the Alpinian geo-tectonic stage, the specific gravity of petroleums increases (a combined change in the contents of paraffins and gasoline is also observed in part). At the same time Cambrian and Silurian petroleums, related to the Caledonian geo-tectonic stage, are heavier than Devonian petroleums.

According to G. P. Tamrazyan, the observed periodicity is explained by the fact that, tied in with the start of tectonic stages, we find fine-grained sediments prevailing which exert a maximum catalytic action on the petroleums, while tied in with the end of the stages we find, on the contrary, coarse grained sediments prevailing which cause the petroleums to be oxidized [5]. The probability should also be noted of the considerable effect of sulfate rocks, more developed at the end of geo-tectonic stages, especially at the end of the Hercynian stage. This effect is first noted on the sulfur content of the petroleums and only later on their specific gravity (refer to Table 2).

Thus the relationship between the composition of petroleums and the age of the containing rocks can only be traced over geologic groups and loses validity in going to separate systems when other factors become significant.

B. DEPTH OF STRATA

The effect of the depth of strata on petroleum properties was first noted by A. Sorokin in Baku [8]. Subsequently this dependence of petroleum properties was observed and described quite frequently in extremely scattered regions of the world. Among the first detailed investigations of this phenomenon, the works of K. Krejci-Graf on Romania [9] and D. Barton on the Gulf Coast region [10] can be indicated. Krejci-Graf tied in the relationship between petroleum quality and depth of burial together with the effect of overburden thickness, Barton did the same for the effect of the geothermal factor.

Actually, the relationship between petroleum composition and depth of burial can only be an outward expression of the effect of temperature, overburden thickness and some other factors. Temperature and the overburden thickness for the accumulation represent the most universally widespread factors. The effect of age (time), as can be seen from the previously presented data, only appears in the case of maximum age differences.

It is absolutely imperative to differentiate between two principally different cases of the relationship between depth of burial and petroleum properties: first, when petroleum properties change as a function of depth within a single accumulation (within a single pool); second, when a corresponding change is observed in passing from one accumulation to another along the section or areally. In the first case we have continuous changes, in the second, discontinuous changes. The first case, representing internal differentiation of petroleums within a reservoir, should be examined quite differently since completely different factors come into play there (see below). Only the second case will be examined here, i.e. the differentiation of petroleums as a function of depth of burial for different accumulations.

First of all it is necessary to establish the overall character of the relationship between petroleum composition and depth of burial.

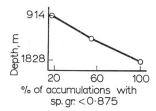

FIG. 3. Changes in petroleum properties with depth in the tertiary sediments of the USA (according to the data of McNab *et al.* [6]).

This can be approached from two basic paths. First of these consists of the examination of a mass of statistical data from a number of fields at one time, just as was done in the preceding section for determining the effect of the age of the containing sediments. In the previously mentioned work of J.McNab *et al.* the relationship between Tertiary petroleum properties in the USA and depth of occurrence was demonstrated. With increasing depth the specific gravity of petroleums decreases with regularity (Fig. 3).

The average characteristics of petroleums from the USSR were calculated (specific gravities for 305 accumulations, content of gasoline–ligroin fractions for 170 accumulations) for different depths of deposition, separately for the Cenozoic, Mesozoic and Paleozoic ages. The values obtained are presented in Table 3 (refer also to Fig. 4).

TABLE 3. *Average specific Gravities and Yields of Light Fractions (to 200°C) for Petroleums of the USSR (according to A. A. Kartsev)*

Age	Depth									
	To 500 m		500–1000 m		1000–1500 m		1500–2000 m		All depths	
	Sp. Gr.	L.F.	Sp. Gr.	L.F.	Sp. Gr.	L.F.	Sp. Gr.	L.F.	Sp. Gr.	L.F.
Cenozoic	0.891 (68)	10 (35)	0.879 (68)	13 (41)	0.867 (45)	11 (22)	0.855 (30)	20 (7)	0.876 (217)	12 (102)
Mesozoic	0.882 (35)	3 (27)	0.850 (9)	15 (7)	0.816 (7)	42 (5)	—	— (39)	0.867 (51)	10
Paleozoic	0.901 (11)	19 (9)	0.879 (14)	19 (10)	0.862 (7)	23 (6)	0.835 (5)	28 (4)	0.876 (37)	21 (29)

Note: 1. In the Cenozoic, for depths over 2000 m = 0.850, L. F. = 23% (6 accumulations). 2. Number of accumulations considered is shown under each value in parantheses.

The data presented in Table 3 (and plotted in Figs. 4a and b) show that, with increasing depth of deposition, the average values of specific gravity for petroleums and their content of light fractions

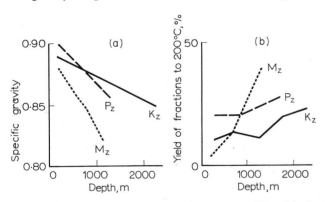

FIG. 4. Changes of petroleum properties in the USSR with depth. K_z = Cenozoic, P_z = Paleozoic, M_z = Mesozoic.

change with regularity; the former decrease, while the latter increase. This is observed separately for the Cenozoic, Mesozoic and Paleozoic and hence the possible effect of age is excluded here.

Thus a mass of statistical data on the characteristics of petroleums from fields in the USA and USSR indicate a definite relationship with the depth of accumulation, the effect of age being excluded.

The other means of determining the relationship between petroleum quality and depths of occurrence consists of the study of differences among petroleums situated in sections having the greatest possible number of separate fields and deriving from this a prevailing rule or law. For this survey it was necessary to use specific gravity as the principal indicator since for many fields this is the only data available. The use of specific gravity as the principal criterion is adequate in the first approximation since the distribution of the balance of primary petroleum properties bears, with very rare exceptions, a definite relationship to the distribution of their specific gravities. The specific gravity is thus a suitable characteristic for deriving fundamental relationships.

The change in specific gravity (and correspondingly other properties) of petroleums of a field with increasing depth of accumulation is called the vertical gradient. This indicator, introduced by D. Barton [10], has only a relative significance and only indicates the direction of changes in petroleum quality with depth: a positive value of vertical gradient results from an increase in the specific gravity of petroleums with depth of accumulation, a negative gradient corresponds to a decrease in specific gravity with depth. As was correctly shown by M. V. Abramovich [11], absolute values of the vertical gradient do not have any significance since such petroleum changes are discontinuous.

Three basic classes of fields can be identified from the direction of petroleum quality changes with increasing depth:

Class I, fields where specific gravity decreases regularly with increasing depth of burial; negative vertical gradient.

Class II, fields where specific gravity of petroleums increase regularly with increasing depth; positive vertical gradient.

Class III, fields where specific gravity remains essentially unchanged with depth (IIIa), or where different rules hold for different portions of the section (IIIb), or, finally, where there is no vertical regularity (as, for example, in sections where the vertical gradient changes its sign) and, in general, can be taken to equal zero (IIIc)†.

The distribution of specific gravity (and, to some extent, other properties) were examined over the sections of more than 250 fields in different countries of the world. The indicated number includes, first of all, over a hundred fields from regions of Cenozoic folding (Caucasus, Turkmenia, Sakhalin, Western Ukraine, Poland, Romania, Czechoslovakia, Austria, Italy, California, Venezuela, Trinidad, Ecuador, Burma, Indonesia, Japan) for which preliminary results were published previously [12]; secondly, it includes over 70 fields related to the Paleozoics of ancient platforms—the Russian and the North American; thirdly, about 50 fields from the salt dome regions of the platform (Emba, Gulf Coast, Germany); and finally a number of fields not included in any of the indicated groups (Fergana, Offshore Gulf, Rocky Mountains, Canada, France, England, Spain, Egypt, Arabia and Argentina).

For 83 fields the data used also included some aspect of the fractional composition of the petroleums, for example, tar content for 44 fields and hydrocarbon composition of light fractions for 40 fields. In isolated cases other data were also used: sulfur content, paraffin content, acidity, total hydrocarbon composition of the distillate portions of petroleums, etc. Of the 250 fields, 175 fall into Class I, 30 into Class II and 45 into Class III.[‡]

Thus the principal class is Class I and the normal rule indicates a decrease in specific gravity with increasing depth (along with the corresponding changes in other properties).

The most striking examples of fields in Class I are Naphthalan, Moreni (Romania), Dominguez (California), Mene Grande (Western Venezuela) in the folded regions of Tertiary age, Tuimazy and Krasnokamsk in the ancient Paleozoic platforms, Kulsari, Makat, Goose Creek (Gulf Coast) in the salt dome zones of the platform (Fig. 5).

An examination of a very large number of separate fields from the most varied geologic provinces tends to support the same relations as established by the average characteristics of petroleums (refer to

† The division of Class III into three subdivisions—IIIa, IIIb and IIIc—presents considerable difficulty.

[‡] These figures are not completely accurate because (1) it is not always clear if there is one field or two (or more) and (2) the rules governing the change cannot be traced too clearly.

preceding section). However, the question of the possible effect of age still remains unanswered since this factor is not excluded in studying different fields. Generally speaking, from the data presented above on the effect of the age of containing sediments, it follows that for individual fields a significant effect of age can only be expected in

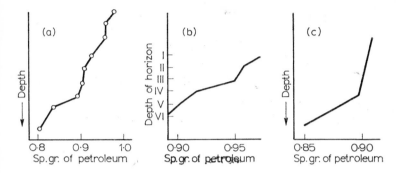

FIG. 5. Examples of Class I fields. (a) Naphthalan, (b) Mene Grande, (c) Tuimazy.

those cases where the accumulations are found in sediments of different stratigraphic groups. Such instances among the 175 Class I fields investigated are few in number. For fields with a narrower stratigraphic oil-bearing range (i.e. for the overwhelming majority) a significant effect of age is quite unlikely. The lack of this effect can be shown in examples of such fields where increases in depth of petroleum accumulation does not coincide with the increased age of containing sediments. The Akhtyrsk–Bugundyrsk field (Western Kuban) can serve as one of these examples. In this field, the overturned Lower and Upper Paleogene oil-bearing sediments result in a sequence of the stratigraphic mirror-image type. An increase in the depth of occurrence within the limits of the Middle and Lower Paleogene corresponds to a decrease in the age of containing sediments (Fig. 6). The specific gravities of the petroleums in the Akhtyrsk–Bugundyrsk field decrease with increasing depth from the oldest to the youngest sediments (Fig. 7). At the same time, in the neighboring Zybza–Glubokii Yar field, the specific gravities in the same, but normally lying (Fig. 8), Paleogene sediments likewise decrease with increasing depth of deposition.

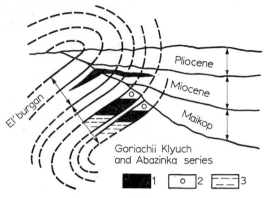

FIG. 6. Conditions of petroleum accumulation in Akhtyrsk–Bugundyrsk field (according to Z. A. Tabasaranskii). *1* petroleum; *2* gas; *3* water.

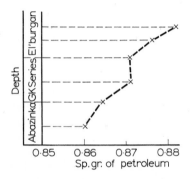

FIG. 7. Changes in the specific gravity of petroleums with depth in the Akhtyrsk–Bugundyrsk field (according to Z. A. Tabasaranskii).

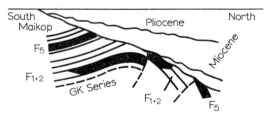

FIG. 8. Conditions of accumulation of petroleums in the Zybza–Glubokii Yar field (according to Z. A. Tabasaranskii).

Consequently, there does not appear to be any relationship between the specific gravity of petroleums and the age of the containing sediments in the given region.

A similar but quite unique instance is observed in the Western Ukraine fields of Bitkov–Pasechnoe and Skhodnitsa. Petroleum is found there in Tertiary and Cretaceous sediments. Principal (average) data are presented in Table 4.

TABLE 4. *Specific Gravity of Petroleums in the Bitkov–Pasechnoe and Skhodnitsa Fields (according to K. Bodganovich)* [13]

Horizons	Bitkov–Pasechnoe		Skhodnitsa	
	Depth(m)	Sp.Gr.	Depth(m)	Sp.Gr.
Tertiary	1150	0.820	350	0.827
Cretaceous	400	0.780	430	0.861

The data presented in Table 4 show that, in both fields, the petroleums occurring at shallower depths are lighter. At Skhodnitsa, however, Tertiary petroleums are found at higher elevations, whereas at Bitkov, where the sediments are overturned, the petroleum accumulations in Cretaceous sediments exist at higher elevations. Consequently, petroleum quality here is also related to depth of deposition and does not depend on the age of the containing sediments. The relationship between petroleum quality and depth of deposition, as indicated above, is a result of the effect of several factors. The most universally widespread of these are temperature and thickness of sediments overlying the oil accumulations. Other factors, the most important of which is hydrogeologic in nature, are not encountered everywhere and do not all have the same effect (see below).

The vertical specific gravity gradient of petroleum is related (in direction) to the geothermal gradient. With increasing temperature, the processes of petroleum metamorphosis, basically involving a decrease in size of molecules, are intensified. Consequently, the negative vertical gradient for the specific gravity of petroleums can be considered the result of processes of petroleum metamorphism. With increasing thickness of sediments overlying petroleum accumulations, there is a decrease in the loss of upward-moving light fractions from the petroleum deposit. Should such upward move-

ment of the light fractions occur, it could explain the inverse relation between depth of burial and petroleum specific gravity.
However, it is necessary to point out that the migration of light
fractions of petroleum does not always occur. With very dense and
very thick cap rock this process cannot have any significant value.

We should consider that, in general, these two indicated processes, metamorphism and escape of light fractions from petroleums
lying closer to the surface, cause the prevailing negative vertical
gradient for the specific gravity of petroleums. General considerations force us to assume that, at relatively shallow depths of deposition, the loss of light fractions by the petroleums has prime
significance while at great depths it is metamorphism. In specific
cases one can attempt to identify the effect of each process, its presence or its absence. However, it is not always possible to resolve
this problem. The basic criteria here must be the presence or absence of differences in the chemical composition of the isolated
narrow fractions. As a result of metamorphism, under the influence
of temperature (and the catalytic action of rock), not only does
specific gravity change, but the chemical composition of the isolated narrow fractions will also change. Under conditions causing
only the loss of light fractions, the composition of the narrow fractions must remain constant. Consequently, the presence of certain
changes in the chemical composition of individual fractions, corresponding to the vertical gradient for specific gravity, must indicate
the effect of metamorphism (but not necessarily the absence of the
effect of loss of light fractions).

Several instances (Class I fields) in which the effect of metamorphism can be established from data on chemical composition
are cited below.

1. Forest Reserve and Bernstein fields (Trinidad)

The data in Table 5 indicate that in this field the aromatic hydrocarbon content of gasolines increase as the specific gravity of the
petroleum decreases and the percent of light fractions increases.
This phenomenon is explained only by the formation of the simplest
aromatic hydrocarbons during the break-down of more complex
naphthenic-aromatic hydrocarbons and the aromatization of
paraffinic hydrocarbons as shown by A. F. Dobryanskii.

This type of break-down is a typical result of the process of petroleum metamorphism.

TABLE 5. *Characteristics of Petroleums from the Forest Reserve Field [14]*

Horizon	Specific gravity	% Fractions boiling off to 200 °C	% Aromatic hydrocarbons in fractions boiling off to 145 °C
Forest	0.936–0.959	12–18	0–1.2
Upper Cruz	0.915–0.921	15–18	0–3.2
Middle and Lower Cruz	0.841–0.893	20–38	1–18

Note: All accumulations are in sandstone. Accumulation is normal.

A similar phenomenon is also established in the neighboring Bernstein field. There the toluene content of the low boiling fraction increases with depth, and gasoline, absent in shallow accumulations [15], is present in deeper horizons, i.e. lower molecular-weight aromatic hydrocarbons are formed at depth.

2. Moreni field (Romania)

This field contains a number of accumulations in Miocene and Pliocene sediments traversed by a salt plug (Fig. 9). The geochemical profile (Fig. 9) shows that with increasing depth the content of

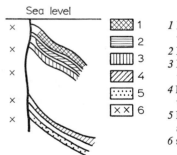

Sea level

1 Petroleum; sp. gr. 0.900, with 9% aromatics in the gasoline;
2 Petroleum, sp. gr. 0.891;
3 Petroleum, sp. gr. 0.866, with 18% aromatics in the gasoline;
4 Petroleum, sp. gr. 0.847, with 20% aromatics in the gasoline;
5 Petroleum, sp. gr. 0.832 (all data are averages for the accumulation);
6 salt plug.

FIG. 9. Diagram for the distribution of petroleum properties along the section of the Moreni field (Romania).

aromatic hydrocarbons and gasoline fractions of the petroleum increases and the specific gravity decreases, i.e. a situation is observed analogous to the case examined first.

It should be noted that the aromatic hydrocarbon content in the kerosene fractions of Moreni petroleums, on the contrary, decreases with depth in the section. Their average content in the kerosenes from Dakiian petroleums is 35%, while in the Meotisse it is 19%. This phenomenon can be explained by the break-down of complex aromatic hydrocarbons in the kerosene fractions and the resulting formation of the simpler aromatic hydrocarbons of gasoline fractions.

3. Kazan–Bulag field (Western Azerbaijan)

In the Kazan–Bulag field the petroleum occurs in Oligocene sandstones. The oil in the upper horizon has a sp. gr. of 0.900, 6% yield of light fractions (to 200°C), 7% aromatic hydrocarbon content in the light fractions, 21% aromatic hydrocarbon content in the kerosene fractions. The petroleum in the lower horizon is correspondingly characterized by the following values: sp. gr. 0.835, yield of fractions to 200°C 27%, aromatic hydrocarbon content in the light fractions 10%, aromatic hydrocarbon content in the kerosene fractions 17%. Consequently, in the Kazan–Bulag field essentially the same phenomenon is observed as in the case of the previously analyzed instances, but less clearly defined. As in the case of Moreni, the changes in the aromatic content of the gasoline–ligroin and kerosene fractions have opposing gradients.

4. Tuimazy field

In the Tuimazy field, as shown by the calculations of A. F. Dobryanskii [4], there is a relative increase in the amount of lighter aromatic hydrocarbons going down the section. In the post-Mississippian petroleums the ratio of aromatics whose boiling temperatures are above 400°C to those boiling below 250°C, $\dfrac{a > 400°C}{a > 250°C}$ is greater than 4 while in Devonian petroleums this value is less than 2. Such relationships, i.e. the greater abundance of the simplest aromatic hydrocarbons in deeper horizons, indicate the formation of those hydrocarbons from heavier ones in the deeper parts of the section and, consequently, on the existence of petroleum metamorphism.

5. Zol'nyi Ovrag and Yablonovyi Ovrag fields

In the Zol'nyi Ovrag field a change in the chemical composition of petroleum is observed with changing depth in the section quite similar to the one cited above for Tuimazy. In post-Mississippian petroleums the value of is equal to 1.6 [16], in Devonian petroleums it is less than 1 [17].

In the Yablonovyi Ovrag field the aromatic hydrocarbon content in the 122–150°C fraction of petroleum from the coal-bearing series of post-Mississippian age comprises only 1%. In Devonian oil the same fraction contains 11% aromatics (in other light fractions there are similar relationships).

6. Kulsary field

In the Kulsary field, where the petroleum has been studied in detail by A.I.Bogomolov and F.B.Indenbom [18], a systematic change in hydrocarbon composition is noted with increasing depth of burial (Table 6).

The data given in Table 6 present essentially the same picture of orderly change in the composition of aromatic hydrocarbons as in the instances examined above, but in the Kulsary field this phenomenon occurs in a more orderly fashion in that it can be traced through a number of horizons. Also toward this end, instead of absolute values of heavy and light aromatic hydrocarbons (as above), the table gives ratios of their percent content in the heavy and light fractions which precludes the effect of differences in the fractional composition of the petroleums.

Furthermore, a value like the ratio of fractional yield to the relative number of molecules in the fraction, decreasing as specific gravity decreases, indicates that the composition of individual fractions changes with depth in the direction of increasing subdivision into smaller molecules.

TABLE 6. *Characteristics of Kulsary Field Petroleums*

Horizon	Sp.Gr.	% Aromatic in the 150–200°C fraction	% Aromatic in the 450–500°C fraction — % Aromatic in the 200–450°C fraction	% 150–200°C fraction — Relative number of molecules in this fraction	Refractive index of solid hydrocarbons in the 500–550°C fraction
Albian	0.889	0.07	20.4	2.1	1.4477
Aptian	0.882	0.06	23.0	2.0	
Neocomian	0.879	0.10	11.6	1.8	1.4445
Upper Jurassic	0.862	0.23	4.8	1.8	
Middle Jurassic	0.823	0.47	1.4	1.2	1.4430
Lower Jurassic	0.793	1.85	0.2	0.6	1.4387

Finally, the decrease with depth of the refractive index for solid hydrocarbons (paraffins and ceresins) indicates the simplification of the structure of these materials in the given direction.

7. Fields in the Gulf Coast region

In fields of the Gulf Coast region, according to data from the voluminous and painstaking investigations of D. Barton on these stratigraphic sequences, the specific gravity of individual narrow fractions changes together with the specific gravity of the whole petroleum, which indicates changes in their chemical composition [19].

Deserving of special attention is Barton's discovery that the depth at which character ("base") of the kerosene fraction changes is displaced with increasing age of containing sediments (Table 7).

TABLE 7. *Transition Depth for the "Base" of Gulf Coast Kerosenes*

Depth of transition (ft)	Miocene	Oligocene	Eocene
From "naphthene base" to "intermediate"	6000	6000	4500
From "intermediate base" to "paraffin"	10,500	9000	8000

In going from the Oligocene to the Eocene and, in part, from the Miocene to the Oligocene an "elevation" of petroleums takes place, i.e. the transition from oils low in saturated hydrocarbons to those high in saturated hydrocarbons occurs at shallower depths. Consequently, the transformation of petroleums in the direction of greater saturation occurs not only with increasing absolute depth of deposition, but also independently of it, with increasing age of containing sediments, and even with relatively small changes in age (Oligocene–Eocene). This very important observation must be considered as indisputable evidence of the influence of thermo-catalytic metamorphism on alterations in Gulf Coast petroleums.

8. Qatif field (Saudi Arabia)

In the Qatif field, as in a number of preceding instances, along with an increase in the yield of light fractions from 20 to 30%, with increasing depth, there is a decrease in the ratio of percent aromatic hydrocarbons in heavy fractions (gas oil) to percent aromatic hydrocarbons in light fractions (gasoline) from 3 to 2.5.

9. Mercedes field (Eastern Venezuela)

Data on the composition of petroleums for this region are presented in Table 8. These data are extremely valuable since only in a very few fields are the results of ring analyses available for petroleums from more than one horizon.

TABLE 8. *Characteristics of Mercedes Field Petroleums*

Horizon	% Tar	% Light fractions	% in light fractions			% Gas oil	% in gas oil		
			Aromatics	Naphthene rings	Alkane chains		Aromatics	Naphthene rings	Alkane chains
Oligocene	35	14	20.5	28	72	29	26	28	72
Cretaceous	11	25	20.0	21	79	35	24	24	76

From these data the presence of a negative vertical gradient for tar content with a positive gradient in the yield of light fractions can be established. The naphthenic ring content in the light fractions, as well as in the gas oil, decreases with depth while the alkane chain content increases. The aromatic hydrocarbon content in the light fractions and in the gas oil fraction change insignificantly, but if the ratio of light to heavy aromatic hydrocarbons is considered, a different picture will result. From the data in Table 8 it can be calculated that the ratio of aromatic hydrocarbon content in the light fractions, as percent of the whole crude, to that in gas oil is equal to 0.38 for Oligocene oil and 0.59 for Cretaceous oil. Similarly, the ratio of percent aromatic hydrocarbons in the sum of the light fractions to that in gas oil is 0.78 for the former and 0.83 for the latter. Consequently, with increase in depth, the relative proportions of light aromatic hydrocarbons increases and the concentration of heavy aromatic hydrocarbons decreases.

If oxidation processes were active here, then, due to the predominant oxidation of heavy aromatic hydrocarbons having a greater oxidation potential, the ratio of light aromatic hydrocarbons to heavy for the shallower (Oligocene) petroleum should be greater than that in the deeper (Cretaceous) petroleum. The reverse is observed, however. If one considers the possibility that the ratio of absolute contents may be effected by the loss of light fractions from the upper petroleum as a result of inspissation, then the fact that the ratio of percentage composition of a fraction changes with lateral displacement of the oils shows that the increase of lighter aromatic hydrocarbons in the lower petroleum occurs independently of possible processes of volatilization.

10. Zhirnovsko–Bakhmet'evskoe field

In the Zhirnovsko–Bakhmet'evskoe field (Lower Povolzh'e) differences between Carboniferous and Devonian petroleums lying at great depths is of considerable interest. Both the Lower Carboniferous and the Devonian petroleums have very nominal specific gravities (0.83 and 0.87 respectively), low tar contents, practically no sulphur, but vary widely in the hydrocarbon content of the light fractions. The naphthene content in light fractions (to 200 °C) for lower Carboniferous petroleum is 49%, for Devonian petroleum, 36%; the aromatic hydrocarbon content is 4 and 8% respectively.

In view of the low specific gravity, low tar content, and absence of sulphur in the Lower Carboniferous petroleum it is impossible to consider that the difference between it and Devonian petroleum is caused by the greater oxidation of the former. Differences in the hydrocarbon composition indicate the extensive metamorphism of the Devonian petroleum.

A review of Class I fields for which data on hydrocarbon composition are available indicates that, in all cases, the changes in composition with depth are essentially the same. There is an increase in the number of molecules in similar, narrow fractions and in the aromatic hydrocarbon content in light fractions, while the aromatic content of the heavy fractions, on the other hand, decreases. This pattern attests to the action of petroleum metamorphism. The condition that the given rule is without exceptions becomes extremely important, indicating that metamorphism of petroleum is universal in the most varied geologic provinces.

The existence of metamorphism alone naturally does not preclude the possibility of the effect of other processes as well, first of all the escape of light fractions. However, sometimes the absence of this factor can be established. Thus, in the Makat field, with a typical negative vertical gradient for specific gravity, petroleums from all horizons completely lack a gasoline–ligroin fraction; differences in the kerosene fraction content, however, are negligible. In the Casave field (Colombia), the light fraction content remains constant but tar content exhibits a drastic decrease with depth.

Occasionally discrepancies are observed between changes in the specific gravity and gasoline content of petroleums from different depths. Thus, in the Romanian fields of Gura-Oknitsa, Ochiur and Beikoi, the deeper-lying petroleums have a lower specific gravity but at the same time have a lower gasoline yield. Consequently, loss of light fractions does not occur in all Class I fields. The special features of Class II and Class III fields will be presented in a later section during the examination of the effects of other geological–geochemical factors.

Special attention should be given to those fields which are characterized by changes (differences) in petroleum properties with depth within individual horizons, i.e. with the sinking and burial of formations, etc. This was first noted by B.M. Sarkisyan [20]. He established that, on the Apsheron peninsula, with the sinking of the Fat'mai–Zikhskoi anticlinal trend along the direction of Balakhany–Surakhany–Zykh, in all of the horizons in the productive mass, there is a gradual decrease in the specific gravity of petroleum and a corresponding change in their other properties [20]. This rule, which was called the "Sarkisyan's law" does not have a *single* exception in that region [21]. Similar data were obtained for the western fields in the Apsheron oil-bearing province [21]. A portion of the data is presented in graphical form in Fig. 10.

Examination of the graphs (Fig. 10) permits one to establish that a decrease in the specific gravity of petroleums occurs not only along the Balakhany–Surakhany–Karachukhur trend, but also along the Binagady–Chakhnaglyar–Sulu-Tepe–Yasamal'skaya Valley and Kush-Khana–Puta–Lok-Batan trends, which also represent directions of submergence and burial of the formations in the productive mass. Thus, the areal distribution of petroleum properties over formations in different accumulations, i.e. changes from field to field, depend here on the depth of deposition.

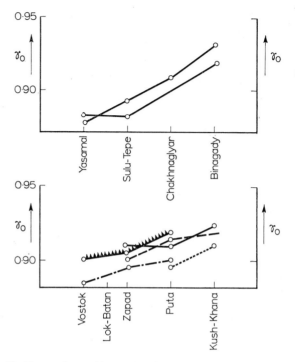

FIG. 10. Changes in specific gravity of petroleums from individual horizons in fields of Western Apsheron.

The given rule cannot be explained by the escape of light fractions. This is opposed by the fact that the gasoline content of the petroleums, which in that case should also change, and change in a most orderly manner, in fact does not have any orderly distribution corresponding to that of specific gravity (Fig. 11). Neither can the effect of oxidation processes serve as an explanation here. Changes in oxidizing conditions, tied to hydrogeologic factors, are nominal here and, most important, are not continuous but often opposing for individual horizons [21], while the observed rule for changes in specific gravity holds over the entire section. As a result, in the case cited, it is necessary to turn to the processes of metamorphism for petroleum. The presence of metamorphic effects here is also established by the orderly changes in hydrocarbon composition of gasoline fractions with subsidence and burial of the formation.

The graph in Fig. 12 shows changes in the aromatic content of gasolines in different horizons from the Surakhani to the Karachukhur accumulations. This graph shows that, practically without exception, the aromatic content of the gasolines is increasing from Surakhani to Karachukhur. This rule is similar to the one established above for changes in hydrocarbon composition with depth. Out of this arises the possibility of extending "Sarkisyan's law" to the geothermal field.

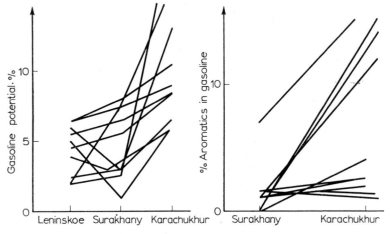

FIG. 11. Changes in the gasoline potential of petroleums over the extent of individual horizons in fields of Eastern Apsheron.

FIG. 12. Changes in aromatic hydrocarbon content in the gasolines of petroleums over the extent of individual horizons on the Apsheron Peninsula (Surakhany and Karachukhur fields).

The concept of the effect of present temperatures on the distribution of petroleum properties in the productive mass of the Apsheron peninsula was first expressed by S. N. Obryadchikov [22]. This idea was developed in the article cited above [21] and does not raise any objections. However, some investigators surmise that the duration of the period of formation for the accumulations plays a role here and this leads to the fact that the more deeply buried accumulations receive additional light crude from the direction of an oil-gathering basin, located even deeper, within the limits of the South Caspian depression.

This point of view likewise does not encounter any particular objections and does not oppose the admission of the effect of temperature. The necessity for the admission of the role of metamorphism, arising from the data on hydrocarbon composition presented above, obtains in this case as well but then this role is tied in with the addition of new portions of petroleum, even more metamorphised in accord with the progressive submersion of the oil-gathering basin.

Unfortunately, phenomena like the one described above for the Apsheron Peninsula are not established for other oil-bearing provinces primarily due to a lack of data but also, probably due to the particular nature of petroleum–geologic conditions of the Apsheron Peninsula. The only instance where it is possible to speak of a somewhat similar phenomenon occurs at Samarskaya Luka. Some data on this region are presented in Table 9.

TABLE 9. *Nature of the Distribution of Petroleum Properties in the Samarskaya Luka Fields*

Horizon	Yablonovyi Ovrag			Zol'nyi		
	Sp.Gr.	% to 200 °C	% Arom.*	Sp.Gr.	% to 200 °C	% Arom.*
Coal-bearing Series	0.878	15	3	0.848	23	17
Devonian	0.860	24	16	0.808	20	

* In the 150–200°C fraction.

The data in Table 9 show that there is a decrease in the specific gravity of Petroleums from the Yablonovyi Ovrag to the Zol'nyi fields in both the coal-bearing series and the Devonian.

Such changes can also be traced further west (Fig. 13). The direction of decreasing specific gravity coincides with the direction of increasing formation depth. S.P. Maskimov explains the relationship cited as the result of the differential filling of traps by lighter and heavier petroleums. Gas and lighter petroleum, as it enters from the oil-gathering basin, displaces the heavier petroleum into traps further and further away from the initial traps, in the case cited from the eastern (Zol'nyi) to the western (Yablonovyi Ovrag, etc.) traps [23]. Data on hydrocarbon composition of the petroleums indicate that the Zol'nyi petroleum is more metamorphised than that from Yablonovyi Ovrag.

In general the metamorphism of petroleums increases here in a regular manner in an easterly direction. For the Devonian (D_p formation), the value $\dfrac{a > 400\,^\circ C}{a < 250\,^\circ C}$ in Yablonovyi Ovrag is equal to 1.7, in Zhigulevsk it is 1.0 and in Zol'noe it is only 0.8 [24]. This phenomenon indicates the prolonged entry of petroleum from the east and the gradually increased metamorphism of the entering petroleum.

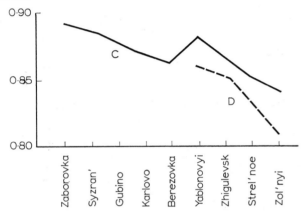

Fig. 13. Changes in the specific gravity of petroleums along the trend of the horizons in Samarskaya Luka fields (according to the data of S. P. Maksimov).

In Turkmenia, the voluminous and detailed investigations of I. S. Starobinets established that a regional barrier separates the zones of occurrence for two different types of petroleum. To the north and east are found naphthenic crudes while paraffinic crudes are found to the south and west, with insignificant differences along the profile [24a]. I. S. Starobinets explains these phenomena by the oxidation of northern and eastern petroleums found in contact with more mobile waters and allows for the cyclization of alkanes to naphthenes [24a].

Such views tie in poorly with hydrogeologic data which do not in the least indicate that everywhere to the north of the barrier, in Nebit-Dag and Cheleken, the waters are less immobile than to the south. The change of paraffinic crude oils to naphthenic as a result of the cyclization of alkanes to naphthenes is inadmissible from the chemical point of view. The explanation of the geochemical phenomena established by I. S. Starobinets can be more readily achieved in a different manner, by recognizing that the formation of accumulations found on different sides of the barrier occurred from different oil-gathering basins, to the south and to the north. The former was buried deeper and the metamorphism of the petroleum in it was therefore more intense. This is also confirmed by geologic data.

It should be noted that petroleums from different zones (in Nebit-Dag) are differentiated also (in addition to group composition and non-hydrocarbon characteristics) by the ratios of normal to iso-paraffins as well as by the ratios of cyclopentane to cyclohexane derivatives. These ratios are lower for petroleums richer in naphthenes [24b]. There is no basis for considering that the oxidation of petroleums is accompanied by the conversion of five-membered to six-membered naphthenes and other such processes.

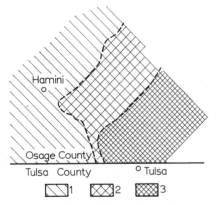

FIG. 14. Zonal chart for the specific gravities of petroleums from the Bartlesville sandstone, Osage County, Oklahoma. Zones of petroleum distribution: *1* sp.gr. < 0.825; *2* sp.gr. < 0.850; *3* sp.gr. < 0.860.

A generalization can be drawn for petroleums in the Pennsylvanian sandstones of Bartlesville, Osage county, Oklahoma. From the schematic chart (Fig. 14) drawn from the data of Neumann and co-authors [25] it may be noted that to the west there is a tendency toward lighter petroleums (in preparing the chart the specific gravities of petroleums from 25 accumulations in the Bart-lesville sandstone were taken into account).

In explaining the above phenomenon the fact should be noted that the depth of the Bartlesville sandstone increases to the west. Processes of migration and oxidation cannot have played a role in the above distribution since the accumulations occur here in isolated sand bodies within a shale formation under conditions precluding any tectonic faulting or movement of waters.

Recently, similar relationships were developed for a number of structures of Class II within the Volga–Ural province. Concurrently, the works of V. F. Raaben, Z. L. Maimin and others established that a structure like the Tatar anticline is characterized by a different trend, namely an increase in the specific gravity of petroleums with depth of burial. The reason for the latter phenomenon is not clear as yet.

The rules or trends analyzed also include such phenomena as the differentiation of petroleums from different tectonic components of a horizon separated vertically through fault displacement. In such cases, within a single field, there may be two or more accumulations in one formation. A survey of the corresponding data shows that, nearly always, the petroleums in the deeper lying tectonic blocks (downthrown, underthrust) are lighter than those in relatively uplifted blocks. This is observed in fields of the Apsheron Peninsula (Surakhany, Bibi-Eibat, Lok-Batan), the Starogroznenski field, in the Kuban (Glubokii Yar and others), on the Emba (Makat), in Venezuela (Mene Grande, Cruces-Manueles), etc.

In this situation one should note one more form of the general trend of petroleum change with depth of occurrence. The immediate reasons may vary for the different cases. Z. A. Tabasaranskii considers that the reason for petroleum differences in separate tectonic blocks lies in the different times of formation for the corresponding accumulations and is not related to depth [26]. As evidence for his point of view he points to the presence of lighter petroleum in horizon VIII at Lok-Batan in the south easterly block, which is relatively uplifted but located in the path of petroleum migration. Even if one allows that a single case provides convincing evidence of the effect of different times of accumulation, one nevertheless has to admit that a factor like a different thickness of overburden for relatively deeper buried and relatively uplifted blocks of accumulation must, in many cases, also have some effect.

The correlation of petroleum properties with depth of accumulation carried out above for four different aspects definitely points to the presence of one dominant tendency—the decrease in specific gravity of petroleums with increasing depth of accumulation. An examination of data on hydrocarbon composition in practically all cases leads to the conclusion that a decrease in specific gravity coincides with indications of processes which increase the number and decrease the size of hydrocarbon molecules.

C. AGE AND DEPTH

The separate relationships between petroleum properties and the age of containing sediments and their depth of deposition was demonstrated in the preceding sections. At the same time it was pointed out that actually, as a rule, the effects of age and depth were in the same direction. The determination of their combined effect can be simplified by the use of representative units called Geokhronobats [27]. The latter, obtained by multiplying depth of petroleum accumulation (in kilometers) by the absolute age of containing sediments (in millions of years), permits petroleum quality to be represented as a function of two variables given in one equation.

The characteristics of fifty petroleums from all of the principal areas of the U.S.S.R. are presented in Table 10 in order of increasing Geokhronobats (values of absolute age in calculating the latter were taken from the data of V. V. Belousov).

The data from Table 10 are represented graphically in the form of a vector diagram (Fig. 15)†. In drawing vector diagrams seven variables were used: Geokhronobats and six petroleum properties (specific gravity, tar content, wax content, yield of fraction to 200°C, aromatic hydrocarbon content in the 150–200°C fraction and the naphthene to paraffin ratio, in the 150–200°C fraction). Notwithstanding the fact that, as was to be expected, the petroleums plotted in order of increasing Geokhronobat's do not yield a strictly sustained trend (which is explained by the effect of a number of other factors besides age) the chart, nevertheless, permits certain geochemical rules to be discerned.

† The use of vector diagrams in the geochemistry of petroleum was suggested by N. V. Vassoevich [27].

TABLE 10. *Characteristics of USSR Petroleums as a Function of Absolute Age of Containing Sediments and Deposition Depth*

Field	Geokhronobat	Sp.Gr.	Excise tars* (%)	Waxes (%) (Holde)	% Fractions to 200 °C	% Content in (150–200 °C) fraction		
						Aromatics	Naph-thenes	Paraffins
Okha	1	0.932	35	0.0	5	5	93	2
Okha	2	0.917	33	0.7	8	7	93	0
Okha	4	0.880	21	1.0	20	15	74	11
Nebit-Dag	5	0.882	27	0.5	15	15	59	26
Leninskoe	6	0.868	18	0.6	18	16	68	16
Bibi-Eibat	6	0.866	18	0.3	20	18	62	20
Neftyano-Shirvanskoe	7	0.875	27	1.5	20	17	67	16
Surakhany	7	0.863	10	1.8	18	18	67	15
Surakhany	8	0.870	10	1.0	16	14	54	32
Starogroznenskoe	8	0.869	20	0.6	18	20	59	21
Karachukhur	10	0.856	10	3.0	18	20	60	20
Starogroznenskoe	12	0.858	16	1.2	17	13	39	48
Oktyabr'skoe	17	0.846	16	4.2	8	14	38	48
Karachukhur	18	0.852	12	1.0	20	21	53	26
Asfalt't. Gora	18	0.850	16	2.0	27	23	37	40
Chimion	20	0.868	23	4.2	18	20	42	38
Starogroznenskoe	20	0.860	14	2.5	19	22	49	29
Changyrtash	23	0.867	13	3.6	21	21	36	43
Sel'rokho	24	0.854	19	2.6	22	21	37	42
Gudermes	25	0.850	16	0.5	23	21	49	30
Shorsu	28	0.826	12	4.0	27	24	23	53
Kuratsetse	29	0.850	18	2.7	20	20	44	36
Bitkov	31	0.840	15	4.9	24	15	29	56
Starogroznenskoe	32	0.846	17	2.6	25	16	31	53
Shirokaya Balka	33	0.848	16	2.3	28	22	44	34
Dossor	35	0.858	3	0.3	13	7	67	26
Alamyshik	36	0.837	8	2.8	26	21	36	43
Izberbash	38	0.840	12	3.0	27	17	33	50
Khanabad	39	0.850	18	3.5	25	22	25	53
Koschagyl	40	0.845	11	1.0	22	13	62	25
Palvantash	48	0.850	18	3.8	24	24	28	48
Andizhan	53	0.838	15	3.5	25	25	25	50
Dossor	54	0.843	5	0.8	18	7	67	26
Buguruslan	60	0.890	43	2.0	19	27	17	56
Novostepanovka	65	0.863	38	2.4	22	23	37	40
Iskine	78	0.843	5	1.4	13	9	79	12
Iskine	82	0.803	3	1.0	30	14	27	59
Dzhaksimai	114	0.840	6	1.2	23	10	48	42

TABLE 10. *(contd.)*

Field	Geokhronobat	Sp.Gr.	Excise tars* (%)	Waxes (%) (Holde)	% Fractions to 200 °C	% Content in (150–200 °C) fraction		
						Aromatics	Naphthenes	Paraffins
Ishimbai	133	0.867	29	1.4	18	23	24	53
Kulsary	140	0.816	5	1.9	30	8	62	30
Iskine	158	0.785	2	1.3	39	12	35	53
Syzran'	260	0.856	27	2.0	23	16	34	50
Yablonovyi Ovrag	270	0.875	30	3.8	18	4	37	59
Syzran'	273	0.859	30	2.3	20	12	29	59
Severokamsk	288	0.841	18	3.8	27	17	30	53
Polazna	296	0.838	16	3.3	32	18	29	53
Tuimazy	300	0.880	30	3.6	18	18	26	56
Il'ya	357	0.870	18	3.0	20	20	47	33
Tuimazy	460	0.850	30	3.5	33	23	18	59
Yablonovyi Ovrag	494	0.860	15	5.8	28	23	24	53

* "Excise tars" is an arbitrary quantitative measure of the tar content of petroleum. Since the excise tar test involves treatment of the petroleum with concentrated sulfuric acid, this parameter indicates not only the concentration of tarry substances, but also the concentration of materials capable of being converted into tarry-resinous substances. [Trans. Ed.]

On the right half of the chart it can clearly be seen that:

1. The specific gravity of petroleums decreases with increasing Geokhronobat.

2. The horizontal projections of vectors increase downward indicating a decreasing tar content.

3. The direction of the vectors gradually changes in a clockwise direction. This means that a decrease in tar content is accompanied by an increase in wax content.

4. Notably conspicuous are several isolated high sulfur content petroleums that are mainly concentrated in the lower portion of the chart (all are from the Ural–Volga region). They are characterized by a high tar content as a result of which they also violate the general rule of change in specific gravities and clockwise rotation of vectors; however, they adhere to the general rule of change in wax content.

On the left-hand portion of the chart some rules evolve on the

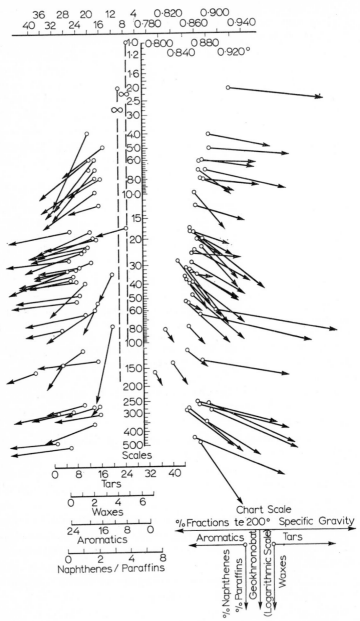

FIG. 15. Vectorial geochemical chart for petroleums of the USSR

hydrocarbon composition of light fractions (the ligroin fraction was selected here in view of the fact that the lighter ones do not occur in all petroleums). The most noticeable tendency on the left half of the chart is the clockwise rotation with increasing Geokhronobat values. This is tied in with the increasing relative content of aromatic hydrocarbons in the composition of light fractions with a simultaneous decrease in the naphthene: alkane ratio. The relationship indicates that naphthenes become displaced by paraffins and aromatics in the light fractions of petroleums with increasing age of containing sediments and depth of occurrence. Essentially, this is the same relationship which was stated above for petroleums from different horizons in individual fields. Here it shows a tendency to depend, in general, simultaneously on age and depth. It is a consequence of the processes of metamorphism of petroleums.

This general phenomenon is violated in part by the behavior of Emba Jurassic petroleums characterized by a low aromatic content (according to the geochemical classification proposed previously [28], these petroleums are classed separately). Thus, the vectorial geochemical chart for petroleums of the USSR, besides illustrating the general relationships, shows the basic deviations from these as well.

With the aid of a unit like the Geokhronobat, and by means of a visual representation like the vectorial chart, it is possible to demonstrate the simultaneous effect of age and depth on petroleum properties.

D. DIFFERENTIATION WITHIN ACCUMULATIONS

As was already noted above, changes in petroleum properties within individual oil pools present a completely different phenomenon. It was suggested by M. V. Abramovich, who investigated the phenomenon of decreasing specific gravity of petroleum with increasing depth of formation within individual accumulations in detail for fields on the Apsheron Peninsula, that the change be called the "formation gradient" [11]. In the case of increasing specific gravity with increased depth the formation gradient is considered to be positive. However, this value though extremely convenient in the case of bedded types of accumulations, loses it significance in the study of massive types of sediments.

Of seventy fields in various countries of the world for which the appropriate data are available, sixty show an increase in the specific gravity of the petroleums with increasing depth of accumulation (i.e. a positive formation gradient for bedded accumulations). Only in ten instances is the reverse phenomenon or irregular variation encountered. Among the sixty fields of the first type, there are a number of multiformation fields containing numerous accumulations with corresponding differences. Consequently, the number of accumulations where the above relationship is actually observed is considerably higher than 60. Thus the increase in specific gravity with depth within oil pools represents the usual case while the reverse situations are rare.

The explanation of the relationship lies in the phenomenon of gravitational differentiation of petroleums within oil pools. Just as there is physical separation (layering) in a formation for gas, oil and water, there occurs a layering within an oil pool according to specific gravity of the oil. A large portion of the tars in solution (as well as, apparently, solid hydrocarbons) accumulates in the lower portions of petroleum accumulations while a large portion of the dissolved gas is found in the upper portions.

Recently this question was studied from the physical standpoint by A.Yu.Namiot [29]. As a result of his calculations Namiot came to the conclusion that for petroleums simultaneously containing many asphalt–tar components, light components, and dissolved gas, a noticeable effect of gravity should be expected. It is quite possible that a significant role was already played by dynamic gravitational differentiation in the formation of oil pools.

The phenomenon of gravitational differentiation becomes more radically expressed the greater the thickness of the accumulation. Hence, the conditions for the differentiation of petroleums within accumulations are more favorable in fields located within folded regions where there is a steep formation dip and the accumulations have a considerable thickness. Classic examples of this type can be found in fields of the Apsheron Peninsula.

Table 11 gives the values of formation gradients for specific gravities of petroleums for some of the Apsheron Peninsula fields (according to M.V.Abramovich, M.F.Mirchink *et al.*). The formation gradient is equal to the change (+, −) in petroleum specific gravity for 100 m of depth.

Some additional understanding of this phenomenon can be obtained by studying the schematic profile section through the accumulation in the PK series in the southeasterly downthrown block of the Surakhany field (Fig. 16). From the diagram it can be seen that the increase in specific gravity occurs continuously throughout a vertical extent of 700 m. A similar character is also established for the phenomenon in Chakhnaglyar [30].

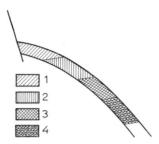

FIG. 16. Petroleum specific gravities in the PK Series of the Surakhany field. Distribution zones for petroleums by average specific gravity: *1* 0.8850; *2* 0.8853; *3* 0.8877; *4* 0.8905.

With nominal thickness of accumulations the differentiation is quite weak. This type of accumulation is especially characteristic of "shelf" fields. This prevents gravitational layering within them. In fact, in the majority of shelf fields no significant inhomogeneity of petroleums within individual oil pools is observed. Even in the vast accumulations of the Tuimazy and East Texas fields, etc., the petroleums are relatively homogeneous.

TABLE 11. *Formation Gradients for Petroleum Specific Gravity in Some Aspheron Peninsula Accumulations*

Field	Horizon	Gradient	Field	Horizon	Gradient
Leninskoe	II	+0.006	Bibi-Eibat	VIII	+0.004
Leninskoe	III	+0.006	Bibi-Eibat	X	+0.006
Surakhany	V	+0.012	Bibi-Eibat	XI	+0.006
Surakhany	Va	+0.027	Bibi-Eibat	XII	+0.006
Surakhany	VB	+0.041	Bibi-Eibat	XV	+0.026
Surakhany	VI	+0.036	Bibi-Eibat	XVI	+0.012
Surakhany	VIa	+0.052	Bibi-Eibat	XVIII	+0.010
Surakhany	PK	+0.001	Bibi-Eibat	XVIII	+0.002
Bibi-Eibat	V	+0.006	Kala	PK-2	+0.005
Bibi-Eibat	VII	+0.004	Binagady	PK	+0.010

Recently the variation of petroleum properties within shelf accumulations was investigated by A.K.Kotina [24] and Z.L.Maimin [31]. These investigations confirm the assumptions set forth above but also establish the presence of a definite increase in specific gravity of petroleums in the direction of the lower portions of the accumulations in some shelf fields, e.g. in Zol'noe Ovrag and Yablonovyi Ovrag. The oil fields of Samarskaya Luka, where petroleum differentiation within accumulations can be noted, are distinguished from typical shelf fields by their more intensely disturbed state.

The above investigators also state the fact that there is a greater change in petroleum properties on the more level flanks of anticlines by comparison with the steeper flanks, which they explain by the relatively stronger action of water on the former in view of the greater areal extent of its water–oil contact. Such a conclusion, however, is in obvious conflict with available data on the different nature of waters on the steep and flat flanks of the indicated anticlines. Hydrogeologic data indicate a more active (in the hydraulic and geochemical sense) nature for the waters on the steep flanks [32]. Hence, the phenomenon can hardly be explained by the hydrogeologic conditions. In any event it requires further investigation.

In the flank depressions of shelves petroleum differentiation within accumulations is encountered frequently, especially in massive accumulations (e.g. Ishimbai), but also in some bedded reservoirs that have considerable vertical extent (e.g. the Graham field in the Ouachita oil-bearing province, Fig. 17).

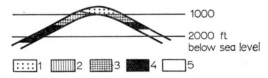

FIG. 17. Specific gravity of petroleums in the Jones Sand, Graham Field, Oklahoma (according to Tomlinson [33]). *1* Gas; *2* petroleum, sp.gr. <0.845; *3* petroleum, sp.gr. 0.845–0.860; *4* petroleum, sp.gr. >0.860; *5* water.

In some instances the observed inhomogeneity in petroleum quality in an accumulation is due to the oxidation effect of bottom or edge waters. Thus, in the Krasnokamsk field, of middle Carboniferous age, a zone of about 10 m in thickness can be traced along the oil–water contact where the petroleum has a much higher specific gravity than in the main body of the accumulation and which, in the opinion of S. F. Fedorov, forms a barrier of sorts and shields the accumulation from the pressure of formation waters [34].

A very characteristic case is represented by the lenticular accumulation of Bush City in Kansas (Fig. 18). As can be noted on the illustration shown in Fig. 18, a drastic increase in specific gravity of petroleum is observed near the oil–water contact. Similar phenomena are also observed in some other fields. It is possible that they are more widespread than was previously assumed since, apparently, relatively thin films of oxidized petroleum near the oil–water contact are easily missed in oilwell production records.

It must be emphasized that the presence of zones with especially heavy petroleums at water–oil contacts and the layering of petroleums over entire accumulations are two different phenomena. It is obvious that the examples, presented above, of the gradual change in petroleum quality over many hundreds of meters can only be explained by the process of gravitational differentiation and can in no way be tied to the effect of edge waters. The relationship between the homogeneity of petroleum in accumulations and the relief in the latter also confirms this conclusion. For the

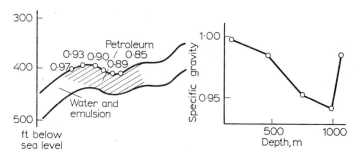

FIG. 18. Petroleum specific gravities in the Bush City field, Kansas (according to H. Charles [35]).

FIG. 19. Petroleum gravities going downdip in the PK Series, Binagadi field (according to V. S. Melik-Pashaev).

Baku fields the gradual changes in petroleum properties moving downstructure and their drastic change near the edge water was recently clearly shown by V. S. Melik-Pashaev [36] (Fig. 19).

With maximum relief in an accumulation the lightest varieties of petroleum, consisting of light fractions alone, can be found at the top. Apparently this phenomenon occurs in the Kimpina field in Romania and the Ventura Avenue field in California. The Ventura Avenue field has long attracted attention as an example of the anomalous distribution of petroleum properties with depth and as the typical representative of Class II fields with a positive specific gravity gradient (see above). Various explanations have been offered. Thus, for example, Taff considered that the deeper accumulations, below the Gosnel series, contain petroleum formed from diatoms while the upper contain petroleum derived from the remains of foraminifera [37]. However, even if one allows for the effect of the composition of source matter this explanation is inadequate. Still remaining to be answered are those differences which can clearly be traced with in the lower as well as within the upper petroleums. It is not possible to speak of the effect of hydrogeologic conditions in this case. No anomalous hydrogeologic conditions can be noted here (the distribution of salinities is normal, increasing downward, all of the waters are primarily calcium chloride solutions, the sulfate content of the waters likewise do not show any anomalies [38]).

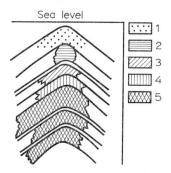

FIG. 20. Schematic section showing distribution of petroleums according to specific gravity in the Ventura Avenue field (California). *1* Gas and oil, sp.gr. 0.749–0.753; Specific gravity of petroleum: *2* 0.759–0.786; *3* 0.814–0.828; *4* 0.870–0.875; *5* 0.875–0.880.

In the opinion of D. Barton the entire series of accumulations in the Ventura Avenue field represent an integral unit. All the accumulations are in communication with each other and gravitational differentiation has occurred within the entire system [19]. This view deserves serious consideration. Here we must, first, take into account the extreme intensity of stratigraphic deformation (the fold represents a rare example, in oil-bearing regions, of a "sharp" anticline), which without a doubt, was accompanied by considerable fracturing and, second, the very nominal thickness of argillaceous partitions (see Fig. 20).

Most probably, the Ventura Avenue field actually represents a rare case of gravitational differentiation of petroleum on a huge scale which led to the appearance of unusually light petroleums.

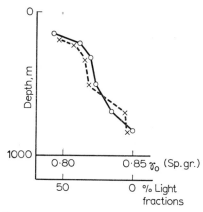

Fig. 21. Distribution of petroleum properties with depth in the Kettleman Hills field.

However, this process, and the hydrologic continuity throughout all accumulations which caused it, apparently occurred sometime in the past followed by the disassociation of the accumulations. The absence of hydrologic continuity between individual accumulations is currently evidenced by the difference in their contours. Similar to the investigated instance in many respects is another Californian field, Kettleman Hills, which is also a characteristic example of a Class I field (Fig. 21).

In Kettleman Hills, as in the Ventura Avenue field, any significant role for the hydrogeologic factor is precluded. The hydrogeologic conditions are practically unchanged throughout the section; all of the waters represent solutions of the calcium chloride type. In the opinion of D. Barton [19], and F. Lahee [39], the positive vertical gradient for specific gravity observed in the Kettleman

Hills field is likewise the effect of gravitational differentiation. F. Lahee indicates that the division between heavy and light petroleums there "represents a near horizontal surface and cuts across the four bottom zones" [39]. This explanation is quite plausible. However, in this case, one should also consider the factor of lithology which plays a significant role here (see below).

Gravitational differentiation of petroleum in structurally complex reservoirs is present in other instances as well, sometimes on a very small scale.

Thus in the Tuimazy field the petroleum in the accumulation has an average specific gravity of 0.852 while the upper accumulation has an average of 0.848. On the basis of such relationships it has been assumed that there is now (or must have been sometime in the past) communication between the first and second horizons. The existence of such communication has been further established by the analysis of production data.

In the Syzran'–Zaborovska field, in the coal-bearing series, the petroleum in the B_1 accumulation is characterized by an average specific gravity of 0.860 and a wax content of 2.2% while the petroleum in the B_2 accumulation, located somewhat lower in the section, is characterized by values of 0.886 and 3.6% respectively. Such an anomalous distribution of petroleum properties, i.e. an increase in specific gravity going down the section, with the simultaneous increase in wax content, can only be explained by gravitational differentiation. The wax content in petroleums usually increases as the specific gravity decreases, due to the effect of chemical processes. With gravitational differentiation of petroleum, however, solid hydrocarbons must collect at the base of an accumulation together with the tars. Considering the nominal thickness of the interbedded argillaceous unit (about 10 m) and the complex form of the oil-bearing sandstone bodies, the presence of hydraulic communication between the B_1 and B_2 accumulations in this field should be considered quite possible.

Something should be said about fields (more accurately–oil pools or accumulations) with anomalous (negative) specific gravity gradients.

Of seven cases, in which this phenomenon is observed, four are represented by California fields containing petroleum in formations outcropping at the surface and sealed therein by asphalt (Midway Sunset, McKittrick, Coalinga and Summerland). Here the increase in specific gravity in an upward direction toward the outcrops is explained by the escape of light petroleum fractions and processes of oxidation.

The remaining instances of negative formation gradients (for example in the Chokrakskii formations of the Starogroznenskoe field, where this phenomenon was studied by G. A. Maksimovich [40]), though not related to formations outcropping on the surface, are likewise explained by processes of escape of light fractions and oxidation. These occur predominately on the domes of anticlinal folds highly disturbed by tectonic faulting (see below). Such instances, as can be seen from the above numbers, are very rare.

The above indicates that the differentiation of petroleums within individual pools (or with the existence of temporary communication between individual accumulations) is primarily caused by the gravitational factor.

E. FACIO-LITHOLOGIC CONDITIONS

The idea of the effect of facio-lithologic conditions on petroleum properties is a very old one. Initially, it arose in the form of recognition of the role of variations in source material and had a very weak factual basis. The understanding of the effects of composition of reservoir rocks on processes of change in petroleums was clearly formulated in the work of C. W. Washburne [41]. H. Hlauschek [2] developed the idea based on the significance of the composition of petroleum-forming organisms, tying this question in with the facies. A. V. Frost [42] and A. S. Velikovskii suggested the probable role of the differences in catalytic properties of reservoir rocks.

At present, knowledge of the effect of facio-lithologic conditions on petroleum quality is in an extremely confused state. On the one hand there is the effect of the nature of source material, connected with the environmental facies of sediment and petroleum formation, and, on the other hand, the effect of rock character on changes in petroleum. These two questions should be treated separately.

The question of the effect of the nature of source material has, in recent times, been widely advanced by H. Hlauschek and V. A. Sokolov. H. Hlauschek considers that the vertical gradient for petroleum properties in fields is related to facies changes with time. The dominance of a negative vertical gradient for specific gravity, however, is explained by the regressive character of the sections in an overwhelming majority of oil fields. In the deeper-water facies, plankton remains, which yield aliphatic compounds (light crudes), predominate as the oil-forming matter, while in the shallower-water facies an increasing role is played by ligno-humic residue from surface vegetation, which yields cyclic compounds (heavy crudes) [43].

Such a viewpoint, confirmed by H. Hlauschek with individual examples, certainly does not survive criticism. The universal relationship between petroleum quality and depth of accumulation and in part the age of containing rocks has been demonstrated above. Hlauschek's views on the regressive character of all oil field sections of course in no way correspond to the facts. Thus, of all of the oil fields in the U.S.S.R., only in several instances does the stratigraphic oil-bearing interval approximately correspond to sedimentary rhythm. A pertinent refutation of the hypothesis of the effect of source composition are the relationships observed, for example in fields of the Western Kuban' and elsewhere where a regular distribution of petroleum properties can be traced in spite of the non-conformance of stratigraphic to absolute depths of accumulation.

Considering the dominance of the relationship between petroleum properties and depths of accumulation, the effect of the facies factor can only be expected in individual instances, and most likely in situations involving an anomalous distribution of petroleum properties with depth, e.g. in Class II and III fields or in situations where petroleums exhibit changes over the extent of horizons with relatively constant depths.

Unfortunately, recently a number of investigators, ignoring or rejecting without evidence the obvious relationship between petroleum quality and depth of occurrence, have emphasized, without adequate grounds, the facio-lithologic factor. Thus H. Hlauschek attempts to explain the difference between Meotissian and Daccian formation petroleums of Romania by facies variation [43]. He thereby ignores the fact that the regular change of petroleum properties in Romania is also observed within units of the Meotisse and Daccian stages (see above, for the Moreni field).

For the oil bearing province of the Gulf Coast. F. R. Haeberle [44] recently attempted to correlate lithologic facies with petroleum properties, namely, the relationship between petroleums with specific gravity of less than 0.800 and "deep-water" facies. Data presented by him, however, not only do not deny, but in fact once more confirm, the earlier conclusions of D. Barton [10] and B. Brooks [45], which, based on widespread and detailed investigations, establish a primary relationship between petroleums in the Gulf Coast region and depths of occurrence. It is quite probable that facio-lithologic conditions do have some effect there, but it is only secondary. Neither the preceding studies nor the work of Haeberle give any indication of the occurence of such an effect (especially when, by Haeberle's own admission, the identification of "deep-water" facies is extremely conditional).

For oil-bearing regions of Wyoming, J. M. Hunt [46] likewise attempts to prove that, within a horizon in a downward direction in an ancient basin, there is a decrease in petroleum specific gravity and sulfur content. But since the indicated direction also usually conforms to the regional downward trend of formations, the given relationship can also be looked on as evidence of the effect of depth of accumulation similar to the instances described above.

The question of the effect of the facies factor is put in a somewhat different aspect by V. A. Sokolov [47]. As the basis of his hypothesis on the effect of facies conditions on petroleum quality Sokolov uses the difference between petroleums of Baku (naphthenic and sweet) and those of the Second Baku (paraffinic and sour). The differences between Kral–Volga region petroleums from carbonate reservoir rocks, and petroleums of Baku from fractured shale reservoirs, V. A. Sokolov assigns to the fact that in carbonate facies, where the contribution from terrigenous sources is small, the main sources of petroleum are plankton albumen and fats which yield end products rich in paraffin and sulfur. In sandy-clayey facies, where terrigenous source contributions include ligno-humic residues from terrestrial vegetation, the source matter is characterized by its highly cyclic and sulfur-free nature.

V. A. Sokolov, himself, admits that this hypothesis cannot pretend to be universal. Its shortcomings arise from the following. In the first place a very large number of paraffinic petroleums is found not in carbonate but rather in sandstone reservoirs. As Sokolov himself reports, the Pennsylvanian petroleums found in sandstones are usually the most saturated. In the second place, Sokolov only considered the composition of light fractions. If lubricating oil fractions are also considered, not to speak of the tars, then it appears that the petroleums from the Second Baku, as a rule, are more, not less, cyclic in composition than those from Baku and similar fields. In general, it is found that petroleums in limestones are more often characterized by a higher tar content. This was noted long ago [41].

Thus the assumption that the facies dependence of petroleum hydrocarbons (in the manner proclaimed by V.A.Sokolov) is a prime factor is not confirmed after all of the facts are taken into account.

As far as the sulfur content of petroleums is concerned, the ideas on its being a primary factor and on its relationship with albumen sulfur likewise suffers from numerous objections. In the first place it should be recognized that "albumen sulfur, which escapes rapidly with decomposition in the form of hydrogen sulfide cannot explain the origin of ... sour crude" [4]. Secondly, the association of sour crudes with carbonate rocks is by no means universal. Numerous examples can be cited of high sulfur content petroleums found in sandstones (the Devonian of the Ural–Volga region, Venezuela, a number of regions in the Southern portion of the North American shelf); also, many low sulfur content petroleums occur in limestones (the Appalachian Basin, Mid-Continent and others).Thirdly, as will be shown later, the distribution of sour petroleums is related to certain geological–geochemical conditions not having any relationship to the origin of the organic source material.

One other fact may be pointed out as a contradiction of the primary nature of high sulfur content in sour petroleums. Recently, A.K.Karimov showed that the aromatic hydrocarbon content in sour petroleums, determined by the general methods, is exaggerated and a correction is proposed for the technique of determining the hydrocarbon composition for such crudes [17]. The correction proposed by Karimov can be applied to tars as well since it is well known that the tar content of sour petroleums is related to their sulfur content (according to Karimov's data the correlation factor for this relation is equal to $+0.63$).

Assuming that the average molecular weight of tars is 500 and the sulfur content in tars is 75% of the total sulfur content of the whole crude,† the content of sulfur-free tars in petroleum (A) can

---

† According to the data of V.A.Uspenskii, 22–43% of all the sulfur in petroleums is found in the asphalt–tar components. In excise tars this quantity must be more than double.

be calculated with the formula

$$A = B - \frac{S(0\cdot75)\,(500)}{32},$$

where B is the % of excise tars† in the petroleum, and S is the % sulfur in the petroleum.

Of course, this is not an analytic computation. Using this formula, however, a tar content value can be obtained which permits a definite ranking of practically all petroleums. Figure 22 shows, in graphical form, data on the tar content for thirty-five petroleums in the USSR in the order of increasing Geokhronobat (see above).

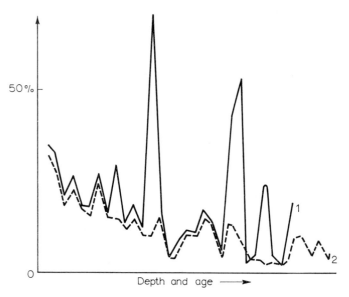

FIG. 22. Relationship between tar content of petroleums and depth of accumulation and age of containing sediments. *1* tar content; *2* tar content corrected for sulfur content.

From the graph (Fig. 22) it can be seen that the tar content of sour petroleums does not fit the general pattern of decreasing tar content with age and depth but, with the introduction of a correction according to the data from the above formula, sour petroleums are

† See footnote to Table 10, p. 65 [Transl. Ed.].

not as conspicuously incongruous in the general ranking. This illustration confirms the view that the sulfur content of petroleums is primarily a secondary phenomenon which complicates the general rule.

All of the above leads to the conclusion that the authors who advanced the facies factor, i.e. the role of compositional differences of source material, were unsuccessful in strengthening their point of view by a single reliable fact. More than that, it must be admitted that it is practically impossible to establish whether or not facies nature of source matter occurs as a prime factor in any one instance or whether it is the effect of some processes which depend on the lithologic peculiarities of the containing rock. Such is the conclusion presented in the above-mentioned work of F. Haeberle and of others.

The properties of reservoir rocks, as well as cap rocks and basement rocks of oil-bearing reservoirs must have a significant effect on geochemical processes in oil fields. Among these properties it is possible to identify, respectively, (1) adsorptive, (2) catalytic, (3) reactive, and (4) hydraulic properties.

Adsorptive properties. Rocks can primarily adsorb asphaltenes and tars from petroleums. The adsorptive ability of rocks increases with increasing concentration of colloidal size fraction and with increasing content of montmorillonite type minerals in these fractions. The so-called bleaching clays used in the purification of petroleum products and some other materials are predominantly montmorillonitic: bentonites, floridins, askanites, nalchikines, etc.*). Having the least adsorptive capability are clean quartz sands and coarsely crystalline rocks.

Catalytic properties. A catalytic effect on some chemical transformations of hydrocarbons and other petroleum components (e.g. redistribution of hydrogen, decomposition of molecules, etc.) is exerted first of all by aluminosilicate minerals (refer to Chapter VI). Unfortunately, to this time there have been no systematic investigations of catalytic properties or even of the mineralogical composition of the clays in oil-bearing sediments. The various available data on the mineralogical composition of clays within oil field sections [48, 49, 50] are completely inadequate for reaching any

---

* These are varieties of clays and clay mixtures whose names are derived from age or place of occurrence, composition, or usage (see footnote, p.295). [Transl. Ed.].

conclusions. This situation severely complicates the determination of the role of lithologic factors in the geochemistry of petroleum.

It is possible that an effect, comparable in part to that of aluminosilicates, is also exerted by the radioactive materials in rocks. The radioactivity of sedimentary rocks is related primarily to their colloidal fractions. Hence, the most radioactive sedimentary rocks are fine clayey deposits.

From the above it must be concluded that increased clay content in rock must, in general, lead to an increase in their adsorptive and catalytic capabilities, which consequently would have an overall effect on petroleums in the direction of decreasing their specific gravities. Such a conclusion agrees with the observations of a number of investigators as noted above, i.e. on the agreement in a number of cases between the direction of decreasing petroleum specific gravity and the transition to more argillaceous ("deep water") sediments (refer also to [51]). Instances in which petroleum composition is observed to be related to the clay content of containing rock are worthy of special investigation.

1. The Kettleman Hills field

This field has already been discussed as an example of the relatively rare gravitational differentiation. Lithologic conditions here are also quite unusual. Moving up in the section the composition of rock (reservoir rocks as well as clays making up the barriers) changes uniformly in the direction of finer grain size. The upper clays are pure bentonites which are known as the best natural adsorbents and catalysts. Correlating these facts with the gradual decrease in specific gravity with decreasing depth in the section and with the presence of the lightest petroleums (specific gravity less than 0.75) in the uppermost portions of the sections, it must be assumed that there exists a definite effect of lithology on petroleum quality. In the upper horizons the petroleums could have lost their heavy polar components as a result of adsorptive processes as well as undergone a greater chemical metamorphism due to clay mineral catalysis.

2. The Coalinga, Belridge, Summerland (California) fields

In three California oil fields, Coalinga, Belridge and Summerland, a decrease in specific gravity is observed with depth, accompanied by increasing clay content in the reservoir rock. In the Coalinga field, within the Temblor sandstones of the Miocene series, petroleum specific gravities decrease from 0.95–0.93 in the zone of well developed clean sands to 0.86 in the pinch out zone of the sand interbeds where the sands are highly argillaceous.

Similar phenomena are observed in the Belridge field within the Etchegoin series of Pliocene age. J. Taff explains these instances by the escape of gas and light fractions from the upper portions of the accumulations and their preservation in the lower portions where the increased argillaceous content complicates the movement of fluids [37]. However, although the process involving the loss of light fractions by the petroleum unquestionably does occur, there is no basis for considering the reservoir rocks to be impermeable to gas. Quite possibly the argillaceous character has another effect here— a catalytic one. In this case, the catalytic effect of the rocks can be relatively more extensive in relatively thin interbeds at the pinch outs due to the smaller mass of the petroleum.

3. The mid-continent fields—East Hominy, Boston, Hittle, Shell Creek, East Medellin, Benton, Winfield, Slick Carson, Wildhorse, Graham

The ten listed mid-continent fields (Oklahoma and Kansas) contain upper oil accumulations in lenticular sandstones of Pennsylvanian age and a lower group in the Ordovician carbonate mass (Arbuckle formation). Most of them contain only two oil-bearing horizons. The specific gravities of the petroleum in the Arbuckle series are either somewhat higher than those of the Pennsylvanian petroleums (in East Hominy and Boston) or completely similar to the latter (Hittle and Shell Creek) or, finally, slightly lower (for example, East Medellin). There is a corresponding distribution for the sulfur and light fraction contents. Thus this group of fields is marked by a more or less obviously expressed anomalous distribution of petroleum quality along the section. The fields are related to Classes II or III.

The Ordovician petroleums lie in carbonate reservoirs while the Pennsylvanian oils occur in sandstone lenses within masses of clay. In the limestones, containing relatively small quantities of alumino-silicate catalysts the process of petroleum metamorphism, leading to a decrease in specific gravity, must be relatively retarded as compared to that in clastic rocks. Some of the chemical peculiarities of the light fractions in the Arbuckle petroleums indicate a relatively lesser (compared to the overlying accumulations) degree of metamorphism. Thus, in the East Hominy and Winfield fields the "correlation indices" for fractions† boiling between 125 and 150 °C are higher than those in post-Mississippian petroleums, which attests to the higher cyclical nature of Ordovician gasolines [52]. In the Benton, Hollow and Washell fields, the light fractions of Ordovician petroleums are characterized by high octane numbers, by comparison with post-Mississippian petroleums, which indicates a more complex structure in the Ordovician paraffinic hydrocarbons.

In view of the considerably greater age and depths of accumulation of the Ordovician petroleums, their relatively lesser metamorphism can only be related to their lithologic peculiarities.

This group also includes several fields, Tidal Osage, Event and others, differing from the preceding examples only in that the deeper accumulations are found not in Ordovician but in Mississippian limestones. Previous statements with respect to influence of reservoir rock composition can be applied here as well.

4. The Aptian petroleums of the Emba province

Of great interest is the genetic relationship between the Neocomian and Aptian petroleums of the Emba oil-bearing province. The Aptian petroleums, overlying the Neocomian petroleums, are significantly different from the latter. This is particularly apparent in the Sagiz field (Fig. 23). Neglecting the Aptian, a normal relationship can be observed there. But the Aptian petroleums are lighter than those in the Neocomian reservoirs. This is also observed in several other fields.

† "Correlation indices" are relative indicators of hydrocarbon composition for the fractions.

G. A. Aixenshtadt considers the Aptian petroleums as having originated from the Neocomian [53]. To substantiate such a view he introduces very convincing arguments. However, one cannot explain the difference between Aptian and Neocomian petroleums by migration and related fractionation processes alone. In the first place, it should be pointed out that light fractions (to 200 °C) are

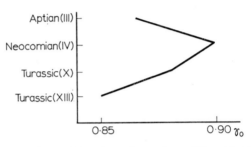

Fig. 23. Specific gravities of petroleums from different horizons in the Sagiz field.

present in Aptian petroleums whereas they are completely absent in Neocomian crudes. Light fractions are also absent in Neocomian petroleums in those fields where there are no oil accumulations in the Aptian and where, consequently, this phenomenon cannot be explained by the escape of light fractions from the Neocomian to the Aptian. Secondly, the fact that Aptian petroleum has a greater tar content as compared to Neocomian petroleum in the East Baichunas field (11 % against 8 %) cannot be tied in with the fractionation process. Thirdly, one also cannot relate the high paraffin content of Aptian petroleums (compared to Neocomian oils) to migration. In the Sagiz and Baichunas fields the paraffin content is higher in Aptian petroleums than it is in the Neocomian. If the difference between Aptian and Neocomian petroleums was only the result of fractionation, wax content should be higher in the Neocomian oils.

Taking the noted situation into account it must be admitted that the difference between Neocomian and Aptian petroleums is the result not only of the migrational origin of Aptian accumulations, but also of the specific metamorphism of petroleums in the Aptian. Such metamorphism must, apparently, be related to the catalytic action of Aptian clays, the peculiarities of which (particularly their highly dispersed state) are well known. Here, apparently, a significant role is played by catalytic rather than adsorptive properties since the action of the latter must be revealed primarily by tar content which is not observed in the given case.

5. The Novobogatinskoe field

In the Novobogatinskoe field the petroleum is found in Jurassic and Tertiary sediments (Fig. 24). The Tertiary petroleum accumulation (sp. gr. 0.775), in a sand lens adjacent to the unconformably underlying Jurassic oil-bearing formations, is considered to have originated as a result of migration from the Mesozoics. However, it is impossible to explain the difference between the Tertiary and Jurassic petroleums by a migration process alone. The Jurassic oil contains 3 % tars and the Tertiary contains 8 %. Such a relationship could not have been created as a result of migrational fractionation (nor as a result of adsorptive processes). The sole explanation here can be the metamorphism of petroleums under the effect of particular catalytic rock properties enhanced by the small size of the accumulation.

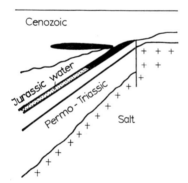

FIG. 24. The Novobogatinskoe field section.

Besides the instances cited the effect of clay content in the rock has been noted in the fields on the Apsheron Peninsula. However, this complex case will be analyzed later in connection with hydrogeological conditions since these also play a part there.

Somewhat puzzling is the distribution of petroleum properties with depth in some fields in Eastern Venezuela (Santa Ana, Santa

Rosa, Oficina, Guarra). In these fields petroleum is found in the Miocene (in the Oficina formation) and in the Eocene (Merecure formation). The whole section consists of alternating clastic sediments. At Santa Ana and Santa Rosa the Eocene petroleums occur in the normal manner, below Miocene petroleums in contact with higher salinity waters. In both fields the Eocene petroleums are heavier than the Miocene oils and in general differ radically from the latter in their properties (% light fractions 12–15 as compared to 35–60, etc.). Perhaps, this is a case of the influence of lithofacies but the nature of their variation is not clear. The effect of vertical migration is not excluded.

Reactive properties. The reactive capability of rocks can be reduced to their oxidizing action. The basic mass of oxygen in sedimentary rocks (in silicas, silicates, aluminosilicates, carbonates) is inert. Only the oxygen in sulfates, free oxides of iron and some of the rarer minerals can be active.

Petroleums associated with sulfate rocks can assume extremely unusual characteristics. Thus in the Uch-Kyzyl field the petroleum in the anhydrites contains more than 70% reactive tars and over 6% sulfur, and, is the most sour petroleum known. In the gypsiferous Kungursk field are found the most tarry as well as sour petroleums. Such instances are rare, however.

V. A. Uspenskii considers the presence of sulfate rocks ("evaporite facies") a necessary condition for the sulfurization of petroleums [3]. However, several cases can be pointed out where highly sulfurous petroleums occur in the complete absence of an "evaporite complex" (specifically gypsum and anhydrite since in general the "evaporite complex" need not contain sulfate rocks). Such examples are numerous: Mexico, Colombia, the Balcones-Mexia zone in Texas, etc. V. A. Uspenskii attempts to explain some of these instances by the effect of an "evaporite complex" supposedly lying somewhere at depth (Balcones zone in Mexico). However, this explanation is unsatisfactory. In the Mexican oil-bearing province there is no justification for assuming the presence of gypsum. Besides, in the faulted Balcones zone there is no upward movement of water as indicated by the fact that the fault zone waters are fresh while the deeper waters are very saline [39]. In general the effect of gypsum, lying deeper in the section, cannot be established anywhere including situations where such relationships are reliably known. For example, in Eastern Fergana accumulations of low sulfur content petroleums are found over the gypsiferous Upper Cretaceous sediments (Gaznau formation). In the Skalistiyi Mountains the Mesozoic petroleum is practically free of sulfur although the underlying Paleozoics contain thick gypsum beds.

The oxidizing properties of rock can also have an indirect effect on petroleum composition. Thus, according to V. A. Uspenskii and O. A. Radchenko, the sulfurization of petroleums basically occurs in carbonate rocks since in sands the hydrogen sulfide, which is the sulfurizing agent formed during the reduction of sulfates, is tied up by the iron which is more abundant there [54, 55, 56]. However, this concept of the effect of the iron content in rocks must be viewed with scepticism. The general agreement on the greater iron content of sands as compared to that of carbonate rocks, based on the data of F. Clarke, cannot be applied to this phenomenon. The point is that it is impossible to speak of the reduction of iron silicates by hydrogen sulfide. We can only speak of free oxides and hydroxides for which the relative concentrations in sands and carbonate rocks have not been established.

According to the data of A. A. Kartsev and V. N. Kholodov, no difference between the content of non-silicate iron in sands and carbonate rocks are observed in the Shorsu field section [57]. At the same time, in the carbonate reservoir rocks of the Shorsu field one finds high sulfur-content petroleums while those with a low sulfur content are found in the sand reservoirs. One can also point to other data. Thus Academician N. M. Strakhov introduces numbers indicating that there is no clear relationship between the carbonate content of sediments and their overall iron content [58]. According to the data of N. M. Strakhov, in the pre-Frannian rocks of the Lower Urals, the average content of common iron in limestones is equal to 1.2%, in argillaceous limestones 2.1% and in sandstones only 0.6% [58]. In Mexico, the Tamaulipas limestones contain large quantities of common iron, while the El-Abra limestones contain several times less [59]. At the same time, both series contain highly sulfurous petroleums.

Even if the overall iron content in limestones in a number of cases is no lower than that in sandstones then this must hold even more for the iron found in the form of free oxides. Even more so, with excess iron oxide, hydrogen sulfide can be oxidized to free sulfur by the process:

$$2\,Fe(OH)_3 + 3\,H_2S \rightarrow 2\,FeS + S + 6\,H_2O$$

Free sulfur, however, reacts with hydrocarbons much more actively than hydrogen sulfide [60]. Consequently, the iron oxide content of rocks must apparently be at least partly responsible for the sulfurization of petroleums. In any event, the overall effect of iron content in rocks is not clear.

Hydraulic properties. The hydraulic properties of rock, essentiallye their water permeability, are responsible (together with other factors) for a greater or lesser water filtration rate and, consequently, the greater or lesser action of water on the petroleum. This factor significantly affects a number of hydrogeologic conditions and will be examined in this connection later. Concluding the survey of the question dealing with the effect of lithofacies conditions (excluding the hydraulic peculiarities of rock) on petroleum quality it must be noted that the effect of specific rock properties (adsorptive, catalytic, oxidizing) is clearly developed in only a relatively few instances and does not involve any basic laws governing the distribution of petroleum quality in fields, but only causes local deviations from these laws. This situation is apparently explained by the fact that the basic mass of oil bearing rocks is relatively homogeneous. The effect of the properties of source matter, i.e. primary facies factors, is practically insignificant as far as petroleum end products are concerned.

F. HYDROGEOLOGIC CONDITIONS

The geochemical action of underground waters on petroleum was suggested by A. Potylitsyn in the preceding century [6]. In recent years the theory of geochemical action of waters on petroleum has been developed further by V. A. Uspenskii [3, 62, 55, etc.] and A. L. Kozlov [63].

Water (more accurately natural aqueous solutions) can have the following effects on petroleum: (a) oxidation, (b) selective solution and (c) catalytic effects. Up to the present time attention has been focused on the first process exclusively. In view of the extensive study of this question the following section likewise gives this aspect the most attention.

Oxidizing action on petroleums can, first of all, be exerted by sulfates dissolved in the waters. The action of sulfates dissolved in water is considerably more significant than that of the sulfates contained in the rocks themselves because the greater mobility of the solution drastically extends the radius of sulfate action.

The interaction between petroleum and sulfates, in the opinion of most investigators, can only occur with the participation of sulfate-reducing bacteria which utilize petroleum hydrocarbons for energy and the oxygen in sulfates for driving the reaction. Consequently, microbiological conditions also affect petroleum changes. However, it is superfluous to examine microbiological conditions here separately since they, so far as is known, are principally determined by hydrogeologic conditions, e.g. rate of movement, sulfate content, salinity, reaction rate and water temperature.

The actual presence of an interaction process between petroleum and subsurface water sulfates is evidenced, on the one hand, by the well-known fact of the absence of sulfates in waters in contact with oil accumulations and, on the other, by the special properties of petroleums in contact with the waters. However, there are a number of complicating instances which must be examined.

The absence of sulfates in the waters can be due to reasons not connected with the effect of petroleum, not, in general, with processes of sulfate reduction. Such a reason can be the precipitation of sulfates from solutions when their concentration exceeds the solubility limit. In that case the sulfates do not decompose but are only removed from the water entering into the composition of the rock.

The solubility of sulfates depends on the character of the sulfates themselves as well as on the character and combination of the other dissolved salts (the general character of the water's salt composition). Least soluble (of the more widely distributed sulfates) is calcium sulfate. Its solubility is especially low in the presence of calcium chloride in the water, i.e. in calcium chloride type waters according to Sulin's classification. Of the sulfates, calcium chloride type waters can only contain calcium sulfate. As a result, calcium chloride type waters can only contain a negligible amount of sulfates. Such waters can frequently, in the complete absence of petroleum, be practically devoid of sulfates, which have precipitated out in the sediment. Calcium chloride type waters, as is well known, are also commonly found in oil-bearing formations. There too, their lack of sulfates, as follows from the above, need not be related to the presence of petroleum.

In addition, as shown by the recent work of N. D. Shustef [64], sulfates can be extracted from water by petroleum by means of their adsorption by the tarry components of the petroleum. The presence of adsorbed sulfates in petroleums, in quantities several times higher than those in adjoining formation waters [64], likewise indicates that the reduction of sulfates by petroleum does not always occur. Thus the absence of sulfates in oil-bearing formation waters in itself is insufficient evidence of the presence of a chemical interaction between petroleum and sulfates.

More significant in this regard are some facts indicating the existence of a relationship between sulfate content of oil-bearing formation waters and their temperature. Thus, according to the data of V. M. Nikolaev, in Grozny field formations having a temperature of over 70–80 °C, the waters contain sulfates (in concentrations up to 0.08 normal) while in lower temperature formations the waters are practically free of sulfates [65]. This phenomenon is explained by the fact that the indicated temperatures place a limit on the activity of sulfate-reducing bacteria and, consequently, to the processes of biochemical reduction of sulfates.

Very low temperatures apparently also oppose the bacterial action as first noted by N. T. Lindtrop [66]. According to the data of this investigator, in one of the fields in the Second Baku, bottom waters in the oil-bearing formation are sulfate bearing at temperatures less than 15 °C. Here we can also point to the high sulfate content of Arctic oil field waters.

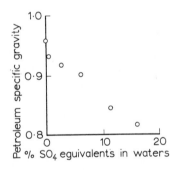

FIG. 25. Relationship between sulfate content in waters and specific gravity of petroleum in the Naftalan field.

Besides temperature, the conditions limiting the development of sulfate-reducing bacteria also include: low pH values (<5), very high water salinity (>20° Be) and high H_2S concentrations [67]. It is possible that high water salinity and its acid reaction are the very reasons for the absence of the reduction of sulfates adsorbed by the tarry components of petroleums. In the Devonian, where this phenomenon was observed [64], these very conditions prevail.

Of definite interest are cases of a systematic relationship between sulfate content in the waters and petroleum quality. Thus, in the Naftalan field, an inverse, straight line relationship is established between petroleum, specific gravity, and sulfate content in the waters of the same horizons (Fig. 25) [68]. The sulfate content of water also increases with depth. This relationship indicates the existence of an interaction between petroleums and the sulfates. It is known that sulfate content in underground waters generally decreases with depth. The sulfides in the rock, however, being an additional source of sulfates, are generally present in uniform quantities over the entire Maikop section of the Naftalan field (where all of the oil-bearing horizons of this field are found).

Thus, changes in sulfate content of the waters in a vertical section does not depend on the depth of accumulation as much as it does on the lithologic peculiarities of a section. Sulfate content here is apparently also independent of the amount of petroleum. It increases in the lower portions of the section where the greater oil accumulations are found.

In view of the indicated independence of sulfate content in Naftalan field waters from accumulation depths, lithologic factors, and oil content in the section, it appears that sulfate content in the waters is a function of petroleum quality. It is possible that such a relationship can be explained by the above cited process of the adsorption of sulfates by petroleum tars. In horizons containing the most tarry petroleums the waters are free of sulfate while in formations containing the least tarry petroleums the sulfate content of the waters is relatively high. A similar phenomenon, but in the presence of considerably lower sulfate contents, is observed in the neighboring Kazan-Bulag field (Fig. 26).

An inverse relationship between petroleum specific gravity and sulfate content of the water is also observed in the Shorsu field (Fig. 27) [57]. A comparison of the sulfate content in the water with the content of various forms of sulfur in the rocks making up these same formations (30 determinations) does not show any trend (the exception lies only in the gypsiferous "K" horizon containing the highest sulfate content waters but this, as pointed out on the graph in Fig. 27, does not violate the basic rule). The significance of the

relationship at Shorsu is apparently the same as in Western Azerbaijan, i.e. the sulfate content of the waters is tied in with petroleum quality.

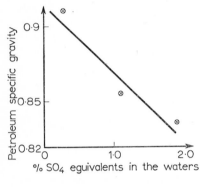

FIG. 27. Relationship between
sulfate content in waters and
petroleum specific gravity in
Shorsu.

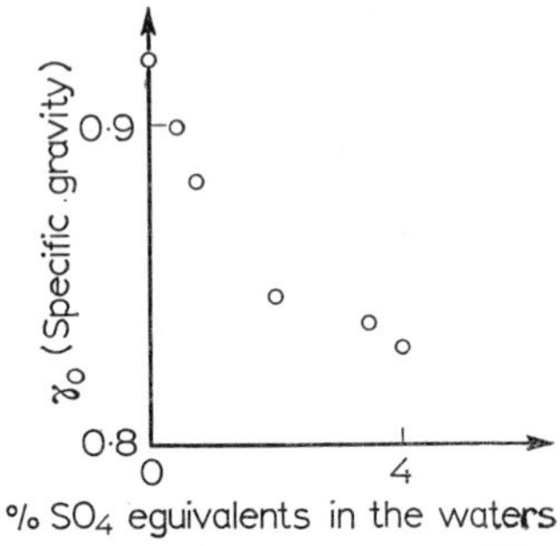

FIG. 26. Relationship between
sulfate content in waters and
petroleum specific gravity in
the Kazan-Bulag field.

The significance of the relationships established above between
sulfate content of the waters and petroleum quality is somewhat
lessened by the existence of reverse situations, i.e. instances where
the sulfate content in the waters and petroleum specific gravity are
related directly (e.g. Tuimazy, Krasnokamsk, Salt Creek).

The various facts presented above prove the existence of interaction processes between petroleums and waters as well as the occurrence, under certain conditions, of reduction of sulfates in the
waters by petroleum. All of these facts, however, still do not prove
that the waters and, in particular, the sulfates dissolved in them,
have a significant effect on petroleum properties.

The instances presented above of the presence of zones of exceptionally heavy petroleums at water–oil contacts can serve as
evidence that petroleum changes can be caused by formation waters.
These petroleums appear to be naturally oxidized varieties; examples of this kind, however, are not very common. Moreover, the
presence of the indicated oxidized zones in the accumulations,
under certain conditions, can even be considered as an obstruction
to the oxidation of petroleum in the remaining portions of these

accumulations. At Krasnokamsk, as indicated above, the oxidized zone is even considered by some to be a barrier screening the accumulation from the pressure of formation waters. V. S. Melik-Pashaev [36] subscribes to a similar opinion with regard to some accumulations in the Baku. In the Hawkins field (Northwest Texas), in the Woodbine sandstone, the oxidized zone is represented by a layer of immobile asphalt only about a meter thick, sharply delineated from the remainder of the accumulation [69]. Under such conditions the mechanism by which the oxidation process spreads to the entire accumulation is not clear.

Nonetheless, accumulations of petroleum which had undergone oxidation by sulfates in the water do exist. Belonging to this group of petroleums are those completely devoid of paraffins, for example the Lechebnaya crude (in the Naftalan field), Horizon III crude (Okha field), Karskaya field crude, Kum field crude and several others. The primary complete absence of saturates is unlikely. The process which led to the formation of such petroleums is viewed by some investigators as the selective "consumption" of saturated hydrocarbons by bacteria and the relative enrichment of petroleum by cyclical components which leads to an increase in specific gravity.

Since all of these accumulations (Naftalan, Karskaya, Okha) are found almost immediately under recent or ancient erosion surfaces (at depths of 100 m or less from these surfaces) and, under conditions favorable for the infiltration of meteoric waters, it is quite possible to assume that they were subjected to the effect of aerobic oxidation by means of dissolved oxygen. In that case the special features of the hydrocarbon composition of the above petroleums should be tied in with aerobic oxidation processes. This problem deserves extensive investigation. Secondly, sulfur-bearing petroleums are also oxidized. The process of sulfur enrichment involves the reactions between sulfur and hydrocarbons, accompanied by polymerization. Sulfur is formed as a result of the reduction of sulfates and the oxidation of hydrogen sulfide.

The following factors must have an effect on the process of oxidation (and sulfur enrichment) of petroleums by sulfates in the waters: (1) the sulfate content of the waters (M_{SO_4}); (2) velocity of water movement (v); the product of these two values ($M_{SO_4} \cdot v$) denotes the amount of reacting material ("dynamic reserves"); (3) the extent of the oil accumulation (Q). The intensity of the oxidation of petroleum can therefore be expressed as

$$\varDelta O = k_0 \frac{M_{SO_4} \cdot v}{Q},$$

where k_0 is a factor depending on petroleum properties, thermo-dynamic and microbiological conditions as well as including some constant. In addition, the magnitude of surface area involved in the water–oil contact is significant.

From the above data it follows that it is very difficult to evaluate the effect of the waters' sulfate contents since the magnitudes of sulfate content can themselves be "secondary", i.e. depend on the reactivity of the petroleum. The sulfate contents of waters in itself by no means has any exceptional significance. A simple calculation shows that with a sulfate ion content in water of 400 mg per 100 g of water (the very high content observed in gypsiferous rocks) and a rate of water movement of 1 cm per year, the "dynamic reserve" of sulfate will not exceed that with a sulfate ion content equal to only 4 mg per 100 g of water and a rate of water movement of 1 m per year.

Thus the hydraulic factor has a very great significance and waters with even a negligible sulfate can have a greater effect than solutions with a high sulfate content.

The rate of water movement in oil bearing formations can be extremely varied: from 10 m per year with significant water entry (for example in some formations of the Grozny region) to values of the order of 10^{-3} per year and less, with an immobile situation (for example in the Lower Carboniferous rocks of the Ural–Volga region according to the calculations of Silin-Bekchurin [70]). The greater the rate of movement of water in contact with the oil the greater the changes in petroleum composition that can occur as a result of the reaction with material dissolved in the water.

V. A. Uspenskii considers that the decrease in specific gravities of petroleums in a downward direction along a section (i.e. the basic rule described above) "is tied in with the different degrees of action that the waters surrounding the accumulation have on the petroleum" and the reason for the inverse relationship "is the reverse nature of the hydrogeologic profile—the increased hydrogeologic exposure of deeper horizons" [71].

However, in actuality this question is much more complex. In the first place, as indicated above, the dominant rule, a negative vertical gradient for petroleum specific gravity, is related to the geothermal factor (through the process of petroleum metamorphism), and to the thickness of the layers overlying the accumulation and hence cannot be completely dependent on hydrogeologic conditions. Secondly, the rate of subsurface water movement is an almost immeasurable value and the available knowledge of the various rates of water movement in the different horizons is in an extremely early state of development.

It is possible to evaluate rates of subsurface water movement from their chemical indications. The mineral content and metamorphism of subsurface waters must generally bear an inverse relationship to their rates of movement. In that case the inverse relationship must exist and be observed between the values of petroleum specific gravity, on one hand, and the salinity of the waters in the same formations on the other. This was first pointed out by V. A. Uspenskii [62]. Actually, in a number of fields, a similarity is observed between the configuration of curves depicting changes in petroleum specific gravity and total water salinity with increasing depth (Fig. 28).

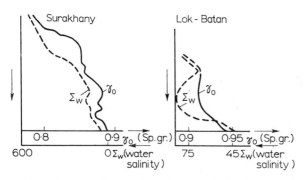

FIG. 28. Petroleum specific gravity and water salinity (in mg-equiv. per 100 g) along a vertical section of some fields of the Apsheron Peninsula.

The situation becomes complicated, however, by the fact that in some instances there is no relationship between petroleum properties and total water salinity, but one can be observed between petroleum quality and the degree of metamorphism of the waters.

Such a phenomenon occurs in the Shorsu field [57] (Fig. 29). Changes in petroleum specific gravities there are inversely proportional to changes in the "secondary salinity" of water. The latter, for calcium chloride types of water, predominant at Shorsu, is a direct index of the degree of metamorphism of the salt solution. This fact, i.e. the correlation between petroleum quality and degree of metamorphism of the waters rather than total salinity, allows one to assume that metamorphism of the water's salt composition rather than the total value of its salinity provides the primary indication of the water's mobility. It should be noted that the divergence between values of salinity and metamorphism represents a rare phenomenon but is by no means a unique case.

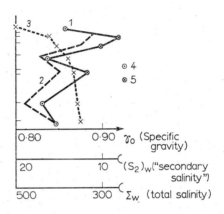

FIG. 29. Changes in Petroleum and Water Properties Along the Section of Shorsu Field. *1* average value of petroleum specific gravity; *2* "secondary salinity" of waters; *3* total salinity of waters; *4* sandstones; *5* limestones.

In the light of the data presented it becomes necessary to compare the number of cases in which the vertical geochemical gradients for petroleums correlate with the corresponding indices for water with the number of cases where such a correlation is lacking. Such a comparison is shown in Table 12. Fields for which a satisfactory correlation between water and petroleum properties is observed (even if it be only between a single pair of properties, e.g. petroleum specific gravity and "secondary salinity" of water, petroleum tar content and water specific gravity, etc.) are denoted as Type "A" in the tabulation, while those fields where no correlation can be established are denoted as Type "B".

TABLE 12. *The Relative Distribution of Correspondence (Type "A")
and Non-correspondence (Type "B") of Changes in the Properties
of Petroleum and Water with Depth*

Class	A		B	
	Number of cases	% of cases	Number of cases	% of cases
I	28	70	12	30
II	13	65	7	35
III	6	35	14	65
All	47	59	33	41

The data in Table 12 show that for Class I fields (i.e. the normal type) a positive correlation predominates. It should be noted, however, that if the number of Class I fields is broken up into geosynclinal (23 fields) and shelf types (17 fields) the following situation is found. All of the Class I shelf type fields fall under Type "A" while the fields in folded regions are divided about equally between Types "A" and "B".

Of considerably greater interest, however, are the anomalous Class II and III fields for which a deciding role for hydrogeologic conditions can be assumed. It should be pointed out that, of the Class II, Type "A" fields, one half consists of fields on the Apsheron Peninsula which will be discussed below. If these are ignored Class II is likewise represented by an equal number of cases of correspondence and non-correspondence. As far as Class III is concerned, it can be seen from the tabulation that cases of non-correspondence predominate. Therefore one cannot agree with V. A. Uspenskii who considers that "cases of irregular fluctuations of specific gravity values are apparently tied in with irregular variations in hydrogeologic conditions" [71].

Recently relationships have been developed, for some regions, between the areal distribution of properties of petroleum and water. Thus Z. L. Maimin showed that the areal distribution of petroleum properties in Devonian sediments in the Ural–Volga region is completely unrelated to the distribution of formation water properties. The work of Yu. A. Pritula leads to the same conclusions regarding Lower Carboniferous rocks. A comparison of the values for all classes shows that, although positive correlations are relatively more numerous, they nonetheless do not justify a general rule. Consequently, there does not appear to be any basis for considering hydrogeologic conditions as the chief factor in the vertical distribution of petroleum properties.

Furthermore, it is necessary to call attention to two further considerations. First, the connection between petroleum and water properties can in some cases be due not to processes of petroleum oxidation by sulfates in the waters but rather by other processes. This will be discussed below. Secondly, the position taken on the relationship between the chemistry of subsurface waters (primarily their salinity) and their mobility, although undoubtedly correct in a general sense, possibly does not have the character of a precise functional relationship. The cases of divergence between salinity and metamorphism noted above confirm this conclusion. It is necessary here to touch on the question of the reasons for the differences in salinity and metamorphism in the different horizons of sections and on the reasons for "hydrochemical inversion", i.e. phenomena of decreasing salinity and metamorphism of water with depth. This question cannot be considered as fully resolved. Besides the relationship between hydrochemical inversions and cases of greater hydrogeologic exposure of deeper horizons, other explanations are also possible.

Thus, of considerable interest is the idea advanced recently by V.S. Melik-Pashaev [72]. According to this author, salt enrichment of water occurs as a result of water being squeezed out of clays and hence depends on the clay content of the section. Although the mechanism of this process requires more study, its admission as a factor determining the character of the vertical distribution of water salinity is in good agreement with conditions observed in a number of regions. Thus, in the Apsheron Peninsula, V.S. Malik-Pashaev shows that the inversion of water salinity is tied to the clay content in the section and does not depend on processes of infiltration and circulation which are practically absent [72].

In the Grozny region, the Neftegorsko-Khadizhenskii region, in Norio (Western Turkmenia) and in some regions of the Mid-Continent, hydrochemical inversion phenomena are also connected with high argillaceous character of the upper portions of sections. In any event, hydrochemical inversion phenomena require additional investigation.

Special attention should be given to the oil fields on the Apsheron Peninsula which represent an extremely complex and unusual case.

The principal fields in this region, Surakhany, Kala, Bibi-Eibat, are typical examples of Class II fields and at the same time, as was shown earlier [21], represent a situation in which a sharply expressed parallelism in the changes of petroleum and water properties with depth in the section may be observed (see Fig. 28).

The anomalous vertical gradient for petroleum specific gravity on the Apsheron Peninsula is explained either as being the result of filtration fractionation in the process of vertical migration through the mass of rock or the oxidizing action of formation waters. Apparently both explanations are inadequate. Filtration fractionation during vertical migration through the mass of rock (the possibility of which in the scale necessary for the Apsheron Peninsula is disputed by a number of authors [73, 74, 75]) cannot explain many factors. In admitting a decisive role for filtration fractionation, the presence of huge masses of gas in the lower portion of the productive section, the Podkirmakinskaya series included, remains unexplained. Also unexplained are local deviations from the basic rule governing changes in petroleum specific gravity and tar content with depth, i.e. the change in sign of the slope for the vertical gradient observed in some parts of the section (see Fig. 28). Multi-stage migration, as assumed by some authors [76], does not eliminate this deviation since, by explaining the rhythmic nature of the changes, it cannot at the same time specify a "continuous" relationship. What is most important, the recognition of an exclusive migrational, physical and physico-chemical origin of petroleum differences with depth does not agree with the observed differences in the chemical composition of narrow fractions.

From the graph (Fig. 30) it can be seen that at Surakhany and Kara-Chukhur the content of paraffinic hydrocarbons in the light gasolines decreases in an upward direction in the section. According to the filtration hypothesis, however, the light paraffinic hydrocarbons should, on the contrary, have their maximum accumulation at the tops of sections and, in general, the shallow accumulations should be lighter petroleums, which does not occur in the cited examples.

Recently, Sh. F. Mekhtiev, by way of a confirmation for the filtration hypothesis, pointed out the curious fact of decreasing specific gravity of bitumens in the reservoir rocks in an upward direction through the section, paralleling the corresponding change in petroleums [77]. He considers the bitumens in the rocks to represent evidence of migration. However, it is possible to explain this phenomenon in a different manner. It is more probable that the bitumens in the reservoir rocks (as is the case in all sedimentary rocks [78]) are primarily syngenetic and changes in their properties with depth in the section are related to facio-lithologic factors.

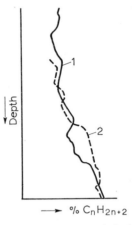

FIG. 30. Changes in the content of paraffinic hydrocarbons in gasolines with depth in the productive section of the Apsheron Peninsula. *1* Surakhany; *2* Kara-Chukhur.

The oxidizing effect of water on petroleums likewise does not explain some of the observed characteristics and cannot, therefore, be accepted as the mechanism responsible for the changes. In the first place, as indicated above, the presence of a considerable circulation of water in the petroliferous sediments of the Apsheron Peninsula is questionable and the hydrochemical inversions observed there could be completely unrelated to the hydrodynamics of the situation. If there are no significant variations in the rate of water movement over a section, one cannot consider that the oxidation process was, in this case, responsible for the changes in petroleum properties with depth in the section.

Secondly, it is improbable that the primary type of petroleum is represented here by the Surakhani series oils having a specific gravity of less than 0.800. At the same time, if increasing specific gravity with increasing depth in the section is due to oxidation then, prior to the oxidation process, all of the petroleums in the productive zones must have been like those in the upper portions of the section in the Surakhany series.

Thirdly, oxidation does not explain the character of the hydrocarbon composition (see Fig. 30). With the predominant development of the oxidation process in the lower portion, its content of paraffinic hydrocarbons should have been reduced due to their selective consumption by bacteria, as some investigators insist. Actually, the opposite occurs (Fig. 30).

The hydrocarbon composition triangle for light gasolines (Fig. 31) also shows a higher aromatic content in gasolines in the deeper horizons as compared to the gasolines in the shallower horizons.

According to the latest data, corresponding regular variations are also present in the relationships between normal- and iso-paraffins as well as between the cyclopentane and cyclohexane

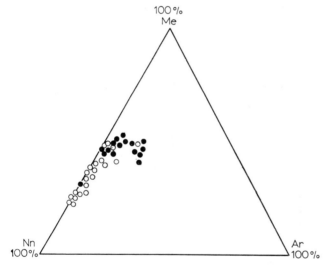

FIG. 31. Composition of petroleum gasolines of the Apsheron Peninsula petroleums (dark circles denote the deeper zones of the producing formation; light circles denote the shallower zones). For a description of apices of triangle, see page 128.

derivatives. There are relatively more normal paraffins and cyclo-pentanes in the lower portion (refer to "Sostav i Svoistva Neftei i Benzino-Kerosinovikh Fraktsii "—" Composition and properties of petroleums and gasoline–kerosene fractions", *Izd. Akad. Nauk, USSR*, 1957).

In order to explain the complex and conflicting rules governing the distribution of petroleum properties in the fields of the Apsheron Peninsula it is necessary to introduce the factors of metamorphism and differentiation. It was shown above that, with increasing depth in the formation, the composition of light fractions increases in aromatic content. Similar changes can be traced along the section in a downward direction (Fig. 31). These changes can be the result of the process of metamorphism of petroleums connected with their increasing depth of burial and, consequently, their temperature,† i.e. the change in the gasoline composition with depth on the Apsheron Peninsula is quite common, the same as in the majority of other investigated cases (see above). The distribution of the gasoline composition here, however, does not correspond to the distribution of other petroleum properties, e.g. specific gravity, tar content, gasoline content, etc.

Changes in specific gravity and tar content of petroleums throughout the productive section corresponds to the change in clay content of the section. A decrease in specific gravity is observed in the upper portions of sedimentary sequences where the rocks are most fine-grained. The correlation between graphs of changes in petroleum and water properties can be explained by the fact that both are basically due to the same general cause, the clay content in the section. The possibility of such an explanation was indicated by G. P. Tamrazyan [79]. The mechanism of the effect of clay content was already discussed above in the section on mineralization of water. The effect of clay content in the rock on petroleum properties, however, can be exerted through the adsorptive process as was noted above in several examples. Adsorptive processes certainly do not have to be connected with vertical migration.

All in all, the distribution of petroleum properties in the producing formations of the Apsheron Peninsula can be explained by the superposition, one upon the other, of a number of processes. In the upper sections these will be predominantly thermo-catalytic adsorptive processes (their role must also be great in the upper portions of the underlying sediments, the Kirmakinskaya series (KS) and the overlying argillaceous Nadkirmakinskaya series [NKG]). In the lower portions a significant role, especially in the formation of gasoline components, belongs to the chemical metamorphism of petroleums. In addition, for the lower division, especially for the

† Possibly also with their location with respect to their source.

Podkirmakinskaya series (PK), one cannot exclude the effect of oxidative processes which can occur there as shown by a number of other criteria.

However, allowing for the simultaneous effect of metamorphism and oxidation, we still cannot explain the origin of the petroleums at the very tops of the section. These extremely light, practically tar-free petroleums with naphthenic gasolines can only be considered specific derivatives of the more normal petroleums but were not formed as a result of thermo-catalytic metamorphism and, of course, not as a result of oxidation processes. The peculiarities of these petroleums are apparently the result of physical processes of differentiation which occurred. These could not be migration through masses of clay, which cannot possibly be considered operative, but could result from free migration through permeable zones, basically related to the disjunctive and eruptive properties of mud volcanoes (see below).

The significance of hydrogeologic conditions is especially noticeable in the process of sulfurization of petroleums.† The geologic-geochemical conditions responsible for the appearance of sulfur-bearing petroleums deserve special study.

In the light of the impossibility, noted above, that high sulfur content is caused by primary factors, sulfates should be recognized as the basic source of petroleum sulfurization since there is no other significant source of sulfur in the petroleum's environment.

Since the interaction between petroleums and sulfates occurs, practically in all cases, with the participation of water, the role of hydrogeologic conditions including hydraulic (reservoir) rock properties will now be considered. The filtration rate of waters depends on rock permeability. The most favorable media in this regard are numerous (but not all) carbonate masses. It is known that the greatest rates, up to several tens of cubic meters per second, are observed at sources flowing from limestone masses. This is related to the development in limestones of water-conducting channels having relatively large cross-sectional areas primarily caused by fractures widened by the dissolving action of water. Carbonate reservoir rocks are also responsible for the greatest petroleum production rates. Thus Permian limestones and dolomites in Texas

† The possibility is not excluded that, at least in some cases, sulfurization already occurs in the "pre-petroleum" period. This is indicated by the variation in sulfur content of syngenetic bitumines.

yielded rates of up to 14,000 metric tons/day (per well), the Tamaulipas limestone in Mexico up to 15,000 metric tons/day, the Asmari
limestone in Iran up to 12,000 metric tons/day, and in Saudi Arabia
the average daily rate of oil production in some areas exceeds
1000 metric tons per well. It should be noted that in all of the cases
indicated above the petroleums are sulfurous. In one of the newest
guidebooks on petroleum geology it is directly stated that "the
production of petroleum from fractured limestones is generally a
simpler and more economic process than that from sands" [80].

In the light of the above it is submitted that the accumulation of
sulfurous petroleums in carbonate rocks is frequently primarily tied
in with their reservoir properties which enable the active circulation
(movement) of water and thereby aid the process of petroleum
oxidation by sulfates. The accumulation of sulfurous petroleums in
carbonate rocks, however, is not a general rule. There is nothing
surprising in this since the reservoir properties of carbonate rocks
are far from the same in different cases. Attention should be drawn
to the case of the accumulation of low sulfur content petroleums in
carbonate rocks as well as to the case of the accumulation of highly
sulfurous petroleums in some non-carbonate rocks.†

Low sulfur content petroleums in limestones are most widespread
on the North American shelf. Thus in the Appalachian region, low
sulfur content petroleums are known to occur in the Paleozoic Big
Lime, Corniferous, Trenton and other limestones. These limestones
differ from the carbonate masses noted above in that they are
represented by thin (5–15 m) beds, having low porosity, lying between impervious shales. In these rocks any significant movement
of water is not too probable.

In the Mid-Continent region low sulfur content petroleums are
known to occur in the Paleozoic Arbuckle, Viola and Hunton
limestones. In comparing these formations with the carbonate masses of the neighboring Permian basin containing sulfurous petroleums, their significantly lower productivity should be noted. The
maximum daily production rates here do not even reach 1000 metric
tons (as compared to 15,000 metric tons) and usually are even much
lower. This is apparently connected with the weaker development
of fracturing in these due to the less intensive tectonic deformation

---

† Cases where sulfurous petroleums accumulate in relatively poor permeability limestones (the Carboniferous rocks in the Ural–Volga region) can be explained by subsequent sealing of fractures by veins of foreign matter.

in the internal regions of the shelf. Thus low sulfur content petroleums are found in limestones in those instances in which the rate of water movement is relatively low.

Sulfurous petroleums are known to occur in sandstones devoid of gypsum and anhydrite (representing an especially rich source of sulfur) primarily in regions with very strong development of disjunctive disturbances such as the downthrown zone of the Balcones-Mexia in Texas, Southern Arkansas (Smackover field, etc.), Western Venezuela, Colombia and others. In the Pueblo Viejo field (Western Venezuela) the production is mainly related to fracturing [81]. In the Elk Basin field (Rocky Mountains) the petroleum in the zone of fracturing contains over 1 % sulfur as against 0.1 % in the "normal" zone within the limits of the same horizon (Second Wall Creek) [82]. Apparently, in these cases the sulfur content of petroleums is also due to the strong movement of waters along fractures. High sulfur content is characteristic of petroleums in sandstones with an anomalously high degree of fracturing.

Anomalously high permeability can be connected not only with fracturing but also with unconformities or with such strata as loose gravels. The latter takes place in the gigantic Quiriquire accumulation in Eastern Venezuela. Thus the great and often decisive role of reservoir rock properties in the process of sulfurization of petroleums should be recognized. The role of reservoir properties is sometimes partially assumed by other hydrogeologic factors, e.g. proximity to the source regions of water-bearing horizons, high hydrostatic pressure, and abundant rainfall which infiltrates the water- and oilbearing horizons. The presence of a combination of the three latter conditions may be assumed for the oil fields of Venezuela and Colombia.

In addition to the hydraulic factors, hydrogeologic conditions also affect the process of sulfurization of petroleums through the chemistry of water. This is tied to the sulfide balance in the waters. In the reduction of sulfates the sulfur can go into various forms, of which the hydrosulfide ion (HS^-) and the molecularly dissolved hydrogen sulfide have the greatest significance. The hydrosulfide sulfur should not react with petroleums since it is tied up by the metals (in an alkaline medium). Consequently, if all of the reduced sulfur ends up in the form of hydrosulfide ions there should be no sulfurization of petroleum. Hydrosulfides exist primarily in alkaline waters, with pH < 6 there can be no hydrosulfides in the water. Hence, if the

4a TP

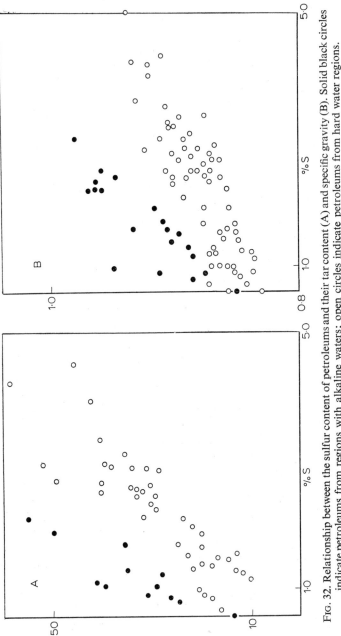

FIG. 32. Relationship between the sulfur content of petroleums and their tar content (A) and specific gravity (B). Solid black circles indicate petroleums from regions with alkaline waters; open circles indicate petroleums from hard water regions.

water is alkaline the conditions are unfavorable for sulfurization. Actually, in the majority of cases, petroleums do have low sulfur contents where the waters are alkaline. Exceptions are the majority of petroleums of Western Venezuela, many of the petroleums of Colombia and some others. It may be assumed that the degree of oxidation of these petroleums is greater than that of their sulfurization since a relatively considerable portion of available sulfur must remain inert with respect to the petroleum. Such an assumption is confirmed by some of the characteristics of these petroleums. Attention was given to the fact that, for a given specific gravity, the sulfur content for Venezuelan petroleums is considerably lower than that of West Texas petroleums [83].

The graph in Fig. 32 shows the relationship between the sulfur content of petroleums on the one hand and their tar content and specific gravity on the other (only sulfurous petroleums are considered here).

An examination of the graph (Fig. 32) leads to the conclusion that there are two classes of sulfurous petroleums. It is the characteristic of one of these classes to exhibit a more rapid increase in sulfur content with increasing specific gravity and tar content than the other. The first class is represented by petroleums from regions with a predominance of hard waters while the second class is comprised of petroleums from regions with a predominance of alkaline waters. To the first class belong petroleums from carbonate reservoir rocks as well as sandstones, from gypsiferous sediments as well as from reservoir devoid of gypsum and anhydrite. Consequently, the chemistry of waters has a considerable effect on the sulfurization of petroleums and determines their relative sulfur contents.

The conversion of hydrogen sulfide into free sulfur represents the next link in the process of incorporating sulfur from sulfides into petroleum and is generally not mandatory since the direct action of hydrogen sulfide on petroleum is not precluded. Sulfur can be formed as the result of the oxidation of hydrogen sulfide by oxides of iron (see above) or by molecular oxygen. In the oxidation of hydrogen sulfide a role is also played by a microbiologic factor in the form of sulfur bacteria. To some extent bacteria also apparently play a role in the reactions between sulfur and the hydrocarbons in petroleum, i.e. in the direct sulfurization of petroleum.

As a result of studying the entire process of the transfer of sulfur from sulfates to petroleum the following principle factors can be identified as being conducive to petroleum sulfurization:

(1) the lithologic factor: the presence of accumulations of sulfate rocks within or overlying the oil-bearing series;

(2) hydrogeologic factors: (a) especially high permeability of oil-bearing rocks, most frequently connected with tectonic fracturing, especially in thick carbonate bodies, (b) other conditions favorable to the active movement of waters (proximity to and high hypsometric position of source regions, etc.), (c) non-alkaline (hard) nature of the waters. Other factors are less clearly defined.

Table 13 gives sulfur content values of petroleums (sulfurous crudes only, i.e. containing over 0.5 % sulfur) for different combinations of the principal factors enumerated above. The data presented in Table 13 substantiate the dominant role of hydrogeologic factors. The average sulfur content of oils in Case II, from reservoirs with especially favorable properties and lacking gypsum, is considerably higher than those of ordinary reservoirs containing gypsum (Case II). The average sulfur content of petroleums associated with alkaline waters (Case IV) is lower than that of oils associated with hard waters, when other conditions are the same (Case III).

The effect of hydrogeologic conditions on petroleum properties solely from the standpoint of the oxidizing action of waters, in connection with the sulfate content of the latter, was examined above. Other forms of this effect are also possible. Thus the selective solubility of petroleum components in water, different for different chemical types of water, is not precluded. This question has not been studied. However, it can be assumed that under conditions of extremely low rates of water movement, characteristic of the majority of oil-bearing formations, petroleum solubility in water can hardly be significant.

The question of the possible catalytic action of subsurface aqueous solutions on chemical transformations of petroleums has never been studied. Attention must first be directed to the acidity of some of the waters in oil-bearing formations. Calcium chloride formation waters have an acidic reaction (pH = 4–6). V. N. Ovchinnikov and others consider that the acidity of calcium chloride waters is caused by the hydrolysis of calcium and magnesium chlorides [84]. Kaveev established the presence of iron chloride (i.e. "tertiary salinity" according to Palmer), a readily hydrolyzable component [85], in some calcium chloride waters in oil bearing formations.

The acidic nature now established for aluminosilicate catalysis and the acidity of calcium chloride waters are two facts which, when mutually compared, suggest a possible catalytic role of calcium

TABLE 13. *Sulfur Content of Petroleums Under Different Geologic-geochemical Conditions*

Geologic-geochemical conditions	Provinces and regions of sulfurous petroleum development	Sulfur content of petroleums		
		No. of analyses	Max. %	Ave. %
I. Gypsum within or overlying the oil bearing series in the section. Reservoir rocks with exceptionally high permeability (carbonate masses, fractured zones). Hard waters	Ural–Volga region, South-Central Asia, Iran, Iraq, Bahrein, Saudi Arabia, Permian Basin, Gulf Coast (cap rocks), Rocky Mts. (Paleozoics)	90	6.3	2.5
II. Gypsum within or overlying the oil bearing series in the section. Ordinary reservoir rocks (sandstones, thin, unfractured limestones). Hard waters	Ural–Volga region (Devonian), Utah, Kuwait, Permian Basin, Michigan, Rocky Mts. (Paleozoics)	35	2.5	1.3
III. No gypsum. Reservoir rocks with exceptionally high permeability (thick, fractured carbonate masses, fractured zones, etc.). Hard waters	Mexico, Southern Arkansas, Balcones Zone, Elk Basin (Rocky Mts.), Calentura (Venezuela)	24	5.3	2.4
IV. No gypsum. Reservoir rocks with exceptionally high permeability (fractured zones, etc.), proximity to a region of abundant rainfall. Alkaline waters	Venezuela, Colombia, some regions of California	45	3.0	1.4

chloride waters on the chemical transformation of petroleums. Calcium chloride waters have the highest salinity and are the most metamorphosed. Consequently, the increased salinity and metamorphism of waters can cause increased metamorphism of petroleums. In the light of this fact the correlation between changes in petroleum and water properties in a number of fields, namely the correlation between increases in salinity and metamorphism of waters and decreases in specific gravity of petroleums, can be partly explained in a completely different manner. This question requires special, including experimental, investigation.

In summarizing the review of the problem of the effect of hydrogeologic conditions on the quality of petroleums we arrive at the following conclusions. Hydrogeologic conditions have a significant effect on petroleum composition, in the first place, by controlling the processes of petroleum oxidation and sulfurization. The action of these factors, however, is not developed universally but only in particular situations. These factors do not contribute any basic rules on the areal distribution of petroleum quality (depth of burial, etc.) but only result in local irregularities.

G. TECTONIC CONDITIONS
AND MIGRATION PROCESSES

An hypothesis concerning the effect of migration processes on the composition of petroleum was first expressed by A. Sorokin [8]. The effect of tectonic conditions and migration processes on petroleum properties was repeatedly mentioned in preceding sections in connection with the review of other factors. The effect of tectonic conditions can be very broad, not to mention the fact that both depth of deposition and hydrogeologic conditions can be viewed partially as a function of tectonic factors, processes of gravitational differentiation, and the variation of petroleums in different blocks separated by fracturing. The role of migration processes was touched upon above in connection with the possible effect of the duration of accumulation or of time difference in the formation of accumulations. In the following we shall examine other aspects of this question. Concerning tectonic conditions, whose role should be specifically defined, attention must be directed towards the disruptive disturbance of sediments and the regional tectonic metamorphism of rocks. Migration processes are very closely tied in with tectonic conditions. Consequently, the effects of both will be examined simultaneously. The following basic questions can be identified:

1. Lateral migration of petroleum. The duration and time difference of the formation of accumulations as a result of lateral migration.

2. Vertical migration of petroleum along fractures and breaks. Escape of light fractions into the atmosphere (degasification). Differentiation of petroleum as a result of "overflow" from lower into upper accumulations. Mixing of petroleums from different horizons.

3. Vertical migration of petroleum through the rock masses themselves. Filtrational fractionation of petroleum with adsorptive processes playing a decisive role.

4. Dislocation and metamorphism of rocks in connection with petroleum properties.

5. Basic differences between petroleums in folded regions and those in shelf areas. Different means of origin of very light petroleums.

1. Lateral migration

The views of several authors on the role of lateral migration in the areal distribution of petroleum were presented above. Especially probable is the role of lateral migration in the region of Samarskaya Luka (see Table 9 and Fig. 13). Lateral migration can, in principle, have a variety of effects on petroleum composition. Here a distinction should be made between instances connected with single-stage migration in which the origin of a group of oil deposits accumulated in the course of a relatively brief period of time, under relatively constant conditions (among them the quality of petroleum supplied from the source), and those related to multi-stage migration over a prolonged period of time.

If the migration and creation of accumulations is of a single-stage type, the basic effect on petroleum properties in the accumulating deposits must belong to the preferential movement of one group of components in the heterogeneous system of the moving "protopetroleum" over that of other components in the system. As a result of the preferential movement of the lighter and more mobile components over those that are heavier and less mobile, the accumulations (or portions thereof) which have the greatest concentrations of light components must be those that are farthest removed from the source. Such a case was theoretically examined by N. A. Eremenko [86]. In the previously noted case of Samarskaya Luka, according to S.P.Maksimov, we have an example of the differential filling of traps by relatively lighter and heavier petroleums which occurs as a result of the displacement of heavy petroleums by lighter ones into traps located structurally higher or, in general, further from the source basin.†

The case involving with prolonged multi-stage migration is considerably more complicated. A variety of combinations of conditions is also possible here. With the prolonged formation of oil accumulations, the composition of petroleum entering from the source basin can be unchanged but, as a result of isolations arising from fractures and the progress of oxidation processes, the continuing migration influences the distribution of petroleum properties. Z.A.Tabasaranskii, as pointed out above, considers this variation to be extremely common [26]. In the Kum horizon of the eastern portion of the Glubokii Yar field (Kuban) the specific gravity of the petroleum on the southerly upthrown flank of the structure is 0.937 and contains practically no paraffinic hydrocarbons while on the north flank the petroleum has a specific gravity of 0.820 and contains 48% paraffins in the distillate. At first glance the southerly petroleum obviously belongs to the oxidized varieties. At the same time it can be assumed that since the north flank adjoins the source basin (the Kuban depression), and the south flank is separated from the latter by tectonic faulting, the differences in petroleums found in the different blocks of the Glubokii Yar field are partially explained by the time difference and different duration of the formation of these accumulations. The accumulation on the north flank could have undergone additional filling during the entire Neogene and later while the southerly accumulation was already isolated from the Kuban source basin in the Neogene and could only have deteriorated, i.e. by loss of volatiles.

The petroleum ("protopetroleum") entering from the source basin during different intervals of time may vary in composition. The differences can be caused by the progressive metamorphism of organic matter in the source beds. As a result of these processes the components entering the accumulation in the latter stages must be predominantly the ones that are more metamorphosed and there-

† This mechanism is essentially similar to the "Differential Entrapment Principle" proposed by W.C.Gussow (*Amer. Assoc. Petroleum Geologists Bull.* **38**, 1954, 816–53). [Transl. Ed.]

fore more paraffinic. As shown above, evidence of such a pheno-menon is observed in fields of the Apsheron Peninsula and Samar-skaya Luka where greater metamorphism is characteristic of petro-leum lying closer to the source and, hence, under conditions where later additions ("supplemental feeding") to the accumulations are probable.

Finally, the possibility that "protopetroleum" moving from the source basin will evolve in the direction of enrichment in heavier components due to the progressive increase in pressure and the related progressive increase in mobility of heavier and more com-plex components of organic matter in petroleum source beds, should not be overlooked. Thus the results of this process may be the reverse of the preceding case.

A brief, primarily theoretical examination of questions dealing with the effect of lateral migration on petroleum properties shows the great complexity and poor state of knowledge of these phe-nomena. Further work in this field must first embrace examination of the existing factual evidence.

2. Vertical migration along fractures

Several possible instances of vertical migration along fractures should be identified here. In the first place, in the presence of frac-tures which could serve as migration channels, the escape of gas and light petroleum fractions into overlying horizons can be facil-itated and, as a result, degasification and increase in specific gravity of petroleum can occur, especially in portions of the accumulations adjoining the fractures. Such phenomena have been stated to exist in a number of fields. Thus, in horizons X and XI of the Mirzaani field, the petroleum from wells penetrating these horizons at the fault plane have anomalously high specific gravities (as compared to the other portions of these accumulation). At Dossor, the petro-leum in horizon III in region 185 at the fault, has a specific gravity of 0.873 as compared with 0.845 in the remaining portions of the accumulation [53]. There are also other instances of this same type.

Secondly, as a result of establishing hydraulic communication between several reservoirs along the channels created by tectonic fracturing, "overflow" of a portion of the petroleum can occur from the lower reservoirs into the upper accompanied by a differentiation of petroleum similar, in principle, to gravitational differentiation as described above. Here we should only distinguish between cases of differentiation within the limits of a reservoir containing a single petroleum accumulation (see above), and cases when the hydraulic communication was temporary, having ceased after effecting the differentiation of the petroleum. The latter situation apparently exists in the Ventura Avenue field. If probably also occurs on the Apsheron Peninsula.

Thirdly, the "overflow" of a portion of the petroleum from certain accumulations into others along channels of tectonic origin can also lead to the mixing (hybridization) of different petroleums. Differentiation as the result of "overflow" must occur at a time when there was initially no petroleum in the upper reservoirs. An anomalous, positive vertical gradient for specific gravity (Ventura Avenue field, for example) must be established under such circumstances. If, however, petroleums were already present in the upper reservoirs and there was a normal, negative vertical gradient for specific gravity, the "overflow" of the predominantly light portion of the lower petroleums into upper accumulations must lead to the mixing (hybridization) of petroleums and may change a negative gradient to a zero gradient, i.e. a transition of fields from Class I to Class III.

With respect to this number of Class III fields are related to anticlines broken up by extensive fractures: Potrero I and II (California), Oficina and Western Guarra (Eastern Venezuela), Andizhan, Palvantash, Powell and North Curry (downthrown Balcones-Mexia Zone), Caddo, Pechelbraun (France) and some others. In these fields, where the vertical gradient for specific gravity is equal to zero, the hydrogeologic factor cannot have a decisive role since the distribution of water properties along the section is normal.

This group should also include in part the Santa Fe Springs field, California, where a normal negative vertical gradient is observed in the upper portion of the section and a gradient approaching zero exists in the lower portion of the section (Fig. 33). The waters in this field are of the calcium chloride type in the lower portions of the section and changes in them have absolutely no correlation with changes in petroleum properties. Apparently, the very small thickness of the argillaceous units and their extremely intensive dislocation lead to the creation of hydraulic communication between the lower accumulations and the mixing of the lower petroleums.

Phenomena observed in the Smackover field, Southern Arkansas, are quite pertinent. This field, related to an anticlinal fold and containing petroleum in Upper Cretaceous sandstones, is characterized by a zero vertical gradient in specific gravity, extensive tectonic fractures, and producing zones separated by relatively thin argillaceous beds. Furthermore, a relationship is observed here between changes in petroleum specific gravities of adjoining horizons and the thickness of separation between these horizons (Fig. 34).

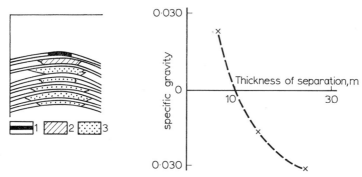

FIG. 33. Chart showing the distribution of petroleum according to specific gravity in the Santa Fe Springs field. Petroleum. *1* 25–28° API;   *2* 28–32° API;   *3* 32–36° API.

FIG. 34.   Relationship between vertical gradient for petroleum specific gravity and thickness of separation between accumulations in the Smackover field.

An examination of the graph (Fig. 34) leads to the conclusion that with large separation the mixture of petroleums does not have any significant effect; the gradient remains negative, i.e. normal. With small separation, however, the gradient exhibits a change in its sign which, apparently, is due to mixing. The presence of such a relationship serves as additional evidence of the existence of the "overflow" and mixing of petroleums. An analogous relationship between changes in the specific gravity gradient in petroleum and thickness of the separation between accumulations has also been stated to exist in the Little Lost Soldier field in the Rocky Mountains.

It is necessary to note that notwithstanding the significant disruptive disturbance of a large number of oil fields, traces of migrational differentiation and mixing are observed only in a relatively small number of cases. Out of several hundred fields, traces of this phenomenon are noticed in only about thirty. Apparently, the effect of vertical migration on petroleum composition is not too significant.

3. Vertical migration through masses of rock
(filtrational fractionation)

Belief that the filtrational fractionation of petroleum during vertical migration across the bedding of undisturbed argillaceous masses, as a result of the adsorption of tars and other polar components by clays formerly was widely accepted. At present the majority of investigators, without rejecting the reality of this process, do not attach to it any great significance. The majority of cases where this phenomenon was assumed earlier can just as readily be explained by other means. V. A. Uspenskii drew attention to a number of petroleums which, in his opinion, represent products of

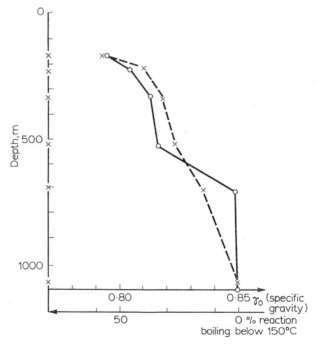

FIG. 35. Distribution of petroleum properties with depth in the Salsa Majore field.

filtration-adsorptive fractionation [3]. However, it is unlikely that all of these petroleums were formed in just this manner. The fact that very light petroleum overlies that which is heavier is not necessarily a corroboration of the filtrational origin of the upper petroleum. As shown above, such relationships can also be the result of the gravitational differentiation of petroleum resulting from establishment of hydraulic communication between reservoirs and by other processes. The possibility of petroleum penetrating consolidated clay strata is extremely questionable.

In the Salsa Majore field (northern Italy), where the existence of filtrational fractionation was assumed to be most probable, a drastic change in the gasoline content of petroleum is observed with change in depth (Fig. 35). Such a situation probably increases the effect of the gravitational factor during "overflow" beyond the effect of the adsorptive factor during filtration since, in the latter case, the change in tar content is more important than the change in gasoline content. In the majority of other cases where filtrational fractionation is assumed there are no data available for drawing valid conclusions.

4. Dislocation and metamorphism of rocks

Oil fields are relatively rare in regions of intense deformation accompanied by noticeable rock metamorphism. Among the best known examples of oil-bearing provinces characterized by unbroken folding and development of overturned and tilted folds are the Carpathian, Apennine and Western Canadian provinces. Petroleum in Carpathian fields (within the bounds of Western Ukraine and Poland) is characterized by properties common to all of the petroleums from these provinces.

First, the significant similarity of petroleum properties and their weak relationship to depths of occurrence should be kept in mind. This is observed for the province as a whole as well as for individual fields, as, for example, in the Borislav field. Such a phenomenon may be partly explained by the significant occurrence of migration and the mixing of petroleums. Also the tendency to uniformity of properties as the result of deformation-metamorphic processes is a possible explanation of the observed similarities.

The second characteristic of Carpathian petroleum speaks in favor of the latter assumption. This characteristic is the lightness of all the petroleums. Out of 70 petroleums from 15 fields not one has a specific gravity higher than 0.880. Characteristic also is the high wax content (up to 10 %) and the high paraffinic content in the gasoline fraction [60–75 % paraffins in the fractions to 180° (7 crudes)].

These characteristics are more than likely explained by the fact that this group of petroleums was subjected to specific chemical changes related to folding. The chemistry of these changes apparently has followed the same basic direction as established for petroleum metamorphism. It is possible that this phenomenon resulted from heat given off as a result of friction within the sedimentary complex during the folding process. Some temporary increase in temperature during folding intensifies and accelerates the processes of petroleum metamorphism.†

Petroleums of the Apsheron province, the tectonics of which is similar to that of the Carpathian province, is likewise characterized by an unusual lightness. Here, apparently, differentiated petroleums are significantly developed but, even the petroleum which must be regarded as "residual", is also very light. In the previously mentioned Salsa Majore field, the very deepest and very heaviest petroleum, devoid of gasoline (to 150°C), has a specific gravity of only 0.850.

In the well-known Turner Valley field (Western Canada), with very intensive recumbent folding, the petroleum is also very light. In the upper horizon, in Lower Cretaceous sediments at a depth of 1 km, the petroleum has a specific gravity of 0.780 while in the deeper horizon, in Mississippian limestones at a depth of more than 2 km, the petroleum has a specific gravity of 0.680. There is no basis for considering this as an example of filtrational fractionation as suggested by V. A. Uspenskii. Apparently, deep metamorphism of petroleum, connected with intensive dislocation processes has taken place here.

An examination of the data which may be obtained from oil fields in regions of particularly intense deformation shows the existence of a relationship between tectonic features and petroleum quality and the increased metamorphism of petroleums in these regions.

---

† Unfortunately, the aspect of increasing temperature during folding has not been investigated at all, so that in this regard the progress of understanding petroleum geochemistry is limited by the inadequate level of development of tectonophysics.

5. Basic differences between petroleums in shelf and in folded regions

In shelf fields, obvious indications of the escape of light fractions and degasification of petroleums are evidenced only in rare instances and only in flank portions of the shelf (for example, in the Timan-Pechora oil-bearing province). Very rarely are indications of the mixing of petroleums from different horizons observed in shelf areas. Examples of pronounced gravitational differentiation of petroleums within deposits are relatively rare in shelf areas (see above). Filtrational fractionation of petroleums is never observed in shelf areas. All these characteristics of shelf fields are a function of shelf tectonics, i.e. smooth deposition and weak development of faults. In shelf fields (excluding the flank portions) very light crudes, with specific gravities below 0.800, are practically non-existent.

The origin of very light petroleum (specific gravity less than 0.800) is theoretically possible by the following means: (1) as the result of advanced metamorphism—at great depths, in areas of intensive folding; (2) as the result of gravitational and migrational differentiation in very thick accumulations or with hydraulic communication established between several reservoirs; (3) as the result of disintegration with partial vaporization of oil in gas at high pressures, i.e. at very great depths.

The four means of origin listed, correspondingly give four genetically light types of petroleum which can conditionally be designated as: (1) "metamorphisates", (2) "differentiates", (3) "filtrates", (4) "distillates". Unfortunately, the chemical criteria of diagnosis for these types has not been developed and the chemical knowledge of the given petroleums is extremely meager.

In shelf fields the conditions for the operation of the processes listed above are usually absent. There are neither the very great depths (over 2–3 km), intensive tectonic processes, great thicknesses of accumulations, nor widespread development of large fractures. Thus the indicated scarcity of very light petroleums in shelf fields can be readily understood (reference is made to the internal portions of shelf areas).

Concluding this review of the effects of tectonic conditions and migrational processes on petroleum composition, we should emphasize the limited significance of independent factors such as tectonics (in the narrow sense in which tectonics is considered here). They either create local deviations from basic processes of petroleum transformation or, in cases of extreme metamorphism, the proposed changes become more pronounced.

H. GASES

Practically every oil field contains gas. In part gas can be considered as the very lightest petroleum fraction. This applies to gases in solution in petroleum as well as to free gases, it being impossible to draw a sharp line between the two types. Oil field gases, however, represent mixtures of components some of which are not related to the petroleum, or are related only indirectly (e.g. nitrogen, hydrogen sulfide). All of the questions on the geochemistry of oil field gases will not be covered below. Only some of the factors showing the effect of geologic-geochemical conditions on the gaseous portions of petroleums will be considered. The chemical interaction of gases, as components of an outer medium, is significant only in the case of hydrogen sulfide.

The following states or conditions of gases can be identified by the conditions under which they are found in an oil field: (1) in solution in petroleum, (2) free (in gas caps), (3) in solution in formation waters, (4) adsorbed by the rocks. These forms can readily pass from one to another. The transition is a physical process. A decisive role in this process is played by pressure, especially the relationship between gas pressure and hydrostatic pressure in the natural reservoir. Chemical properties of the gases, petroleums, waters, and rocks themselves are of significance. The composition of each of the four forms also depends on the solubility of the individual gases.

A special situation is presented by pure gas accumulations, which can be found in oil fields in formations lying above or below oil-bearing horizons as well as in isolated locations. However, it is difficult to draw a sharp distinction between oil-associated gas and "pure" gas accumulations since gas accumulations sometimes contain nominal quantities of petroleum dispersed in the gas.

The question of the chemical composition of gas mixtures in oil fields is complex. The composition of only those gas mixtures which were sampled under the same physio-chemical conditions can be compared with each other. Usually considered is the composition of free gases and that portion of the dissolved gases which are given off when formations are exposed.

The hydrocarbon components of oil field gases is of the greatest interest, in the first place, because they are their basic constituents and, in the second place, because gaseous hydrocarbons are considered as the gas fraction of petroleum. Hydrocarbons, as a rule, comprise not less than 40% and usually the dominant portion of oil field gases. Among the other gases. nitrogen and carbon dioxide may comprise a large fraction. These latter gases, especially nitrogen, may have an independent origin and not be related to the petroleum.

Hydrocarbon gases found in oil fields are formed in conjunction with the petroleum as a component part of the latter, as one of the products of the origin of petroleum or as a result of the metamorphism of petroleum.

It must also be recognized that gases have a great mobility. A significant portion of the gas in a formation may be of migrational origin, perhaps having come from lower horizons. Consequently, it is not surprising that the degree of gas saturation in petroleum deposits is complex. Hence, it follows that any attempt to establish general rules for the quantitative relations of gas and oil is quite difficult.

How does the quantitative relationship between gas and petroleum depend on basic geologic-geochemical conditions, viz. depth of accumulation, age of surrounding sediments, lithology, tectonics, etc.? The following facts are pertinent to these question.

A regular increase in relative gas saturation with depth and age can be observed. A striking example of this rule can be found in the Seal Beach field (Los Angeles basin, California). Data on initial gas–oil ratios and the percent of gas content in petroleums from different horizons in this field are presented graphically in Fig. 36.

Numerous facts indicate that at great depths and in older rocks, in a number of areas (mainly in folded regions), the number of gas accumulations increases relative to those that contain petroleum, e.g. Eocene and Cretaceous in California, Cretaceous in Fergana, etc. Contrary situation may also be observed, however. In a number of provinces gas accumulations are found above sediments containing petroleum (Volga region, Rocky Mountains).

Gas saturation increases relative to oil content in regions showing evidence of increased metamorphism, e.g. Appalachian basin (refer to the work of D. White), Arkansas basin and hydrocarbon (methane) gas flows in a number of intensely disturbed regions.

On the other hand, V. S. Melik-Pashaev pointed out the existence of a direct relationship between relative gas saturation and clay content in reservoir rocks [87]. Similar phenomena were also noted by A. V. Ul'yanov [88] and V. E. Khain [89].

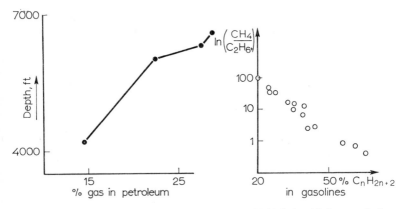

FIG. 36. Changes in gas saturation of petroleum with depth in the Seal Beach field (California).

FIG. 37. Relationship between hydrocarbon composition of gases and paraffinic hydrocarbon content in light fractions of petroleum in the same formations.

The comparison of a number of observed facts with known relationships, relative to the composition of petroleum, leads to the conclusion that the direction of increasing relative gas saturation coincides basically with the direction of decreasing petroleum specific gravity, and increasing gasoline fraction content. Naturally, such a coincidence is not due to chance but rather to the fact that a common cause provides the basis for the relationships observed for petroleum quality and relative gas saturation in petroleum accumulations. The basic cause is the metamorphism of petroleum which leads to intensified gas formation and ultimately, to the transformation of petroleum into gases. These processes proceed the farthest the greater the absolute age of the petroleum, depth of the accumulation, and tectonic intensity of the region. With increasing clay content in the rocks, catalytic activity also increases which leads to intensified gas formation through the disintegration of liquid hydrocarbon molecules.

The relative predominance of gas accumulations in the upper portions of a section observed in some cases is explained in part by processes of migrational differentiation and perhaps in part by the fact that, at relatively shallow depths, only gas (methane) accumulations can occur since the heavier components are not yet capable of migration at the corresponding pressures and, consequently, of forming accumulations [63].

The basic nature of the hydrocarbon composition of gases is the quantitative ratio of methane to heavier hydrocarbons $\dfrac{CH_4}{C_2H_6+}$ the index of gas "dryness". This value is related to the nature of the petroleum. It is inversely proportional to the paraffin content in the light fractions of petroleums in the same formations (Fig. 37).†

The greater the concentrations of saturates in the gasoline fraction, the greater the amounts of C_2H_6+ in the gas. The reason for this phenomenon lies in the increased vapor pressure of the lower molecular weight paraffins as compared to that of lower cyclic hydrocarbons (the content of the latter in gases is quite negligible). As a result of this relationship, for example, rich gases are characteristic of the Grozny and Ural–Volga regions where petroleums have large amounts of saturates in their gasoline fractions. The hydrocarbon composition of gas, however, also depends on other factors. Unfortunately, complete data for resolving this question is not available. Nevertheless the following facts can be pointed out.

TABLE 14. *Gasoline Content in Elwood Field Gases (per M. Hill [91])*

Horizon	Depth (ft)	% Gasoline in the gas (gal./MCF)	Crude oil sp. gr.
Templor	3000	1.5–3.0	0.870–0.970
Vaqueros and Upper Sespe	3650	1.0–1.5	0.835–0.865
Bell 14 Zone	4600	1.0	0.815
Lower Sespe	5800	0.75	0.830

† A. A. Cherepennikov, utilizing a reverse quantity, the "coefficient of gas richness", establishes a similar relationship [90].

In the Elwood field (Ventura basin, California) a decreasing gasoline content (i.e. vapors of liquid hydrocarbons: pentanes and higher) is observed in the gases with increasing depth (Table 14). The data in the table show that the richness of the gas decreases with increasing formation depth. Such a relationship cannot be explained either by (1) increased pressure, since this should have the opposite effect, facilitating the vaporization of liquid hydrocarbons (see below), or (2) by the nature of the petroleum inasmuch as the

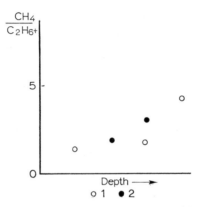

FIG. 38. Changes in "dryness"–"richness" of gas with depth in the Palvantash field. *1*, gas dissolved in petroleum; *2*, free gas.

deeper petroleums should contain more saturates in the gasoline fractions and, consequently, be accompanied by richer gases. In the Palvantash field the richness of gases, both free and in solution, decreases with depth (Table 15 and Fig. 38).

TABLE 15. *Nature of Palvantash Field Gases*

Horizon	Type of Accumulation	Petroleum sp. grav.	% C_nH_m	% CH_4	% C_2H_{6+}	$\dfrac{CH_4}{C_2H_{6+}}$
IV	In petroleum	0.87	93	53	40	1.3
V	Free	0.85	98	58	40	1.45
VII	Free	0.78	95	71	24	2.9
VII	In petroleum	1.10	97	57	40	1.4
VIII	Free	0.68	96	84	12	7.0
VIII	In petroleum	0.82	95	71	24	2.9

The petroleums here are practically the same in all horizons with specific gravities of 0.848–0.851. Consequently, this factor cannot have any effect on gas composition. Rock masses affected by significant metamorphism are known to contain gases whose hydrocarbon fractions consist only of methane. Significant quantities of heavier hydrocarbons are not encountered. Reverse relationships are also known to occur. Thus, in the Izbaskent field, the gas becomes richer with depth, which correlates with the decrease in specific gravity of associated petroleums (Fig. 39). Similar relationships are noted in some of the fields in Japan [92].

Phenomena of decreasing richness of the gas and increasing methane content in the gas with increasing depths of accumulation, age, and degree of rock tectonism is explained by metamorphic processes which lead to the transformation of heavier, more complex hydrocarbons into the more simpler forms, the simplest of which is methane.

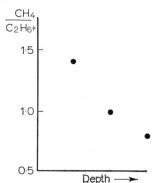

FIG. 39. Changes in "dryness"–"richness" of gas with depth in the Izbaskent field.

The opposite phenomenon, increasing richness with depth of accumulation, is also associated with metamorphic processes but in an indirect way: by changes in petroleum composition (increase in saturates in their gasoline fractions) and a general increase in gas saturation, which facilitates the vaporization of lower-boiling liquid hydrocarbons. Of great significance here also is the increase in pressure which likewise facilitates such vaporization. Thus far it has not been possible to determine the reasons for the existence of the opposing phenomenon in different fields.

It is desirable to note again the previously mentioned phenomenon of vaporization of heavier hydrocarbons. This process occurs at very high pressure (over 300–400 atm) with a sufficient quantity of gas and leads to the petroleum passing into a homogeneous single phase gas state. This phenomenon, improperly called "reverse vaporization", is explained by the peculiarities of the phase equilibria of binary gas–oil mixtures. Increased temperatures aid the process.

Oil fields containing petroleum in a single-phase state, the so-called gas-condensate fields (on the surface the gaseous petroleum condenses into liquid "condensate"), are known to occur in significant numbers, especially in the Gulf Coast region. The accumulations are found at great depths, below 2500–3000 m, and the petroleums (under atmospheric conditions) are characterized by special qualities: a low specific gravity (less than 0.800), the predominance of gasoline-ligroin fractions, negligible (less than 5%) content of oil fractions and the absence of tars. As shown by the experiments of M. A. Kapelyushnikov, high tar content petroleums cannot be successfully brought to a single phase condition even at the very highest pressures. In the case of low tar content petroleums, however, the tars drop out in the form of a sediment [93].

Processes of petroleum vaporization can effect the composition of petroleum, causing it to lose its tars and result in the appearance of a special form of a very light petroleum. It should be noted that the role of petroleum vaporization processes is currently being greatly exaggerated, principally due to the influence of the experimental work of M. A. Kapelyushnikov and his co-workers. This work has resulted in a tendency to regard almost all petroleums as natural condensates that have passed through the single-phase state, and to regard the numerous relationships among petroleum properties in fields as the result of phase transformations. Such views should be recognized as incorrect since they oppose the established facts and completely ignore the data of geochemistry.

Petroleum which has passed through the single-phase state, as previously mentioned, is lacking in tars. This one condition alone shows that the distribution of phase changes for petroleums is very limited in nature since the overwhelming portion of petroleums contains tarry matter in significant quantities.

The dominant relationship for the distribution of petroleum properties with depth of occurrence in fields, the negative vertical gradient for specific gravities, can in no way be explained by phase transformations and related phenomena. If the latter did indeed play a leading role, a reverse relationship should be observed. With the increase in pressure and temperature, everything else being equal, heavier and heavier fractions of petroleum should in that event have been vaporized and, consequently, the "condensates" should then have had a more and more complex composition and an increasing specific gravity. Moreover, the vaporization of petroleum itself depends on the chemical metamorphism of petroleum, which provides the necessary conditions for this phenomenon to exist, namely, a sufficient quantity of gas and a relatively low content of high molecular weight matter.

I. BASIC RELATIONSHIPS

All of the above shows that the basic relationships for the distribution of petroleum properties in fields are related to depths of accumulation. Age and the deformational metamorphism of the containing sediments affect it in the same direction as depth of accumulation, i. e. in the direction of decreasing specific gravities and tar content, increased content of saturates, etc. The combined effect of depth and age was illustrated above with the aid of the Geokhronobat. It appears practical then to characterize the total effect of the three similarly acting factors, (1) depth of burial, (2) age and (3) degree of deformation of the containing sediments, and to neglect the remaining factors which, as demonstrated above, only occur sporadically, but nevertheless cause a variety of deviations from the basic relationships.

Evidence was noted above for the effect of deformational metamorphism only on petroleums located within the limits of the more intensely deformed regions. It should be expected, however, that in less deformed provinces this factor should also have a corresponding action but to a lesser degree.

It is possible to characterize the total combined action of depth of accumulation, age and degree of metamorphism of containing sediments on petroleum properties with the aid of another conditional term, the Geotectokhronobat, obtained by multiplying the Geokhronobat by different numerical factors characteristic of various tectonic provinces having different degrees of metamorphism.

The Geotectokhronobat is calculated according to the following formula:

$$G_{TKB} = \frac{A \cdot B \cdot C}{10},$$

where A is the depth of petroleum accumulation in kilometers; B is the absolute age of containing sediments in millions of years; C is a factor characterizing the degree of metamorphism of the particular region.

Unfortunately, an accurate approach to the determination of the latter factor is extremely difficult. From the relationship between typical angles of dip for formations in different tectonic provinces, factor C can be taken as equal to the following: for shelves $= 1$, for

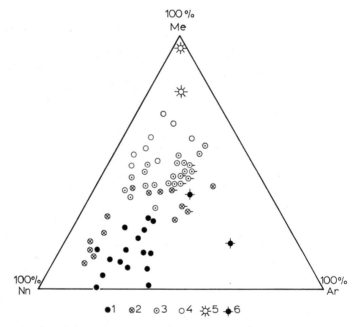

FIG. 40. Hydrocarbon composition of petroleums in relation to Geo-tectokhronobats. *1* Geotectokhronobat <10; *2* ditto, from 10 to 20; *3* ditto, from 20 to 50; *4* ditto from 50 to 100; *5* ditto >100; *6* sulfur content $>1\%$ (remaining signs denote sulfur contents $<1\%$).
The apices of the triangle correspond to petroleums with 100% contents of paraffinic (Me), naphthenic (Nn), and aromatic (Ar) hydrocarbons in the distillate fractions ($<550°$C).

provinces of a transitory nature = 5, for folded provinces with interrupted folging = 10, for provinces with complete folding (Carpathian province, etc.) the factor can be taken as equal to 20. All of these values are conditional or arbitrary but, as will be shown below, they do permit the primary relationships to be taken into account.

Our knowledge of the basic chemical composition of petroleums at the current stage of technology is limited to the hydrocarbon group composition of distillate fractions ($< 550\,^{\circ}$C). It is therefore necessary to determine the relationship between the hydrocarbon group composition of petroleums and Geotectokhronobats. Toward this end it is convenient to use the triangular diagram for hydrocarbon composition of petroleums. The relationship between Geotectohkronobats and petroleum properties is presented graphically in Fig. 40. The data used as the basis for constructing this graph are presented in Table 16 (the petroleums in the tabulation are listed in order of increasing Geotectokhronobat).

An examination of the triangular diagram leads to the conclusion that a relationship exists between the hydrocarbon composition of petroleums (more accurately, their distillate portions) and "Geotectokhronobat" values characterizing conditions of their accumulation. By this same token the latter values are indirectly confirmed and it becomes possible to recognize important geochemical relationships.

A previously published classificational geochemical diagram [28] permitted some general relationships to be noted between the chemical and geologic indices of petroleums: the predominantly paraffinic nature of Paleozoic shelf petroleums and the predominantly naphthenic nature of Cenozoic petroleums. However, in view of the fact that this former diagram did not take into account such indices as depth of accumulation and the metamorphism of the region, it was not possible to establish a definite relationship.

On the diagram presented in Fig. 40 the relationship between the hydrocarbon composition of petroleums and the Geotectokhronobat values characterizing conditions of their accumulation is quite adequately illustrated. The basic relationship derived from the diagram consists of the fact that with increasing geotectokhronobat there occurs a decrease in naphthene content and an increase in paraffin content, i.e. a transition is observed from naphthenic to paraffinic petroleums. A definite trend of Geotectokhronobat values on the diagram can be noted for the zones extending from the

TABLE 16. *Composition and Properties of Petroleums as Functions of Depths of Accumulation, Age of Containing Sediments, and Degree of Metamorphism*

Field, horizon	Geotecto-khronobat	% in fraction to 550° (distillates)			% Fraction to 550° (distillates)	% Excise tars	Sp. gr.
		Aromatics	Naph-thenes	Paraffins			
Okha, 4	1	35	65	0	68	35	0.929
Okha, 7	2	35	57	7	74	33	0.919
Naphthalan	2	20	60	0	65	36	0.958
Okha, 11	4	23	61	16	72	20	0.867
Balakhany	5	18	76	6	76	14	0.876
Nebitdag	5	18	57	25	66	32	0.880
Bibi-Eibat	6	20	68	12	80	8	0.865
Buguruslan†	6	34	32	38	55	23	0.893
Surakhany	7	13	71	16	82	8	0.848
Chusovskoe†	7	58	24	18	62	12	0.954
Maikop	7	30	45	25		24	0.893
Inglewood	10	33	56	11		23	0.934
Ekhabi	10	24	47	29	82	12	0.824
Dzhaksymai	11	10	57	33	69	5	0.843
East Texas	12	20	43	37		18	0.830
Ishimbai†	13	38	29	33	61	6	0.895
Ishimbai†	13	34	32	34	60	6	0.867
Santa Fe	16	25	53	22		24	0.882
Shugurovo†	16	37	18	42	62	9	0.925
Dossor	17	11	78	11	84	12	0.866
Oktyabr'skoe	17	13	47	40		15	0.844
Makat	19	17	71	12	60	12	0.902
Zholtybai	19	12	69	19	74	11	0.904
Starogroznenskoe	20	30	55	15	73	24	0.887
Koschagyl	20	11	72	17	73	12	0.857
Shorsu, 8	21	26	33	41	62	15	0.872
Changyrtash	23	17	68	15	50	13	0.862
Sel'rokho	24	13	50	37	71	21	0.857
Maikop	25	22	39	39		14	0.848
Krasnokamsk†	26	24	42	34	64	16	0.857
Severokamsk (Carboniferous)†	26	19	39	42	68	10	0.840
Syzran' (Vereian)†	26	28	29	43	64		0.888
Syzran' (Vizeian)†	27	27	31	42	66	18	0.859

† Sulfurous petroleums. Tar contents shown for these were calculated on the basis of Karimov's formula (refer to preceding section).

TABLE 16 *(contd.)*

Field, horizon	Geotecto-khronobat	% in fraction to 550° (distillates)			% fraction to 550° (distillates)	% Excise tars	Sp. gr.
		Aromatics	Naph-thenes	Paraffins			
Zol'noe (Carboniferous)†	28	23	26	51	80	6	0.847
Khaudag†	30	29	25	46	65	10	0.939
Tuimazy (Vizeian)†	30	37	25	38	53	5	0.899
Tuimazy (Turneian)	30	28	25	47	59	5	0.887
Shorsu	30	19	30	51	79	10	0.832
Starogroznenskoe	32	13	48	39	80	12	0.844
Achisu	35	10	45	45		14	0.829
Oklahoma City	35	15	45	40		10	0.830
Alamyshik	36	15	45	40	90	7	0.836
Iskine	37	10	50	40		4	0.843
Severokamsk (Devonian)†	44	16	31	53	80	12	0.832
Tuimazy (Devonian)†	46	24	24	52	73	15	0.851
Palvantash	48	17	40	43		20	0.852
Yablonovyi Ovrag†	49	28	23	49	81		0.860
Bavly†	49	28	13	58			
Andizhan	53	19	36	45		14	0.837
Kipyachaya	56	18	34	48	87	10	0.820
Zol'noe (Devonian)†	58	21	16	62		6	0.808
Kulsary	65	7	38	55		5	0.824
Klyuchevskoe	70	17	30	53	87	17	0.818
Kulsary	70	8	21	71		4	0.778
Iskine	80	7	42	51	80	4	0.786
Ozeksuat	160	12	12	76			0.830
Siberia (Devonian)	250	6	1	93	62	6	0.830

† Sulfurous petroleums. Tar contents shown for these were calculated on the basis of Karimov's formula (refer to preceding section).

lower left corner of the triangle to the right side of the latter. Moving from lower to higher Geotectokhronobats we move upward (and somewhat to the left on the diagram. Inasmuch as the principal changes of petroleum as a function of Geotectokhronobats is in the relationship between naphthenes and paraffins it is desirable to examine this relationship thoroughly.

Table 17 shows calculated average values of Geotectokhronobats and naphthene: paraffin relationships for the same Geotectokhronobat gradations of the 57 petroleums plotted on the diagram in Fig. 40.

TABLE 17. *Average Geotectokhronobat Values*

Geotecto-khronobat gradation	Number of petroleums	Average Geo-tectokhronobat	Naphthenes / Paraffins
0–10	13	5	5.5
10–20	12	16	3.3
20–50	23	32	1.0
50–100	7	64	0.5
>100	2	≈200	0.05

The numbers presented in Table 17 clearly illustrate the same relationship as does the diagram in Fig. 40. It might be assumed that if Geotectokhronobats did indeed accurately reflect the degree of intensity of tectonic processes, the relationship noted would have been expressed even more precisely.

Thus, with increasing depths of accumulation, age and degree of metamorphism of containing sediments, a transition is observed from petroleums of naphthenic composition to aliphatic petroleums. This can only be explained as the result of petroleum metamorphism under the effects of temperature and catalysis, accelerated with intensive metamorphism and intensified by prolonged duration of its action.

By considering Geotectokhronobats, the petroleums which had appeared strange, e.g. Ozeksuat [94] and Siberian (Devonian) [95] petroleums, fall into place. These petroleums located closest of all to the "paraffinic" corner of the triangle represent the most "paraffinized" and "de-naphthenized" products of metamorphism. This fact is in complete agreement with their extremely high Geotectokhronobat values, over 100–200 (only gases occur at the "paraffinic" peak itself).

An examination of the graph also leads to the conclusion that oxidation processes do not have a great effect on the evolution of the hydrocarbon composition of petroleums. As can be seen from Fig. 40, among saturated petroleums, there are many that are sulfurous and consequently oxidized. The degree of their oxidation, however, "narrows" with increased metamorphism. At the same time many of the cyclic petroleums can in no way be considered to be oxidized. The petroleums located at the base of the triangle, i.e. completely lacking in saturates, can be considered to be oxidized.

Oxidation and various other physical processes merely introduce secondary deviations in the basic relationship clearly seen on the triangular diagram. However, it should be kept in mind that this relationship is established only on the basis of studies of the hydrocarbon composition of liquid petroleums (and gases) forming accumulations of commercial significance.

Thus the basic conclusion drawn from the study of the geochemical diagram for the hydrocarbon composition of petroleum, which conclusion does not violate the facts presented above on the effect of individual geologic-geochemical conditions, would be the following. "The primary direction of the geochemical evolution of petroleums is the transformation of those having a predominantly cyclical composition into those having a predominantly saturated composition, a transformation resulting from the action of temperature, catalysis and time, and accelerated by tectonic processes." Deviations are subordinate in nature and are superimposed on the basic process.

Analysis of the relation between the properties of petroleum and the geologic-geochemical conditions of their occurrence indicates that the basic process for the transformation of petroleum in nature is metamorphism due to the action of depth factors, traces of which are especially noticeable in the more ancient petroleums and in those from intensely metamorphosed regions.

It is necessary to note that the question of the geologic stage of petroleum existence, the "protopetroleum" stage or the "petroleum" stage after the accumulations were formed, and during which metamorphism has its greatest effect, remains unclarified. The effect of other processes is secondary. Oxidation processes, basically associated with hydrogeologic conditions, determine such petroleum properties as their sulfur content.

BIBLIOGRAPHY

1. Höfer, H. *Petrol. Zeitschr.* **18**, No. 31 (1922).
2. Hlauschek, H. *Naphten- und Methanöle*, Stuttgart, 1937.
3. Uspenskii, V.A. and Radchenko, O.A. *The Question of Genesis of Crude Oil Types*, Lengostoptekhizdat, 1947.
4. Dobryanskii, A.F. *Geochemistry of Crude Oil*, Lengostoptekhizdat, 1948.
5. Tamrazyan, G.P. *DAN SSSR* **94**, No. 3 (1954).
6. Vassoevich, N.B. and Amosov, G.A. *Geol. Sbornik, NITO VNIGRI*, No. 2 (5), Lengostoptekhizdat, 1953.
7. McNab, J.G., Smith, P.V. and Betts, R.L. *Ind. Eng. Chem.* **44**, No. 11 (1952).
8. Konchine, A. *Guide des excursions du VII Congrés Geologique Internationale*, **24**, SPb (1897).
9. Krejci-Graf, K. *Basic Questions on Petroleum Geology* (translated from German), ONTI, 1934.
10. Barton, D. *Problems of Petroleum Geology*, Tulsa, 1934.
11. Abramovich, M.V. *Trudy Geol. Instituta Azerb. Fillialla AN USSR*, vbl. 19, Izd. Azerb. Fil. AN SSSR, 1959.
12. Kartsev, A.A. *Trud. Mosk. Neft. Instituta*, Issue 14, Gostoptakhizdat, 1955.
13. Bohdanovicz, K. *Bull. Am. Ass. Petr. Geol.* **21** (1937).
14. Morton, F. and Richards, A. *J. Inst. Petr.* **29**, No. 230 (1943).
15. Barr, K., Morton, F. and Richards, A. *Bull. Am. Ass. Petr. Geol.* **27**, No. 12 (1943).
16. Dobryanskii, A.F. and Bogomolov, A.I., *Trudij VNIGRI*, Issue 28, Lengostoptekhizdat, 1949.
17. Karimov, A.K. *An Investigation of Aromatic Hydrocarbons in the Sulfurous Crude Oils of the Second Baku*, Izd. VNIGRI, 1953.
18. Bogomolov, A.I. and Indenbom, F.B. *Trud VNIGRI*, Issue 57, Lengostoptekhizdat, 1951.
19. Barton, D.G. *Bull. Am. Ass. Petr. Geol.* **21**, No. 7 (1937).
20. Sarkisyan, B.M. *Relationship Between Crude Oil Quality and Geologic Conditions*, Aznefteizdat, 1947.
21. Kartsev, A.A. *Neft Khoz.*, No. 9 (1951).
22. Obryadchikov, S.N., *Sbornik "Proiskhozhenie Nefti i Prirodnovo Gaza"*, Izd. Is. T. M.T.Nefti, 1947.
23. Maksimov, S.P. *Neft Khoz.*, No. 10 (1954)
24. Kotina, A.K. *Trudy VNIGRI*, Issue 82 (*Sbornik "Ob Uslovyakh Obrazovaniya Nefti")*, Lengostoptekhizdat, 1955.
24a. Starobinets, I.S. *Isd. Akad. Nauk Turkmen. SSR*, No.1 (1956).
24b. Amosov, G.A. *Geol. Sbornik NITO VNIGRI*, No. 2 (1953).
25. Neumann, L.M., *et al. Bull. Am. Ass. Petr. Geol.* **31**, No. 1 (1947).
26. Tabasaranskii, Z.A. *Trudy Moskv. Neft. Instituta*, Issue 14, Gostoptekhizdat, 1955.
27. Vassoevich, N.B. and Kartsev, A.A. *Trud VNIGRI*, Issue 83 (*Geol. Sbornik*, No. 1), Lengostoptekhizdat, 1955.
28. Kartsev, A.A. *Azerb. Neft. Khoz.*, No. 3 (1954).
29. Namiot, A.Yu. *Trudy Vsesoyuz. Nefte-Gaz. Inst-ta*, Gostoptekhizdat, 1954.

30. GABRIELYAN, A.G. *Azerb. Neft. Khoz.*, No. 10 (1948).
31. MAIMIN, Z.L. *Trudy VNIGRI*, Issue 82, Legostoptekhizdat (1955).
32. KROTOVA, V.A. *Geol. Sbornik NITO VNIGRI*, No. 3 (6), Lengostoptekhizdat, 1955.
33. TOMLINSON, C.W. and STORM, W. *Bull. Am. Ass. Petr. Geol.* **8**, No. 5 (1924).
34. FEDOROV, S.F. *Trudy Instit-ta Nefti AN SSSR*, vol. 1, Issue 2, Izd. AN SSSR, 1950.
35. *Stratigraphic Type Oil Fields* (A Symposium), Tulsa, 1941.
36. MELIK-PASHAEV, V.S. *Neft. Khoz.*, No. 9 (1955).
37. TAFF, J.A. *Problems of Petroleum Geology*, Tulsa, 1934.
38. JENSEN, J. *Problems of Petroleum Geology*, Tulsa, 1934.
39. LAHEE, F.H. *Problems of Petroleum Geology*, Tulsa, 1934.
40. MAKSIMOVICH, G.A. *Groznenskii Neftyanik*, Nos. 5–6 (1932).
41. WASHBURNE, CH. *Bull. Am. Ass. Petr. Geol.* **3** (1919).
42. FROST, A.V. *Usp. Khimii*, No. 6 (1945).
43. HLAUSCHEK, H. *Bull. Am. Ass. Petr. Geol.* **34**, No. 4 (1950).
44. HAEBERLE, F.R. *Bull. Am. Ass. Petr. Geol.* **35**, No. 10 (1951).
45. BROOKS, B.T. *Bull. Am. Ass. Petr. Geol.* **33**, No. 9 (1949).
46. HUNT, J.M. *Bull. Am. Ass. Petr. Geol.* **37**, No. 8 (1953).
47. SOKOLOV, V.A. *Outline of Petroleum Genesis*, Gostoptekhizdat, 1948.
48. KOSSOVSKAYA, A.G. *Lithologic- Mineralogical Charakteristics and Conditions of Origin of Clays in the Productive Masses of Azerbaijan*, Izd. AN SSSR, 1954.
49. KAZMINA, T.I. *Trudy VNIGRI*, Issue 28, Lengostoptekhizdat, 1949.
50. BROOKS, B.T. *Ind. Eng. Chem.* **44**, No. 11 (1952).
51. KHAIN, V.E. *Geotectonic Bases For Petroleum Exploration*, Aznefteizdat, 1954.
52. Research Committee of Tulsa Geological Society, *Bull. Am. Ass. Petr. Geol.* **25**, No. 9, (1941).
53. AIZENSHTADT, G.A. *DAN SSSR*, **58**, No. 4 (1957).
54. RADCHENKO, O.A. *Sbornik Pamyati Akad. I.M.Gubkina* Izd. AN SSSR, 1951.
55. USPENSKII, V.A. and RADCHENKO, O.A. Geochemistry of bitumens (from the text *Sputnik Polevogo Geologa-Neftyanika*), Lengostoptekhizdat, 1952.
56. USPENSKII, V.A. and RADCHENKO, O.A. *Neft Khoz.*, No. 8 (1954).
57. KARTSEV, A.A. and KHOLODOV, V.A. *Neft. Khoz.*, No. 6 (1954).
58. STRAKHOV, N.M., *et al.* *The Formation of Sediments in Contemporary Aquifers*, Izd. AN SSSR, 1954.
59. MUIR, J. *Problems of Petroleum Geology*, Tulsa, 1934.
60. *Sovetskie Nefti*, Gostoptekhizdat, 1947.
61. POTYLITSYN, A. *Zh. RFKhO* **4**, Issue 7 (1882).
62. USPENSKII, V.A., GORSKAYA, A.I. and KARPOVA, I.P. *Izv. AN SSSR, Ser. geol.*, No. 4 (1947).
63. KOZLOV, A.L. *Problems on the Geochemistry of Natural Gases*, Gostoptekhizdat, 1950.
64. SHUSTEF, N.D. *Neft. Khoz.*, No. 7 (1954).
65. NIKOLAEV, V.M. *Regimens of Oil Fields in the Tersko-Sunzhenskii Oil Bearing Province*, Grozn. Obl. Izd., 1946.
66. LINDTROP, N.T. *Sbornik "Pamyati Akad. I.M.Gubkina"*, Izd. AN SSSR, 1951.

67. Shturm, L.D. *Mikrobiologiya*, **19**, Issue 1 (1950).
68. Kartsev, A.A. *Neft. Khoz.*, No. 9 (1950).
69. *Occurrence of Oil and Gas in North Texas*, Austin (Tex.), 1951.
70. Sillin-Bekchurin, A.I. *Trudy Lab. Gidrogeol. Problem AN USSR* (1949).
71. Vassoevich, N.B. and Uspenskii, V.A. Petroleum geology (from the text *Sputnik Polevogo Geologa-Neftyanika*, Issue 2, vol. 2), Lengostoptekhizdat, 1954.
72. Melik-Pashaev, V.S. *Azerb. Neft. Khoz.*, No. 9 (1954).
73. Gorin, V.A. *Azerb. Neft. Khoz.*, No. 8 (1940).
74. Veber, V.V. *Izd. AN SSSR, Ser. geol.*, No. 2 (1945).
75. Apresov, S.M. *Azerb. Neft. Khoz.*, No. 9 (1946).
76. Sarkisyan, B.M., *Azerb. Neft. Khoz.*, No. 2 (1947).
77. Mekhtiev, Sh.F. and Digurova, T.M. *Trudy Inst-ta Geologii AN AzSSR*, vol. 15, Izd. AN AzSSR, 1954.
78. Kartsev, A.A., Tabasaranskii, I.A., Subbota, M. and Mogilevskii, G.A. *Geochemical Methods of Exploring for Oil and Gas Fields*, Gostoptekhizdat, 1954.
79. Tamrazyan, G.P. *Relationships in the Distribution of Oil Fields of Eastern Azerbaijan*, Izd. AN AzSSR, 1952.
80. Titatsoo, E.N. *Petroleum Geology*, London, 1951.
81. Gonzales de Juana, C. and Rodriguez, L. *Proc. III World Petrol. Congr.*, sec. 1, Leiden, 1951.
82. Espash, R.H. and Nichols, H.D. *Petroleum and Natural-gas Fields in Wyoming*, U.S. Bureau of Mines Bull., No. 418, 1941.
83. Nelson, W., Martorano, J. and Fombona, F. *Proc. III World Petrol. Congr.*, sec. 6, Leiden, 1951.
84. Ovchinnikov, B.N., Vereshchagin, A.N. and Tsiganov, P.I. *Neft. Khoz.*, No. 3 (1952).
85. Kaveev, M.S. *DAN SSSR*, **61**, No. 2 (1948).
86. Eremenko, N.A. *Vestn. Moskv. Univ-ta*, No. 9 (1948).
87. Melik-Pashaev, V.S. *Neft. Khoz.*, No. 2 (1950).
88. Ul'yanov, A.V. *Sbornik Pamyati Akad. I.M.Gubkina*, Izd. AN SSSR, 1951.
89. Khain, V.E. *DAN AzSSR* No. 11 (1953).
90. Cherepennikov, A.A. *Trudy VNIGRI*, Issue 82, Lengostoptekhizdat, 1955.
91. Geologic Formations and Economic Development of the Oil and Gas Fields of California, USA, 1943.
92. Damperov, D. *Neft. Khoz.* No. 6 (1927).
93. Kapelyushnikov, M.A., Zhuze, T.P. and Ushakova, G.S. *Trudy Inst-ta Nefti AN SSSR*, vol. 3, Izd. AN SSSR, 1954.
94. Vassoevich, N.B. and Strigaleva, N.V. DAN SSSR **101**, No. 1 (1955).
95. Bogomolov, A.I. *Trudy VNIGRI*, Issue 83, Lengostoptekhizdat, 1955.

CHAPTER III

PROCESSES OF SPONTANEOUS ALTERATION OF ORGANIC MATTER

THE geochemistry of petroleum is concerned with processes of alteration and transformation of organic matter over large increments of time. Petroleum is encountered in practically all sedimentary rocks beginning with those of Silurian and Cambrian ages. In still more ancient sediments one frequently encounters almost completely carbonized matter.

One characteristic of these processes is that they occur spontaneously under relatively mild conditions of temperature and pressure, as a rule without interference of external active agents. Another one of their characteristics is that the alteration of organic molecules occurs under very gradually changing temperature and pressure conditions resulting from the slow processes of burial or elevation of formations containing the organic matter. Finally, a third characteristic of the transformation processes is the complexity of the material and the energy exchange between the system of organic matter and the outside media.

There is little analogy between a system of organic matter changing under natural conditions and that observed in an organic chemistry laboratory because of the discrepancy between the time intervals required for geological sedimentation processes and those of known chemical reactions. On the other hand, classical organic chemistry, as a rule, operates either with individual chemical compounds or with relatively uncomplicated systems. In a natural environment, however, the processes occur in systems which are more complicated from the standpoints of complexity and composition. Laws governing the processes of change in these natural systems are, so far, completely unknown and are probably more complex than those for systems of individual compounds.

Thus it is necessary to approach an analysis of the processes of

5a TP

alteration of organic matter over geologic periods of time from a special point of view without necessarily seeking an analogy between natural processes and those of experimental organic chemistry. It would appear more rational to use the general laws of nature to uncover relationships for changes in the complex system of organic matter, including the more general laws of organic chemistry. The relationships found in this manner should be checked, however, using actual material found in nature.

The latest achievements of the chemistry of synthetic high molecular-weight compounds have shown that all relationships found to be applicable to relatively low molecular-weight substances do not hold for high molecular-weight matter, even though these are structurally similar to the former. It was found, for example, that the reactive capability of individual functional groups, which are well known for the simplest compounds, changes drastically with molecular size. In view of this, all of the properties of the compound as a whole also change.

It is logical to assume after this, that in even more complex systems made up of a number of low as well as high molecular-weight compounds, as is characteristic of natural organic compounds, the properties of fractional groups and, consequently, the properties of the whole molecule and the system of molecules as a whole, will not resemble either the properties of individual low molecular-weight materials or the properties of synthetic high molecular-weight compounds, more homogeneous in terms of weight and created according to the same plan. For natural systems of organic matter it is also necessary to take into account the possibility of the mutual effect of individual functional groups on each other, as well as the very possible development of initiated reactions known in classical organic chemistry. The more complex the system, the more probable are combined, initiated processes of chain-type transformation within it, and there is every basis for assuming a wide, possibly primary development and even the dominance of these processes in nature.

Neither should we overestimate, however, the difficulties arising in the path of the investigator who sets before himself the problem of studying the complex natural systems of organic matter. Current knowledge possesses an arsenal of firm natural laws having general significance such as the laws of conservation of energy and matter, the laws of thermodynamics, etc. On the basis of these laws it is always possible, with more or less accuracy, or in certain instances only qualitatively, to determine the general direction of changes in the investigated system, the approximate rate of change and even to predict the behavior of this or that type of matter under certain conditions. Neither should the already known laws of change for this or that matter be rejected. These should be approached from the point of view of the overall system of the change in organic matter in general and a proper place should be found for them in this system.

Undoubtedly, it is only possible to explain the striving of individual investigators to back away from this problem and to transfer the burden of its solution on to the shoulders of allied disciplines or even extremely distant branches of learning, by the intuitively recognized difficulties in discovering new relationships and the inapplicability of particular laws to a qualitatively different system of natural organic matter. This, for example, was the case with the attempt to give widespread recognition to the microbiologic factor as the one explaining the many characteristics of natural compounds such as crude oil. If the significance of the proposed explanations is investigated it is relatively simple to become convinced that this factor not only fails to explain anything but is also completely barren. Nonetheless such attempts are known to exist in special literature by investigators of the geologic as well as the chemical profile.

We had already called attention to this situation in our own time [1]. The futility of such an approach to the solution of actual problems in the geochemistry of crude oil does not require any special proof. Obviously, with the possession of such a tool it is possible to "prove" anything that may be desired including the non-organic hypotheses of the origin of petroleum. Actually, according to the understanding of individual investigators, different micro-organisms can generate as well as transform and, finally, completely destroy petroleum. Although this situation is strictly speculative it is considered that the source of interaction between organic matter and micro-organisms depends only on which bacteria function in the specific process. Such an approach even satisfies the supporters of the non-organic theory on the origin of petroleum.

A. DIRECTION OF PROCESSES IN THE ALTERATION OF PETROLEUM

With the development of knowledge of the composition of petroleums lying in different stratigraphic horizons and under different conditions of temperature and pressure, as well as in different types of reservoir rocks, investigators became more and more convinced of the existence of a multitude of diverse types of petroleums. In this regard, numerous attempts were made to reduce the knowledge of petroleum composition to a system by means of creating classification schemes. With the development of knowledge on the detailed structure of petroleums and their compositions the schemes became more complicated and each time new and different indicators were taken as the bases for the classifications. The latest, in terms of time, is the classification of A. F. Dobryanskii [2] based on comparing the hydrocarbon composition of petroleums and which takes into account the shortcomings of previous schemes.

A. F. Dobryanski's classification scheme encompasses all of the currently known types of petroleums and foresees the probable appearance of new types unknown at the present time. Thus, for example, during the development of the classification scheme, the Cretaceous petroleums of Ozek-Suat (Grozny region), where the petroleum has a very peculiar character quite unlike that of Tertiary petroleums of the same region or Cretaceous petroleums of other regions, were still unknown. In spite of this, a proper place was found for these petroleums in the classification scheme [3]. Without a doubt any other petroleum, capable of being discovered with the development of oil well drilling technology and the uncovering of new oil-bearing horizons, will find its rightful place in this system, e.g. Siberian crude oils [4, 5].

The early, relatively primitive schemes for classifying petroleum composition forced investigators to stop and think of the genetic relations between individual petroleum types. Actually, a far from indifferent question and one having a serious practical significance is that of knowing which of the following petroleum types were more transformed by secondary processes—the tarry oil comprised predominantly of cyclic compounds or the low tar content crude oil containing paraffinic hydrocarbons. The direction of exploratory work in poorly studied regions governs, to a lesser degree the further development of the theory on the origin of petroleum.

As was often the case with the theory of petroleum chemistry, supporters were found for both solutions to this question. Some of the investigators stated that the primary crude oil is one which has a low tar content, is light and is predominantly paraffinic in its hydrocarbon composition. The secondary crude oil has a high specific gravity and high tar content and is cyclical in its hydrocarbon composition and is created from the primary paraffinic crude oil as a result of processes of oxidizing transformation in the zone of hypergenesis.

Extremely characteristic of this hypothesis is its system of argumentation based exclusively on geologic evidence, completely neglecting all other forms of evidence, including chemical evidence. As a method of solution for the presented question, authors have selected the statistical treatment of data existing in the literature on the composition of the crude oils produced in the world as they relate to a definite geologic system. Another group of investigators, initially in the minority, came to the exactly opposite conclusion [2] on the basis of a number of chemical ideas corrected, to a certain extent, by the geological facts.

Examining the dynamics of the change of crude oil types with time and not assigning the decisive role to the oxidation factor in the genesis of their types, investigators have come to the conclusion that the primary type of crude oil is one which is tarry, with a high specific gravity and has a relatively high concentration of cyclic hydrocarbons. This conclusion was confirmed from the chemical point of view on the basis of data on the transformation of hydrocarbons as well as of oxygen-, sulfur-, and partly nitrogen-containing compounds over aluminosilicates at nominal temperatures.

The transformation of the hydrocarbon portion of petroleum, by means of hydrogen disproportionation reactions, into a system consisting primarily of paraffinic hydrocarbons (the process of "paraffinization" of crude oil) was determined empirically and confirmed experimentally.

A definite choice between these two points of view on the direction of processes of change of petroleum in nature was to a certain extent complicated by the condition that the investigators of the geologic profile did not take chemical evidence into account and based their conclusions exclusively on empirical facts observed in nature.

Observations in nature of changes in petroleum type with

changes in depth of occurrence, indicating the increasing cyclic nature of crude oil with the transition from the more ancient to younger horizons, confirmed by a great volume of statistical material, taken by themselves can permit diametrically opposing interpretations.

In examining the quite noticeable increasing content of cyclic hydrocarbons with decreasing distance between their horizons of accumulation and the surface, the self-evident conclusion is that the reason for such a change in petroleum composition is none other than the singular factor which continuously increases in its intensity in the same direction, the factor of oxidation. Making a comparison between the continuous increase in intensity of the oxidation factor with decreasing distance from the surface and the continuous increase of the degree of cyclization and tar content of petroleum in the same direction, it is possible to consider one of these phenomena dependent on the other. Naturally, the increased intensity of oxidation should be considered as the independent variable since this phenomenon is also observed in those regions where the absence of petroleum has been proved. From this comes the conclusion that petroleum properties are a function of the degree of intensity of oxidation conditions. The conclusion appears to be obvious, standing to reason, quite exhaustively covering the essence of the matter and not requiring the introduction of any other system of argumentation.

It is not hard to see that with such an approach to the facts, the line of reasoning for the explanation of the movement and development of matter is directed to external conditions, and the ability of the matter to move and change due to internal causes is completely discarded. It should be noted that such an approach greatly simplifies the problem of the investigator. Actually, from these points of view, it is relatively simple to explain not only the general relationship but also all of the deviations from it. It will be quite sufficient to point out that the reason for the distortion of the general relationship in each concrete case is a local violation of the general relationship for the change in intensity or capacity of the oxidizing factor. A check of such an explanation is impossible in the majority of cases.

Acceptance of the explanation that petroleum changes result from natural external conditions originates from the silent admission of the apparent stability of organic matter in the absence of oxidizers over the extent of relatively short increments of time. Here people lose sight of the fact that inanimate matter has a time scale for its changes such that it absolutely cannot be compared with the general duration of an experiment. Obviously, it will be completely improper to extrapolate the absence of changes in a system of organic matter over the extent of short increments of time to the entire duration of the system's existence.

In view of the imperceptible nature of the changes in organic matter in a catalyst-free environment, over the extent of short increments of time, a conclusion is drawn on the stability of the system in the general absence of any external causes. At the same time the rapid nature of the changes in organic matter under the effect of oxidizers gives a basis for maintaining that the sole reason for the changes lies in fact in the action of external oxidizing factors. Investigators appear to lose their perspective of time and approach the solution of the basic problems, having long time periods for their basic co-ordinate, with time scales comparable to the human life span.

It is easy to show that the reason for the transformation of matter lies, not in external influences or conditions, but rather in the matter itself and is its inseparable property. We consider this situation to be apparent and proven repeatedly. The question of the relative role of external conditions and internal factors was recently discussed in detail in the literature [7]. It was concluded that the reason for the movement and change of matter lies within it, while the role of external conditions in the final accounting is reduced to the acceleration or retardation of the processes of development and change of matter with time. We will return once more to this question in the section dealing with the rate of transformation of a system of organic matter but for the present we will focus our attention on a well-defined solution of the problem of direction of the processes of petroleum transformation in nature.

We have shown the incongruity of the approach to the explanation of direction from the position of the oxidation hypothesis, which serves as a basis for maintaining that even the conclusions drawn on the basis of this hypothesis as to the direction of change for petroleum with time from paraffinic to cyclic varieties, cannot be recognized as being factual.

At the same time even the opposite point of view, based on the same factual data in conjunction with chemical experimental data, is not completely convincing. A substantial objection to it is the argument of its opponents that it is impossible, without significant corrections, to transpose relationships observed in a chemical experiment to the laboratory of nature where all phenomena are highly complicated and have completely different rules.

One cannot but agree with this objection, even if only partially. Some new data are presented in this book which confirm the hypothesis on the direction of the paraffinization of petroleum. For example, on the determination and proof of the catalytic role of moist clays for processes of petroleum transformation, quite convincing experimental data are introduced on the noticeable rate of transformation of hydrocarbons and other organic matter even at nominal temperatures in the absence of aluminosilicates, and so forth.

However, it is possible to solve the problem of the principal direction of processes of change in organic matter in an environment free from oxidizing agents only in very general terms, based on a minimum of assumptions and working with completely unquestionable relationships. We have already noted the fact that the thermodynamic method [7, 8] is the method for determining the direction of processes of petroleum change in nature. Until recent times thermodynamic methods found little application in the analysis of natural processes [9, 10, 11, 12] and were not used at all in the analysis of processes of the formation and change of petroleum under natural conditions.

The reason for this situation still is not clear to us. There are justifications for suspecting that some of the formal complications of the thermodynamic method and the known abstract nature of some of its concepts, as well as the approach to the solution of problems from completely general standpoints, became the reasons for overlooking this powerful method. Attempts are known to have been made, without any basis, to declare this method inapplicable in principal to the analysis of the phenomena which interest us. Occasionally, the thought would even slip through that since the organic hypothesis of the origin of petroleum has synthetic processes in a live organism as its basis and since, in the opinion of individual investigators, the laws of thermodynamics do not apply to these, then the thermodynamic method is supposedly inapplicable in general to the entire sum of processes for the origin and change of petroleum in nature.

The absurdity of such thinking is obvious. The laws of thermodynamics are unconditionally applicable whenever and wherever we are concerned with processes of change of individual forms of energy and the inseparably connected processes of transformation of matter regardless of whether or not these processes occur in a living organism or in inanimate nature. The law of conservation of energy and that of degradation of energy, on which thermodynamics itself is based, at least under the conditions on the earth's surface and in the layers of the earth's crust known to us, always remain in force and do not have any exceptions. From these completely general principles a number of quite logical and experimentally founded deductions and conclusions are made in thermodynamics which then have the character of natural laws.

The condition which appears to be negative at first glance, the abstract nature of the thermodynamic method compared to the concrete characteristics of matter, is in our case its positive feature. In view of the poor state of knowledge of petroleum itself and of the organic source matter often related to it, as well as the poor state of knowledge of the products of subsequent changes in petroleum, it becomes absolutely imperative to either completely reject the analysis of these processes and to concentrate all of the attention only on the accumulation of factual material, or to take the position of only solving the basic questions in general terms for the present, only detailing conclusions where this appears possible in view of the existence of factual data.

The first approach appears to offer us little perspective, especially with regard to attaining practically useful results in a short period of time. If it is also kept in mind that petroleum geochemistry is not yet endowed with the necessary specific methods for the recognition and study of complex natural systems of organic matter and operates only with the methods of classical organic chemistry, then the fruitlessness of this path becomes obvious.

The second approach, based on the solution of problems in general terms, is useful even if it only makes possible the drastic limitation of existing hypotheses to those which do not stand in open contradiction to the basic laws of nature. In addition, the thermodynamic approach permits the discovery of causal relationships between individual forms of natural organic matter and can form a sound basis for creating a better founded genetic scheme for the classification of caustobioliths. Finally, the thermodynamic method also permits us to establish the direction in which petroleum changes in nature; this being the objective of the current section.

A necessary, determining condition for the possibility of a specific process proceeding under given conditions is the decrease in the level of free energy or the increase in entropy of the changing system. The process which does not satisfy this condition is always extremely improbable and practically impossible.

If the position of individual groups of hydrocarbons in the free energy scale [7] is noted, it is relatively easy to see that of all of these, acetylenes and aromatics† have the highest level of free energy per atom of carbon. Next, after these, one finds the unsaturated hydrocarbons with double bonds. Still lower on the free energy scale are found the saturated five- and six-member cyclic hydrocarbons and, finally, lowest of all are the paraffinic hydrocarbons. At the same time the entropies of hydrocarbons in the order of benzene → cyclohexane → hexane increase from 64.46 to 92.45 entropy units/mole.

From these data if follows that, in the system consisting of hydrocarbons of all classes, those that are paraffinic are the most stable under standard conditions. All spontaneous changes known to occur in the direction of decreasing free energy and increasing entropy in the reacting system can only occur with noticeable effect in the given case in the direction from aromatic to the paraffinic hydrocarbons. The reverse path of transformation in the direction from paraffinic to cycloparaffinic and further to aromatic hydrocarbons is much less probable under conditions of low temperatures and nominal pressures.

F. Brickwedde and M. Aston [13] have calculated the constants in the equation for the reaction of the hydrogenation of benzene to cyclohexane at various temperatures and compared the obtained data with experimental results. It was found that at $400°K$ the equilibrium constants are approximately equal to 10^8, i.e. the reaction

$$C_6H_6 + 3H_2 \rightleftharpoons C_6H_{12}$$

is shifted to the right, in practice, and for one molecule of benzene in the equilibrium state there are 100,000,000 molecules of cyclohexane. This means that if, under the same conditions, we start with pure cyclohexane, regardless of the time that the system was left to come to an equilibrium state and no matter what catalysts

† It is impossible to compare values of free energy per gram-molecule in view of the differences in molecular weight.

were introduced into the system, it would still be impossible to obtain more than one molecule of benzene to a hundred million molecules of cyclohexane. The calculation coincides very well with experimental data.

Calculations further indicate that an increase in temperature leads to a rapid decrease in the equilibrium constant. Thus, for example, even at temperatures of $500°K$ ($237°C$) the magnitude of the constant is only about 135, while at a temperature of $600°$ it is about 0.0255. This means that in the range $500–600°K$ the reaction in the system benzene–cyclohexane–hydrogen is reversible and, if the reactions for the transformation of benzene to cyclohexane are possible in systems at temperatures up to $500°K$, then above $600°K$ the reverse reactions for the transformation of cyclohexane to benzene with the splitting off of hydrogen will start to predominate. If it is taken into account that the majority of petroleum accumulations known at the present time is found at temperature conditions not exceeding $150°C$ or $423°K$, it can be seen that under such conditions the dominant reactions developed in the system will be those for the transformation of benzene to cyclohexane if, of course, there will be sufficient reserves of free hydrogen in the system.

From this, by the way, follows the conclusion that with the development of drilling technology and the movement toward the exploitation of deeper lying accumulations of petroleum, in which the temperature will exceed $300°$, one cannot expect cycloparaffinic hydrocarbons to be present in the petroleum. This also serves to explain the situation that up to the present time no petroleums have been found the composition of which would represent a system of only paraffinic and aromatic hydrocarbons. S. S. Nametkin [14] even considers that such systems are "prohibited" for petroleum in general and, in his classification, does not leave an appropriate place for such petroleums. Thermodynamic analysis, however, shows that such petroleums must occur in nature and that they should be sought at great depths where high temperature conditions prevail. There is no doubt that such petroleums will be found sooner or later and will take their place in a reasonable classification. Evidence of this can be seen in the very characteristic composition of Ozek-Suat petroleum lying in deeply buried formations at a temperature of $145°K$, as we already had occasion to point out above, as well as in the composition of Minusian petroleum.

Similarly, the simplest thermodynamic analysis of processes for the transformation of paraffinic hydrocarbons shows that, under temperature conditions up to 1070 °K (797 °C), the transformation of compounds of the open chain type into five- or six-membered cyclic, hydrocarbons is not too probable while, at the same time the reverse process of opening the cyclic compounds and the formation of paraffinic hydrocarbons of the open chain type is quite reasonable [7, 8]. As we will show below, however, one should differentiate between processes for the transformation of low and high molecular weight paraffinic hydrocarbons. If the low molecular-weight paraffinic hydrocarbons are not inclined to change into cycloparaffinic compounds at relatively low temperatures, then the high molecular-weight paraffinic hydrocarbons will be inclined to change directly into aromatic hydrocarbons, avoiding the cycloparaffinic (or naphthenic) stage, at relatively low temperatures in the presence of aluminosilicates.

Cycloparaffinic hydrocarbons, depending on conditions, are capable of change in two directions. Under one set of conditions they may transform into open chain compounds, in the presence of excess hydrogen, while under other conditions they may, with the splitting off of hydrogen, change to aromatic structures. These processes, usually, under the conditions of limited resources of associated hydrogen in an oil accumulation and the absence of free hydrogen in general, proceed jointly and the transformation of naphthenic rings into aromatics simultaneously leads to the origin of additional quantities of paraffinic hydrocarbons.

Thus the thermodynamic analysis of processes for the transformation of hydrocarbons under conditions of an isolated system and nominal temperatures shows that there can occur an increase in paraffinic and aromatic hydrocarbons at the expense of cycloparaffins and a general decrease in the molecular weights and, consequently, the specific gravity of the system. If one considers, however, that with an increased degree of condensation of aromatic hydrocarbons the conditions of their existence in the form of a molecular solution in a gradually paraffinizing system becomes drastically less possible and that they will sooner or later leave the system in the form of a solid phase, it is relatively simple to come to the conclusion that, with the increasing depth of processes, the face of the petroleum changes in the direction of progressive lightening and paraffinization. Thus spontaneous processes in a thermodynamically isolated system of petroleum hydrocarbons cannot lead to either an increase in the quantity of cyclic compounds at the expense of paraffinic compounds or an increase in specific gravity.

It is possible to arrive at a similar conclusion with respect to the direction of processes for the transformation of hydrocarbons on the basis of an examination of the magnitude of entropy change in the reactions discussed. Thus, for example, the reaction for the hydrogenation of benzene into cyclohexane leads to an increase in entropy of 6.82 entropy units/mol. Further transformation of the cyclohexane into normal hexane is likewise accompanied by an increase in entropy of 10.14 entropy units/mol. Reverse reactions for the hydrogenation of paraffinic to cycloparaffinic hydrocarbons and further to aromatic hydrocarbons is accompanied by a decrease in entropy and, consequently, is not too likely.

B. EQUILIBRIUM AND IRREVERSIBILITY

It is well known that, in chemical processes involving organic matter, especially hydrocarbons, the reactions generally do not proceed instantaneously but rather over longer or shorter intervals of time and never completely exhaust all available reserves of source material. Organic reactions, in the majority of cases, achieve a state of equilibrium, i.e. for each specific combination of temperature, pressure and concentration conditions, a definite relationship is established in the reacting mixture between the amount of source materials and end products.

This characteristic of reactions involving organic matter is a consequence of the relatively small changes in the values of free energy of reactions between organic materials whereas the changes in free energy attain considerably higher values for reactions among inorganic materials. For example, the reaction for the formation of methane from elements leads to a lowering of the value of free energy by only 12.14 kcal/mol, while the reaction for the formation of carbon dioxide from carbon and oxygen is accompanied by a decrease in the value of free energy of 94.26 kcal/mol. For reactions with hydrocarbons, the decrease in value of free energy seldom exceeds 20 kcal/mol, while for inorganic substances, reactions leadnig to a decrease in free energy of hundreds and thousands of kilocalories are quite common.

From the expressions for the relationship between the equilibrium constant and change of free energy during a reaction

$$\Delta F_t^\circ = RT \ln K$$

and

$$K = e^{-\Delta F_t^\circ / RT}$$

it follows that even a nominal additional decrease in the value of free energy during a reaction leads to a significant increase in the value of the equilibrium constant since the values of ΔF_t° enter into the power of the function.

From this same expression it follows that values of $K = 1$ are attained at $\Delta F_t^\circ = 0$, i.e. in the case when the value of free energy does not change in the course of a reaction. Under these conditions the source products are half used up and, at the moment of equilibrium, one will find source and end products in the reacting mixture in equimolecular quantities.

Continuing our analysis of the expression for the relationship between equilibrium constant and change in free energy it is possible further to come to the conclusion that nominal positive values of change in free energy, for the situation in which only source materials exist in the system prior to the start of the reaction and the reaction for their conversion to end products proceeds in one stage, lead to the appearance of noticeable amounts of transformation products in the composition of the reacting mixture at the moment of equilibrium. Thus, for example, for the case examined by us, of the reaction for the hydrogenation of benzene to cyclohexane, the value of $K = 5.66 \times 10^{-5}$ at a temperature of 700°K, corresponds to values of free energy change of approximately $+13$ kcal/mol. Under these conditions, if equimolecular quantities of benzene vapors and molecular hydrogen are given off from the mixture, at the moment of equilibrium approximately 1.7×10^6 molecules of benzene will be found for each molecule of cyclohexane. Notwithstanding the fact that the effect of the change in free energy for this reaction at a temperature of 700°K represents a positive quantity, one will find small, but nevertheless measurable as fractions of a percent, quantities of cyclohexane in the reacting mixture.

From these approximate calculations the conclusion can be drawn that for practical purposes one can and must consider the equilibrium of those processes for which the change in free energy comprises either nominal negative values or positive values not larger than $+10$ kcal/mol. Values of change in free energy lying in the positive region and having an absolute value greater than 10 kcal/mol indicate the practical impossibility of the given reaction.

An analysis of the relationship between equilibrium constant and the value of change in free energy allows one to better understand the physical meaning of the irreversibility of chemical processes. This is especially important for an understanding of the general relationships of the process for the transformation of organic matter in an environment characterized by the absence of oxidizers, the origin of petroleum and its further transformation over the extent of geologic periods.

The understanding of the irreversibility of chemical processes follows from the idea of their spontaneity. In essence, each chemical process is spontaneous and occurs only when conditions of temperature, pressure and concentration of source reagents are combined in such a manner that the source system has a higher level of free energy as compared to any other. If it is possible for the source system, due to some other reasons, to re-orient the existing bonds by means of the simplest processes so that it would pass into a new system marked by lowered values of free energy then that reaction will have a place in reality and vice versa.

Since such a process was spontaneous and resulted in the passage of the system to a lower level of free energy, then one cannot expect the resulting system, under the same conditions, to return once more into its source state as a result of a spontaneous process. Such a change would contradict the law of conservation of energy since it would require the expenditure of a certain amount of energy with high potential. There is no source of such energy in an isolated system. It could also have been expected that it would be possible to attain the complete return of the system to its source condition by corresponding changes in temperature and pressure. This assumption would have been actually proved in practice in the case when the energy activating the direct and reverse processes would have been exactly equal.

In the overwhelming majority of cases, however, such is not the case. The energy activating the direct and reverse reactions are not equal. As a result, the rate of the direct and reverse reactions are also unequal, especially at the start of the process. Only at the moment that equilibrium is established, when the change in free energy is equal to zero, the rates of the direct and reverse processes equalize in such a manner that they maintain the relationship between starting and end reaction products constant with time.

Strictly speaking, under real conditions, every chemical process is irreversible since it occurs, especially with organic matter, in a finite time with quite definite values of force differences acting on the system (and counteracting these) and, what is very important, it is always accompanied by different irreversible losses: heat transfer, diffusion, etc.

Only in the idealized case can the process be reversible in the thermodynamic sense—when it proceeds at infinitely slow rates, with strict equality between the acting and reacting forces, and under conditions of the complete absence of any kind of losses.

Applying these thermodynamic considerations to the analysis of processes occurring in an oil accumulation it can be clearly seen that the conditions of their existence is such that there is no possibility for speaking of the reversibility of these processes. A petroleum system is far from any material or energetic insulation. In such an uninsulated system the processes are always tied in with greater or smaller losses of matter and energy by means of diffusion and heat transfer. In such a system processes are also possible which lead to the introduction of new quantities of different substances and different forms of energy.

On the other hand, processes within a system of hydrocarbons occur in such a manner that each time a new system of bonds arises within it, the next process will differ from the preceding in having a greater value of energy of its origin. In order to return to the previous state the newly arising system must expend a known amount of high potential energy from an outside source. However, there is no such energy source either in the petroleum itself or in the inorganic matter surrounding it.

As we shall see below, in the system of natural petroleum matter under conditions in which it is found, numerous interrelated processes of change occur in separate groups of this matter. Material formed as a result of one reaction serve as source products for other reactions, thereby drastically changing the conditions of equilibrium of the whole system in general and making the changes within it irreversible. In order to return to the basic relationships in any one portion of the system, one must set in motion a considerable mass of matter, not directly participating in the investigated equilibrium but related to it by a number of subsequent reactions.

Of course, this situation cannot but lead to a deepening of the irreversibility of the processes under way since the path of each process and its irreversibility is in turn tied in with a definite set of conditions. One cannot propose such a program of subsequent change in external conditions, the strict adherence to which could lead to the quantitative transformation of the system from methane and graphite into the system of hydrocarbons of the Grozny petroleum, although it is quite obvious that methane and graphite are both end products of the transformation of any petroleum. If we do not consider the entire process for the transformation of petroleum to its end products then there is every justification to maintain that each individual stage in this process is likewise irreversible. One cannot, for example, imagine a change in external conditions which could lead to the transformation of Grozny paraffinic petroleum into Grozny paraffin-free petroleum. At the same time the reverse process for the transformation of paraffin-free petroleum into the paraffin type can be achieved by means of spontaneous processes occurring within the system of matter in paraffin-free petroleum with a relatively nominal increase in temperature.

As in the overwhelming majority of natural processes, the process for the transformation of petroleum in nature is irreversible, and one cannot attain the quantitative transformation of a given system into the source system by changing the external conditions, even if the limitations imposed by the factor of time on any changing system are not observed.

C. MOTIVATING FORCES FOR PETROLEUM TRANSFORMATION PROCESSES IN NATURE

Every process involving changes in molecular structure takes place by means of chemical energy. If the source molecule does not have the required reserve of chemical energy then it is impossible to expect any significant changes in it, even in the distant future.

The overall reserve of chemical energy of all matter is determined by the characteristic of its composition and structure, as well as by the external conditions in which it occurs. However, it is not the overall reserve of energy which determines the reactive capability of the given matter, but only that portion of it which can be transformed into useful work by one process or another. With one and the same overall energy reserve, the matter having the greater reactive capability will be the one which has the lower specific heat under the given condition, i.e. the one which contains a lesser amount of tied up energy and more free or active energy.

The portion of the overall energy in matter which can be transferred to useful work is called free energy. The remaining portion which, under the given conditions, cannot be a source of useful work, in particular the work of changing the composition and molecular structure of matter, bears the name of unavailable energy. The sum of free and unavailable energy makes up the overall energy reserve of matter.

$$H° = F° + T \cdot S°.$$

All matter can obtain and provide energy from or to the external medium. Depending on the characteristics of composition and structure of matter, a greater or lesser portion of the energy absorbed from an external source will be transformed into free energy and can become a further cause for chemical and physical processes. The molecule which is inactive under the given condition, but potentially capable of transformation can, by means of changing the external conditions, be changed into one that is active and capable of chemical transformation if only it contains a sufficient reserve of free energy.

These general situations are commonly known and would not have to be repeated were it not for the existence of some erroneous reasoning on the motivating forces in the problem of petroleum origin. The majority of investigators recognizing the development and change of petroleum matter with time are inclined to see the reason for these changes in the effect of external conditions [6]. This situation exists because these investigators did not make the effort to analyze the details of the mechanism of the processes and limited themselves to the phenomenological side of the question. Besides, the relative stability of petroleum hydrocarbons with time under conditions of the absence of oxidizers and the nominal temperatures and pressures, created a misleading impression of the principal incapability of such matter to change. Naturally, in view of these conditions, the reason for the changes was shifted to the external conditions, completely setting aside from consideration the reasons based on the internal order. Thus, for example, we have the hypotheses of V. B. Porfir'ev and I. V. Greenberg on the high temperature origin of petroleum, the oxidation hypothesis for petroleum types, etc.

Let us examine the conditions for the existence of petroleum accumulations and the processes possible in the system of petroleum matter. Analysis of the material presented in the section of this book on the conditions for existence of petroleum accumulations indicates that the conditions which should be considered common include a temperature not higher than 100–150° and a pressure not over 100 atm. Under these conditions the stability of the majority of petroleum hydrocarbons, as compared with the stability of the elements comprising them, is little different from the stability under normal conditions.

From this it follows that feasible temperature and pressure changes for typical petroleum accumulations cannot be responsible for the basic change in the direction of transformations. An increase in temperature can only be responsible for a displacement of equilibrium conditions in the direction of the thermodynamically sound process, i.e. an increase in the equilibrium constant along with the increase in the rate of transformation.

The presence of a reserve of free energy within the system represents a constantly acting factor among all of the possible causes for petroleum changes, a factor which acts constantly in one and the same direction although perhaps with varying intensity. This condition is especially important because, among all of the other possible factors, one cannot find any which would act consistently in one and the same direction throughout the entire history of a petroleum. No matter how small such constantly acting influences would appear to be at first glance, by gradually accumulating over large intervals of time they lead, in the end, to significant changes in the system.

Examining the relative role of external and internal factors in the processes of petroleum change under natural conditions, one should especially underline the non-essential and periodic role of unusual external conditions as opposed to the essential, general and constant nature of internal factors. A necessary and sufficient reason for petroleum changes in nature are the internal factors while the external conditions do not have either a necessary or sufficient character.

By analyzing the role of external conditions and factors in detail, in one of our books [6], we came to the conclusion that among these it is possible to differentiate between conditions which stimulate the processes of petroleum change with time, those which retard such changes and, finally, neutral conditions not exerting any significant action on the flow of the processes.

Among the possible stimulating external conditions we included, for example, conditions such as contact with rocks having significant catalytic properties, elevated temperature conditions, the possibility of material exchange with external media, and sulfur content of petroleums. Processes which lower the energy level are also stimulated by such external conditions as oxidizing action on the petroleum system, even though they do, with widespread development, lead to considerably different end products.

Processes of natural metamorphism of petroleum are retarded by such external conditions as the absence of suitable catalysts or the presence of negative catalysts (inhibitors), low temperatures conditions, material and energy isolation of a petroleum system, increase in pressure and some others.

Thus the role of external conditions reduces, in essence, to the periodic possibility of accelerating or retarding the processes of natural petroleum changes proceeding under the influence of internal causes.

The periodic action of external conditions over the extent of the history of a petroleum makes the precise resolution of all specific processes that occurred extremely difficult. If all petroleums accumulated in nature under identical conditions then all of their differences would be reduced to a single variable, the greater or lesser duration of their existence in the depths of the earth's crust.

Such a view, however, obviously does not correspond to reality. On the basis of data on petroleum composition it is sometimes possible to establish a minor reflection of the effect of one external factor or another on the rate of its transformation and peculiarities of character of the end products of change.

From the point of view of some investigators, the entire history of petroleum in essence represents an endless chain of chance and the petroleum itself represents only a passive objective for the action of external forces and conditions. Such a hypothesis is completely fruitless and essentially explains nothing. If one adheres to such a point of view, then the role of the investigator is reduced merely to that of selecting, from the available arsenal of data, a number of external conditions for a more or less logical explanation and description of the peculiarities of composition and structure of the investigated petroleum. It is impossible to predict in advance the properties of petroleum under these or the other conditions of occurrence or even to establish the direction of its development with time with the aid of such a system of thought. Each external factor taken by itself may or may not have acted during the history of a petroleum and it is impossible to predict this fact in advance.

If, however, one takes the stand on the point of view that the motivating force of processes for the development and change of petroleum in nature is provided by internal causes, acting unchangingly in the same direction over the extent of the entire history of the petroleum, and that external conditions do not exert any significant effect on the general direction, but only accelerate or retard the course of the natural process, there appears a possibility of creating an orderly system of views on the course of this process.

According to this system, the general direction of processes involved in the change of petroleum matter under natural conditions is that of the reduction in the level of free energy acquired by the atoms of hydrogen, carbon and others in the process of photosynthesis. Within limits the system strives to attain a level of free energy characteristic for carbon dioxide and water.

The tendency to lower the level of free energy can be attained most simply and most rapidly by means of the oxidation of petroleum matter by an excess of oxygen. However, under the conditions of occurrence of the majority of petroleum accumulations, an excess of oxygen, or even the presence of more or less detectable concentrations of oxygen, are non-existent. Consequently, this simplest path is impossible for petroleum.

Under conditions of the absence of oxidizers the only available means for reducing the level of free energy is that of re-orienting the system of bonds between the atoms present in a manner that would lead to the formation of compounds with the minimum possible level of free energy. For the carbon and hydrogen atoms making up the system of petroleum matter, such compounds, in the absence of oxidizers, can only be methane and graphite. This is the final and limiting result which the petroleum system strives to attain.

Examining all of the imaginable conditions associated with sedimentary rocks, one is readily convinced of the fact that no external factors, either taken separately or in any spontaneous combination, can either serve as a source of energy for opposing processes within the system of petroleum matter or radically change (reverse) the course of the process, i.e. from methane, graphite, carbon dioxide, water and others to petroleum. Furthermore, one should not expect that the petroleum system can return to a former state of its development, no matter how close, due to any change in external conditions.

Notwithstanding the fact that the various external factors or combinations of them can lead to different changes in the material composition of petroleum, the energy content of their action remains constant and unchanging. External factors only accelerate or retard the natural process of reduction of the free energy level for the system of petroleum matter.

D. RATE OF TRANSFORMATION PROCESSES
OF PETROLEUM MATTER

Time is the most important co-ordinate for processes of petroleum change. In no division of experimental organic chemistry does the investigator have the opportunity to observe the results of processes for the transformation of organic matter over the extent of such an extended period of time as in the geochemistry of petroleum. This greatly broadens the boundaries of organic chemistry in general and, in particular, the study of slowly occurring chemical processes, as well as making these processes available if not for experimental investigation, then at least for investigation from the phenomenological point of view.

Significant variations in the composition and properties of petroleums lying in different stratigraphic horizons and the established direction of change of petroleum properties forced investigators to suppose that time is a significant factor in the development of petroleum. This point of view was first formulated on a scientific basis by V.A. Sokolov [15]. A.A. Kartsev [16] assigns a significant place to time in the system of factors changing the form of petroleum by introducing it in the value of the Geotectokhronobat.

In classifying the processes of petroleum change we noticed that, of all of the possible processes, it is possible to identify those in which high activation energy is inherent. Although those interested in the theory of chemical kinetics are referred to special guiding texts [17, 18] we nevertheless must mention some of the basis tenets of this science at this point.

For each individual form of chemical process in which the original molecule participates, there exists a characteristic value of activation energy. Before entering a chemical reaction the molecule must obtain a definite reserve of kinetic energy, as a result of collisions with other molecules, and only then will it become "active" and enter into the reaction.

Under all given conditions of temperature and pressure there exists in the basic mixture a very definite amount of active molecules, usually quite small but one that grows rapidly with time. Thus, for example, for a reaction with an activation energy of 60 kcal/mol at a temperature of 573 °C there will only be about a 10^{-17} mol-fraction of active molecules in the mixture. Increasing the temperature by 10° increases the fraction of active molecules by 30%. A further increase of 50° leads to an increase in the number of active molecules by 7.25 times and an increase of 100° by 3^{10} times. The greater the number of active molecules arising in a unit of time the greater the total rate of the reaction.

The magnitude of the energy of activation depends on the type of reaction and on the molecule's structure. The more complex the structure of the molecule the lower, in general, is its energy of activation for one and the same reaction, and the greater the transformation rate. Hydrocarbons having an especially simple structure are characterized by high values of energy of activation, for example, in reactions connected with a significant change of the hydrocarbon framework.

The activation energy value enters into the numerator of the power for the expression describing the constant for the reaction rate, in view of which even a relatively small decrease or increase in energy of activation leads to a significant change in the rate constant. Thus, for example, the rate constant for a bi-molecular reaction is equal to $K = c \cdot e^{E/RT}$ and with an energy of activation value of 60 kcal/mol a decrease of only 4.0 kcal/mol accelerates the reaction by some 500 times.

The realm of gradual reactions starts with values of activation energy of 20–30 kcal/mol and for hydrocarbon reactions these values are usually about 50–60 kcal/mol. It is especially important to recognize that the energy of activation is a characteristic of the reaction and not of matter. This energy differs in magnitude depending on whether the reaction proceeds independently or under the influence of catalysts. It also differs for different catalysts.

The role of catalysts in a chemical process reduces to decreasing or increasing the energy of activation for a given reaction, in view of which it becomes possible to either drastically increase the rate of or to retard such reactions. In the absence of catalysts such reactions occur in terms of completely different time scales. Simple calculations show that with a value of energy of activation for the reaction involving the disintegration of the simplest methane hydrocarbons of 60–70 kcal/mol, their stable existence will be assured over the extent of billions of years under nominal temperature conditions. If we nevertheless have unquestionable evidence in nature of the existence of processes for hydrocarbon transformation over considerably shorter increments of time, then this can only attest to the fact that positive catalysts played an important role in such processes for petroleum matter and that without catalytic processes the composition of natural petroleums would have been completely different from that actually observed. Furthermore, it can be proved that in the absence of catalytic processes one not only cannot expect petroleum to be present in Tertiary sediments but typical petroleum probably would not be found in Paleozoic rocks because noncatalytic processes for the transformation of buried organic matter in the period from the Cambrian to the present could only have led to the formation of highly viscous mixtures with a minimal content of low molecular weight hydrocarbons. This curious conclusion can probably serve as direct and unquestionable evidence for the presence of catalytic processes in the system of buried organic matter in sedimentary rocks.

Depending on the state of development of processes for the change of buried organic matter, the materials accumulating in the system in the form of end products would have high energy of activation values for processes of their further transformation under stable conditions of temperature and pressure. As a result of these transformation processes, less stable materials are eliminated and more stable materials are generated. If one considers that the less stable matter will be subjected to transformation first, and only afterwards will the more stable compounds with increasing energy of activation be affected, it is possible to conclude that the source compounds for the formation of hydrocarbons had an energy of activation for the transformation lower than that for the reaction with hydrocarbons. Compared to source matter, hydrocarbons have lower transformation rates in view of the increased values of energy of activation in the processes of their further transformation.

The presence of hydrocarbons in the organic matter in contemporary sediments (the composition of these hydrocarbons precludes the possibility of their synthesis by live organisms) suggests the fact that there are components of the buried organic material whose activation energy is nominal in the process of hydrocarbon formation. The absence of significant accumulations of petroleum in Quaternary sediments, however, attests to the fact that large-scale hydrocarbon formation takes place in those reactions where the energy of activation comprises no less than 30–40 kcal/mol under conditions when positive catalysts are present. It is possible that the formation of nominal quantities of high molecular-weight hydrocarbons during the initial stages of burial has as its basis the action of extremely energetic biochemical catalysts, i.e. ferments. However, the action of these catalysts terminates quite rapidly since the ferments are inclined to rapid deactivation. The mass formation of hydrocarbons probably occurs, however, under the effect of mineral catalysts which are not as effective as the ferments but which act over a more prolonged period of time and under more favorable conditions of elevated temperature.

The poor state of knowledge of specific reactions for transformations in the complex system of petroleum hydrocarbons and the absence of data in the literature on activation energy values soon place a limit on any attempts at quantitative calculation of the rates of processes for the transformation of hydrocarbons. This situation is not insurmountable, however, at least from the qualitative point of view. Relying on known data on the composition of petroleums it is possible to draw at least some preliminary conclusions regarding activation energy values for the basic directions of processes involved in the transformation of various types of hydrocarbons.

It will be shown below that the predominant direction for the change of aromatic hydrocarbons in a natural environment are condensation processes with the preservation of aromatic rings. These processes are probably differentiated by not too high values of energy of activation since already in Paleozoic petroleums, in the majority of cases, there is no aromatic structure in the presence of complex condensed hydrocarbon molecules. This can be explained by the fact that the processes for the formation of complex condensed structures had progressed so far that the compounds formed had already dropped out of the system due to loss of solubility.

The transformation of complex naphthenic hydrocarbons is probably characterized by even lower energies of activation. This can be seen from the fact that the naphthene content decreases in going from Tertiary petroleums through the Mesozoic to the Paleozoic. The high temperature conditions of petroleum accumulations already leads to the disappearance of complex naphthenes in petroleums of Mesozoic age.

The highest values for energy of activation belong to the processes for the transformation of paraffinic hydrocarbons. Tracing the changes in petroleums from the Tertiary period to the Paleozoic one can observe a continuous increase in the paraffin content indicative of the low transformation rates for this class of compounds.

Characteristic for petroleum hydrocarbons is the gradual or possibly progressive slowing down in the transformation rate at each subsequent stage. Within limits, with the exhaustion of basic reserves of free energy, the rates of all transformations in the system of petroleum matter are inclined toward zero. "Young" petroleums have the highest transformation rate. Perhaps, for this very reason, poorly transformed compounds of A. F. Dobryanskii's "oxy-asphalts" are so rare in a natural environment, at least in the concentrated form. This type of matter is so rare that even its occasional discovery in nature is attributed not to processes of the initial stages of change in organic matter but rather to processes of petroleum oxidation in a subaerial environment.

E. PHENOMENOLOGY OF SPONTANEOUS TRANSFORMATION PROCESSES OF ORGANIC MATTER

Processes occurring in one system or another only become noticeable as a result of the change of properties in the basic system. If in the course of a known interval of time the properties of the system persist without noticeable change, it can be claimed that, within the time limits of observation, no irreversible processes occur with the system.

The chemical molecule in itself exists in a constant state of flux. Changes occur in the distances between atoms, the order of the relationships between these, etc. Some of these processes do not lead to a change in the chemical individuality of the molecule while others can lead to such significant changes that the molecule ceases to be that which it was an instant earlier.

Since one cannot imagine the isolated existence of an individual molecule and since in the actual case there can only be a collective co-existence with similar or structurally different molecules, external conditions existing for the examined molecule will have an additional effect on its properties. Every substance has within its nucleus the possibility of becoming another under a new set of conditions.

A stage on the road of spontaneous transformation of organic molecules is represented by processes which lead to an irreversible change in the structure of the basic molecule without changing the overall number of molecules in the system. These processes bear the special title of isomerization processes. Naturally, with a change in the structure of a molecule, its physical and chemical properties as well as the properties of the system as a whole also change. The phenomenon of isomerization is widespread and is common to both hydrocarbons and other organic compounds.

Isomerization processes occur with quite a noticeable change in the energy state of the molecule and require a considerable energy barrier to be overcome in the course of its development. As a result, the rates of isomeric transformations are quite nominal at times and only become noticeable with increases in temperature or with the action of catalysts.

If one looks closely at the source of isomerization processes, for example in the case of the relatively simplest hydrocarbon cases, it is possible to identify a number of interesting relationships. In the first place a characteristic which strikes the eye and which was previously discovered by Butlerov, Flavitskii and Favorskii, is that in the isomerization processes of many hydrocarbons a definite tendency is observed toward the formation of compounds containing in their composition a greater number of methyl groups than was present in the source matter. For example, it is known that hydrocarbons of normal paraffin structure have a tendency, under certain conditions, toward isomerization with the formation of iso-compounds

$$CH_3-CH_2-CH_2-CH_3 \rightarrow \begin{matrix} CH_3 \\ \diagdown \\ CH_3 \diagup \end{matrix} CH-CH_3.$$

Reviewing the data of Rossini [19] on the composition of equilibrium mixtures formed as a result of isomeric transformations of paraffinic hydrocarbons, it can be seen that iso-compounds will be the most stable at low temperatures. With increasing temperatures the equilibrium is shifted in the direction of hydrocarbons having a normal structure.

In this regard, in discussing the relationships of the hydrocarbon composition of petroleums, one should keep in mind that the presence of iso-compounds among paraffinic hydrocarbons can serve as a type of geochemical indicator of the degree of petroleum change under natural conditions. The greater the number of compounds with a branch type hydrocarbon structure in the composition of petroleum hydrocarbons the greater the degree of petroleum transformation, everything else being equal. This relationship can take on great significance under the definite condition that the sources for the formation of isoparaffinic hydrocarbons and the paths of their further transformations over the extent of geologic time will be known.

Probably a greater significance for the solution of problems in the geochemical correlation petroleums can be attributed to data on the relative content of methyl groups as compared to the overall amount of carbon and hydrogen in the system rather than on the absolute content of isoparaffinic hydrocarbons. Actually, the energy saturated compounds characteristic of live organism cells differ by their minimal carbon content in methyl groups while, in the products of the final transformation of petroleum, a considerable portion of the carbon is concentrated in the molecules of methane, in compounds representing a methyl radical saturated with hydrogen. Consequently, according to the development of petroleum transformation processes in nature, there is a tendency for the hydrogen and part of the carbon to shift from the internal portions of the molecules to the periphery and to form methyl groups. If the petroleum system was completely isolated, then at any subsequent stage of development it would be possible to state that there is an increase in the content of methyl groups joined to the principal portion of the carbon reserve in the system by C—C bonds or in the form of free methane molecules.

The greater or lesser degree of isolation of the petroleum system creates various possibilities for the loss of methyl groups from the system in the form of methane and other simple volatile hydrocarbons. In this regard the actual increase in methyl group content in petroleum systems cannot be of a continuous nature. Depending on the degree of isolation of the system this process can have an important influence, since the release of methane in equilibrium with the balance of the molecules in the system also has an effect on the structure (including the methyl group content) of the less mobile components in the system. The discovery of the relationships for the change in methyl group content represents the foremost problem of the scientific investigation of petroleum. In all probability, it is these specific characteristics of the formation and liberation of methyl groups from the system which are responsible for the observed deficiency of ethane in the composition of petroleum gases.

The thermodynamic relationship for isomerization processes can be clearly seen from a comparison of the free energy for normal and isomeric hydrocarbons. Thus, for example, in the isomeric hexanes the highest level of free energy is found in n-hexane (-1.04 kcal/mol) while isomeric 2-methyl pentane has a free energy value of -1.95 kcal/mol. Further accumulation of methyl groups leads to a further decrease in free energy; so that the free energy of 2,2-dimethyl butane is -2.82 kcal/mol. Similar relationships exist for pentanes, heptanes, octanes, etc. Thus the spontaneous development of the system at low temperatures can only proceed in the direction of the accumulation of iso-compounds and, consequently, in the direction of the accumulation of methyl groups.

Studying the processes of isomerization in a number of cyclic hydrocarbons it can be seen that the above relationship holds for these too. For example, it is known that all substituted cyclic compounds with long side-chains (greater than methyl) are inclined under favorable conditions to isomerize spontaneously into polymethylene derivatives. N. Ya. Dem'yanov [20] established that in the decomposition of aromatic rings under moderate conditions the liberated carbon atoms do not break away from the original structure but remain tied to it in the form of methyl groups (for example, methyl-cyclohexane). It is also known that the splitting of substituted cyclo-paraffinic hydrocarbons during reduction occurs in such a manner that the bonds between carbon atoms not having any substitutes are broken:

$$
\begin{array}{c}
\text{H}_2\text{C}\!-\!\!-\!\!-\!\text{CH}\!-\!\text{CH}_3 \\
\text{CH}_3\!-\!\text{HC}\diagdown\quad\diagup\text{CH}_2 \\
\text{CH}_2
\end{array}
+ \text{H}_2 \rightarrow \text{CH}_3\!-\!\overset{\overset{\displaystyle\text{CH}_3}{|}}{\text{CH}}\!-\!\text{CH}_2\!-\!\overset{\overset{\displaystyle\text{CH}_3}{|}}{\text{CH}}\!-\!\text{CH}_3
$$

and branched hydrocarbons are formed in preference to straight chains.

Numerous instances of isomeric transformations of unsaturated hydrocarbons are known which, in the absence of inflow of energy from the outside, lead to the formation of compounds with a greater number of methyl groups than there were in the source molecule [21, 22]. Although processes with these hydrocarbons do not have a direct relationship to the transformation of petroleum they illustrate the general rule very well. In the isomerization of unsaturated compounds one can observe the displacement of the unsaturated bond from the periphery to the center of the molecule as, for example,

$$CH\equiv C-CH_2-CH_2-C\equiv CH \rightarrow CH_3-C\equiv C-C\equiv C-CH_3$$

or in the case of unsaturated cyclic compounds

$$
\begin{array}{ccc}
& C{=}CH_2 & \\
H_2C & \diagup \quad \diagdown & CH_2 \\
H_2C & \diagdown \quad \diagup & CH_2 \\
& CH_2 &
\end{array}
\longrightarrow
\begin{array}{ccc}
& C{-}CH_3 & \\
H_2C & \diagup \quad \diagdown & CH \\
H_2C & \diagdown \quad \diagup & CH_2 \\
& CH_2 &
\end{array}
$$

In reality these examples are only local cases of the more general relationship for the accumulation of methyl groups during the spontaneous transformation of organic molecules. As in the case of saturated paraffin hydrocarbons, the general direction of the process in the series studied will be towards a reduction in the level of free energy. The greater the number of methyl groups in the unsaturated hydrocarbon molecule and the closer the unsaturated bond is to the center of the molecule then the lower will be the level of free energy for such a hydrocarbon. Similar relationships are inherent not only in hydrocarbons but are also the property of compounds containing oxygen, sulfur, nitrogen, halogens, etc., in their composition.

From this point of view the structural characteristics of molecules which enter into the composition of a live organism become understandable. Fats, being the material and energy reserve of the organism, are built in the form of a chain of carbon atoms without any branches, i.e. they possess more excess energy for one and the same number of carbon atoms even by comparison with structurally isomeric compounds. A live organism, so to speak, selects the more "spacious" forms of molecular structure for the storage of its energy reserves for one and the same number of atoms. The same relationship holds for sugars, representing a vegetable organism reserve, and for molecules which enter into the composition of the albumin reserve of animals and plants.

At the same time organic molecules which do not play the part of reserve resources in a living organism, as for example hormones, vitamins, alkaloids, as a rule have a carbon frame in the form of a cyclic structure with a large number of methyl groups. This also has a definite significance since precisely such a molecule is more compact, more unstable and, for one and the same number of atoms, permits a considerably greater variety in its structure and hence in its properties. These molecules play a completely different role than do the reserve fats and albumins and continuously participate in the exchange of matter taking place in a living organism. In general isoparaffinic structures are not characteristic of a living organism and their presence in petroleums can only be explained by subsequent processes in already dead matter.

Of very great theoretical and practical interest is the development of relationships for the co-existence in petroleum of normal and iso-hydrocarbons depending on the stage of petroleum transformation. Investigating the question in general terms it can be stated that certain iso-type hydrocarbons appear in noticeable quantities only during a certain stage of a system's development and disappear in an orderly manner during subsequent stages, being once again transformed by means of the loss of methyl radicals in the form of methane, into normal type hydrocarbons but now with a lower molecular weight.

Each stage of petroleum development is characterized by a lower free energy level compared to the one preceding and, consequently, isoparaffins are probably products of change of the more energy laden decomposed cycloparaffins with side chains or of normal paraffinic hydrocarbons having a greater or equal molecular weight. Iso-type hydrocarbons have an increased free energy level compared to a system of normal hydrocarbons, only in the case when the latter are lower in molecular weight but in general when their molecular weights are similar to those of the original. Thus, for example, 2-methyl butane in the presence of excess hydrogen is inclined to go to a system of normal butane and methane. This transition will be accompanied by a lowering in the free energy level of 12.39 kcal/mol.

$$CH_3-\overset{\overset{\displaystyle CH_3}{|}}{CH}-CH_2-CH_3 + H_2 \rightarrow CH_3-CH_2-CH_2-CH_3 + CH_4.$$

From this point of view one can also explain the regular appearance of solid paraffins and ceresins at a certain stage of petroleum development since for these one can also expect the same relationships between values of free energy as found in the case of low molecular weight normal and iso-hydrocarbons.

One cannot draw a sharp line between processes of isomerization and processes of disproportionation of elements. Actually, processes of isomerization are, in the majority of cases, processes of disproportionation of elements within a single molecule. Processes of accumulation of methyl groups in the composition of a molecule cannot be called anything other than processes of intramolecular disproportionation of elements which lead to the collection of a surplus of hydrogen atoms in one portion of the molecule and the simultaneous paucity of these in another portion. Simultaneously, one part of the molecule is made rich in carbon and another poor.

In this manner, studying the processes within a molecule it is possible to extend the ideas of A. F. Dobryanskii on processes of intermolecular disproportionation of hydrogen to intramolecular processes, extending these ideas to other elements besides hydrogen. These processes are not characterized by as great a depth or as significant a change in system properties as in the case of intermolecular disproportionation but do likewise lead to results that are similar and represent one of the stages in the preparation of the molecule for more radical changes.

Processes of intramolecular disproportionation of elements is extremely widespread and much is known about them in organic chemistry. Processes of intramolecular oxidation-reduction [23, 24, 25] lead, from the phenomenological point of view, to the accumulation of oxygen in one part of the molecule and a corresponding stripping of it from another. Processes are known to exist which lead to the accumulation of halogens, sulfur, nitrogen and other elements in one portion of a molecule.

Descriptions of all of these most interesting processes are scattered through individual chapters of organic chemistry and original articles and bear the name of rearrangements largely named after the investigators discovering them. For example, we know of the rearrangements of Beckman, Kurtsius, Danilov, Favorskii, Freese, the pinacol rearrangement and numerous others. A somewhat outdated summary of data from the literature on rearrangements is available in V.Khyukkel's work [27].

To the present time attempts have not been encountered in the literature to generalize all of these spontaneous intramolecular changes in organic molecules from any general points of view although a number of common characteristics become immediately obvious in studying the entire series of such reactions.

It is possible to note at least two common phenomena inherent in these reactions which appear at first glance to be quite different. First, all of them are accompanied by a reduction in the free energy level of the original system and, under constant external conditions, they proceed irreversibly. Second, studying the structural characteristics of the original and end products it is possible without difficulty, in the overwhelming majority of cases, to become convinced of the fact that the molecules in the end products are put together in such a manner that they have a large fraction of some element concentrated in some portions of it while carbon predominates in another. Both of these occurrences, one relating to the energy side of the phenomenon and the other depicting its phenomenology, have one common property and that is the one allowing all of these previously varied processes to be united into one group of processes involving the intramolecular disproportionation of elements.

We do not have the opportunity here of illustrating this conclusion in detail with numerous examples and will return to this problem in a separate work. At this time it will suffice for us to state the fact that processes of intramolecular disproportionation of elements are widespread and occur spontaneously.

Thus if one leaves a system of homogeneous molecules by itself, then, under constant external conditions of temperature and pressure, processes of intramolecular transformation will sooner or later become apparent within it and these will tend to bring the molecules of matter to a state having the lowest possible reserve of free energy under the given conditions. A known principle of organic chemistry is that of least change in molecular structure for any chemical transformation or, as formulated in a different manner, the principle of step-wise occurrence of chemical reactions [26].

In accordance with this principle, the primary processes in a system left to itself will be those which are not tied in with any significant change in the internal structure of source molecules. Subsequent stages after this will have the nature of deeper changes. However, here too, the molecule will tend where possible to change its original structure by the least amount.

So far, in such a system, not all of the possibilities for lowering the level of free energy by means of intramolecular processes will be exhausted. The change in the total number of molecules, i.e. the deep disintegration of the structure, will occur at the lowest level. The principle of least change in the structure of the original system will first apply to processes of isomerization or the disproportionation of elements within a molecule. Consequently, these processes will be the primary ones compared to processes for any deeper change in the system.

Consequently, a deeper stage of change in the original system will consist of processes of intermolecular redistribution of elements leading also, from the phenomenological point of view, to the disproportionation of elements, i.e. the accumulation of certain elements in one portion of the system and the stripping of these from another part of the system.

Processes of intermolecular disproportionation are no less plentiful than those that are intramolecular. Individual examples of these can be found in the original works of various investigators and, in recent times, in the theoretical writings of A. F. Dobryanskii.

Without dwelling on the details of the mechanism for these reactions it can be stated here that in the end they lead to the isolation of carbon from the other elements, such as oxygen, hydrogen, sulfur, nitrogen, etc., existing with it in a living organism. In the course of this a portion of the carbon leaves the system in the form of simpler compounds loaded to the limit with hetero elements of carbon dioxide and methane while the other portion remains in place in a state approaching pure carbon. A portion of the hetero elements splits off in the form of compounds made up of various combinations of themselves rather than with carbon, e.g. water, hydrogen sulfide, ammonia, etc. Some hetero elements like nitrogen can split off in an elemental state.

Here we see how processes of intermolecular disproportionation gradually pass into combined processes of disintegration of some and enlarging of other molecules in the original system. This probably occurs when the possibilities of intramolecular lowering of the free energy level is already exhausted to a considerable degree. This latter, concluding stage of existence for the original system is characterized by fundamental changes in its properties which is reflected not only in the structural changes of individual molecules but also in a change of their total number. In the end the total number of molecules increases and this increase basically depends on the carbon-hetero element relationship in the original system.

Out of this by the way follows the curious conclusion that during the initial stages of change, when there is a large number of hetero elements in the system, the latter is capable of forming the greatest number of small molecules, i.e. during the initial stages of change of organic matter, in an environment lacking in oxidizers, gaseous products are predominantly formed.

The order of occurrence for various processes in a system of organic matter reviewed above from a phenomenological point of view does not at all mean that at each stage within it only one type of change can occur, as, for example, only isomerization processes. In view of the great complexity of the system itself as well as of its processes, at any given moment the most varied transformations can occur in the system, starting from the delicate ones which do not change the properties of the molecules and ending with processes of disintegration. The order of the processes is related to one separate molecule rather than to the system as a whole. Each separate molecule sooner or later passes through the orderly sequence of changes from beginning to end to complete disintegration but this does not at all mean that the whole system in general will pass through this sequence in a given time. Molecules will be found in it which, under the prevailing conditions, will be quite stable over considerable increments of time and these are the molecules that can accumulate while the external conditions remain constant.

Our system strives toward those molecules that are structurally most stable. Somewhat of a natural selection of molecules occurs, as a result of which only the most stable under the given conditions can "survive". A general levelling of molecular structure will occur.

Among hetero compounds, the most stable products probably are molecules of asphaltic matter and the simplest mineral compounds. Among hydrocarbons, paraffinic compounds and ultimately methane are found to be the most stable. Graphite and materials close to it are stable forms for the existence of carbon.

There is probably no need for a reminder that each subsequent stage of change is characterized by reduced values of free energy relative to the preceding stage and by higher values of activation energy for the possible reactions in the system. The development of the system proceeds at the expense of its internal energy resources and is not lacking in a constant source of external energy. If, however, local conditions provide a source of external energy, then, because of the general irreversibility of processes in a system of organic matter, the development will proceed not in a reverse direction but rather in such a manner that it will lead to the intensification of processes of disproportionation of elements with the formation of products of complete system degradation. The destruction of the system will be attained in a much shorter time.

BIBLIOGRAPHY

1. ANDREEV, P.F. Geol. Sbornik 1 (Geol. Handbook 1), Trudy VNIGRI, Nov. Seriya Issue 83, p. 140, Gostoptekhizdat, 1955.
2. DOBRYANSKII, A.F. Geokhimiya Nefti (Geochemistry of Petroleum), Gostoptekhizdat, 1948.
3. BOGOMOLOV, A.I., ANDREEV, P.F. Zh. prikl. Khimii, **29**, Issue 9, p. 957 (1956).
4. BOGOMOLOV, A.I. and VASIL'EVA, G.M. Geol. Sbornik 2, Trudy VNIGRI, Issue 25, p. 405, Gostoptekhizdat, 1956.
5. BOGOMOLOV, A.I. Geol. Sbornik 1, Trudy VNIGRI, Issue 83, p. 506, Gostoptekhizdat, 1955.
6. ANDREEV, P.F. Geol. Sbornik 2, Trudy VNIGRI, Issue 95, p. 266, Gostoptekhizdat, 1956.
7. DOBRYANSKII, A.F. and ANDREEV, P.F. Bull. Acad. Sci. Estonian SSR **3**, 193 (1954).
8. DVALI, M.F. and ANDREEV, P.F. Sbornik "Proiskhozhdenie Nefti" (Origin of Crude Oil), Gostoptekhizdat, 1955.
9. SAULL, W.A. Geoch. et Cosmic Ac. **8**, 86 (1955).
10. BLOOM, H.F. Time, Arrow and Evolution, New York, 1951.
11. LEBEDEV, V.I. Vestnik LGU, No. 11 (1948).
12. KELLER, W.D. J. Sed. Petrology, **24**, No. 1, 62 (1954).
13. BRICKWEDDE, F.I. and ASHTON, J.G. J. Res. Nat. Bur. St. **37**, No. 5, 263 (1946).
14. NAMETKIN, S.S. Khimiya Nefti (Chemistry of Petroleum), GONTI, M–L, 1939.
15. SOKOLOV, V.A. Ocherki Genezisa Nefti (Outline of Petroleum Genesis), Gostoptekhizdat, 1949.
16. KARTSEV, A.A. Azerb. Neft. Khoz., No. 3 (1954).

17. KIREEV, V.A. and FEDULOV, I.F. *Uchebnik Fizicheskoi Khimii (Textbook of Physical Chemistry)*, Gostoptekhizdat, 1954.
18. RAKOVSKII, A.V. *Vedenie v Fizicheskuyu Khimiyu (Introduction to Physical Chemistry)*, ONTI, 1938.
19. ROSSINI, F.D. Crude oils, *Chemical Thermodynamic Properties of Hydrocarbons, the Science of Petroleum*, vol. 5, p. 1, OUP, London, New York, Toronto, 1950.
20. DEM'YANOV, N.YA. *Sbornik Izbrannikh Trudov (Handbook of Selected Works)*, Izd. AN SSSR, 1936.
21. REZNICHENKO, M.S. *Sbornik Nauchn. Rabot Leninskovo Inst. Sovetsk. Torgovi (Handbook of Scientific Works of the Lenin Institute of Soviet Trade)*, Issue 9, p. 96, 1955.
22. REUTOV, *Teoreticheskie Problemy Organischeskoi Khimii (Theoretical Problems in Organic Chemistry)*, Izd. MGU, March 1956.
23. DANILOV, S.N. Problemy Kinetiki i Kataliza (Problems in Kinetics and Catalysis), VI. Geterogennyi Kataliz (Heterogenous Catalysis), *Trudy Vsesoyuzn. Konf. po Katalizu*, Izd. AN USSR, 1949.
24. DANILOV, S.N. Sbornik "Problemy Mekhanizma Organich. Reaktsii" (Handbook of Problems in the Mechanism of Organic Reactions), *Trudy Kievsk. Soveshch.*, 2–5 June 1952, Izd. AN USSR, 1953.
25. DANILOV, S.N. *Sbornik "Reaktsii i Metodi Issled. Soed." (Handbook of Reactions and Methods for Investigating Compounds)*, No. 4, Goskhimizdat, March 1956.
26. OSTWALD, W. *Zeitschr. f. Phys. Ch.* **22**, No. 3, 298 (1897).
27. KHYUKKEL', V. *Teoreticheskie Osnovi Organicheskoi Khimii (Theoretical Principles of Organic Chemistry)*, Vol. I, I.L., 1956.

CHAPTER IV

THERMODYNAMICS OF LOW TEMPERATURE TRANSFORMATION OF HYDROCARBONS

IN THIS section we will examine the transformation of previously formed petroleum by means of the internal energy of the molecules. This transformation primarily refers to the hydrocarbon mass of the molecules since the formed petroleum only contains nominal amounts of heterogenous molecules connecting it with the basic material. The effect of catalyzers and increased temperature is reduced to overcoming the internal resistance of the molecules to change, which is also possible without the indicated factors. If petroleum is formed from material deposited with the argillaceous mineral particles, the basic transformations must have already occurred in the source rocks. The displacement of petroleum into more suitable reservoir rocks made up of porous rocks, not having catalytic properties, reduces the possibility of petroleum transformation but does not eliminate it completely, i.e. it creates the possibility of the petroleum existing in one transformed state or another, thereby determining the petroleum type.

The thermocatalytic transformation of petroleum and the origin of petroleum itself are interrelated processes and should not be viewed as single-stage processes having a successive nature. The source material of petroleum, as well as the petroleum itself, represents a complex mixture of various classes of organic matter. These materials are potentially capable of being transformed, in a reducing environment, into other more stable products, first of all into hydrocarbons, carbon dioxide, and water. It is therefore possible that some components of the basic material will be transformed into hydrocarbons or other stable forms while other components will be completely unaffected by the transformation process. From this it follows that the most varied combinations of natural and transformed molecules can be encountered in nature, with the systems designated as petroleums being those in which the products of transformation prevail. It then follows that there is no possibility of rejecting in principle the existence of primary petroleums to which the altered source materials of a still unfinished hydrocarbon transformation cycle are related. It is also understandable that there is no logical possibility of drawing a sharp distinction between the source material of petroleum and petroleum itself since these limiting states of matter are related by the transitory stages of primary petroleum.

Technological diagnostics of petroleums do not coincide with the chemical, and hence, any understanding of primary petroleum appears to be redundant from the practical point of view, while chemical diagnostics could significantly narrow the scope of this understanding. Petroleum containing over 50% heterogenous compounds, including tarry material, is not a purely hydrocarbon product from the chemical point of view, not yet having completed its transformation cycle, and hence is not yet a petroleum, in spite of the fact that from the manufacturing point of view it appears to be petroleum with many of its distinctive characteristics. Petroleum is first of all a natural mixture of hydrocarbons which must quantitively predominate over all other components.

It would have been impossible to expect a hydrocarbon petroleum to be found somewhere in nature close to its unaltered source material. This would have been an unexplainable discovery since it is difficult to imagine that under one and the same geochemical conditions only a portion of the material, regardless of chemical structure, would have been transformed into petroleum while another would have remained in its initial state. It would have been equally strange, however, not to encounter petroleum in association with those materials which directly form it, at the nearest stage of transformation, and which are sufficiently far removed in their properties from the original buried material.

In view of the hypothesis of gradual transformation of source material into petroleum, one should consider the primary petroleum matter to be the deeply altered material which had not preserved the distinctive properties of the basic material and consisting of new matter not present in the original. The initial matter of petroleum must consist almost exclusively of heterogenous compounds with an incidental admixture of hydrocarbons of inherited character. The partial transformation of heterogenous material into hydrocarbons increases the content of the latter to a certain limit when the whole system attains mobility and, under favorable conditions, is capable of partially separating out, during migration from the source beds, in the form of predominantly hydrocarbon mixtures called petroleum. A portion of the heterogenous material, if it is soluble in petroleum, migrates together with it and could further be transformed into hydrocarbons and into stable heterogenous compounds which are present in all petroleums. Such heterogenous matter is represented by tarry material containing oxygen, nitrogen and sulfur. Heterogenous matter, not capable of dissolution during petroleum migration, remain in the source rocks and are then incapable of forming hydrocarbons on a large scale. The existence and separation of such matter depends on the geochemical conditions of conversion of the source material as well as on the initial composition of the latter. In this manner a portion of the tarry petroleum substance is viewed as a residue of source matter not completely transformed into petroleum and as matter which is soluble in petroleum but already incapable of mass transformation into hydrocarbons.

The origin of other types of tarry matter can be varied. On the one hand this is primary material synchronous with the formation of petroleum and in part causally related to petroleum. On the other hand, tarry matter can be the residue from the disproportionation of hydrogen in hydrocarbons. Finally, on the zone of surface oxidation, as a result of biogenetic and abiogenetic processes, the creation of new, secondary tarry matter† is possible. All forms of tarry matter in petroleum can be present simultaneously, forming mixtures which cannot be differentiated by current analytical methods based on physical evidence of their solubility, since one solvent or another can extract certain components from tarry matter regardless of whether it is of a primary or secondary nature. It is impossible to speak of the nature of tarry matter without regard to the extent of petroleum transformation.

The initial stage of transformation of basic petroleum substance is the destruction or transformation of energy-saturated molecules of matter which are close to being a live substance. The termination

---

† To these one could also relate tars created by way of a parallel product in the sulfurization of petroleum but the lack of accurate experimental data does not allow this question to be resolved.

of the life process deprives some molecules of the basic condition for their existence and they unavoidably change into new forms of matter which are thermodynamically more stable. Mutual reactions, different from the process in a live organism, are already possible at this stage. The general pattern of changes consists of the loss of water, carbon dioxide, nitrogen, hydrocarbons and other matter, i.e. the loss of hetero atoms, which brings the system closer to a state of carbonized compounds.

As a result, materials are formed which do not preserve the elements of the original structures. This is an important condition which does not allow any inherited vestiges of the original material to be seen in the properties or composition of petroleum. Processes of initial change of the basic material of petroleum are sufficient reasons for leveling the properties of the most varied chemical structures of living matter. The deeper the transformation process occurs, the less the differentiation in the composition of primary petroleum. In this regard, it can be said that all petroleums come from buried organic matter, according to one plan, and any deviation from it depends on secondary, often local, conditions.

The initial process of change in the original material probably occurs sufficiently fast since it is tied to the corresponding energy possibilities. Further transformation proceeds at reduced rates. The transformation process does not terminate, however, and under a suitable geochemical environment continues on to form a system of hydrocarbons, which in turn enter into new reactions of the retarded type. This whole cycle of transformation is irreversible.

The process of transformation for the hydrocarbons themselves is a normal one, although it need not occur in each individual case, because the change in geochemical environment can preclude the action of stimulating transformation factors and the process can slow down or even practically terminate at one stage or another. In the statistical sense such interruptions in the evolution of petroleum must be considered as exceptions. A normal process will ultimately lead to the destruction of petroleum into gaseous molecules and carbon in the form of graphite and other highly carbonized minerals.

Besides the discontinuity in the evolution of petroleum, exceptional phenomena not foreseen by any of the schemes are also possible. However, as a result of further study of such "abnormal" petroleums, it will probably become possible to explain their composition by either the specific action of the containing rocks or the secondary phenomena of selection of some hydrocarbon components. At the present time such cases have not yet found any acceptable explanation.

Theoretical notions on the transformation of petroleum emanate from a whole assembly of relationships which, in the aggregate, cannot be otherwise explained although each of them separately can be explained without resort to the idea of transformation. In this case, however, the individual relationships conflict with each other.

POSSIBLE TRANSFORMATION PATHS FOR INDIVIDUAL CLASSES OF PETROLEUM HYDROCARBONS

1. Aromatic hydrocarbons

Aromatic hydrocarbons have positive values of free energy. Their creation out of the elements was accompanied by the expenditure of high potential energy. In this regard hydrocarbons of this class are capable of numerous chemical transformations as opposed, for example, to paraffinic hydrocarbons. For benzene $\Delta F^{\circ}_{298^{\circ}}$ $= 29,580$ cal/mol, while for normal hexane $\Delta F^{\circ}_{298^{\circ}} = -1040$ cal/mol [1].

Possible changes of aromatic hydrocarbons are generally quite probable and varied in view of the high level of free energy. However, under the conditions that oil accumulations occur, these possibilities are highly limited.

A lowering of the level of free energy under these conditions can be attained by two means:

(a) the addition of hydrogen and transition to naphthenic hydrocarbons with subsequent unlocking of the cyclic compounds and formation of paraffinic hydrocarbons;

(b) the loss of hydrogen as a result of condensation processes and transition through polycyclic hydrocarbons, ending in graphite.

An analysis of the thermodynamic possibility of these two means of change is presented below taking into account the environment of petroleum accumulation.

(a) *Hydrogenation and decyclization*

Processes of hydrogenation of aromatic hydrocarbons by simple hydrogen are thermodynamically quite feasible. For example, the reaction for the hydrogenation of benzene to cyclohexane and then to hexane is accompanied by a lowering of the level of free energy

$$C_6H_6 + 3H_2 \rightarrow C_6H_{12}; \quad \Delta F_{298^\circ}^\circ = -23\,670 \text{ cal/mol}$$

$$C_6H_{12} + H_2 \rightarrow C_6H_{14}; \quad \Delta F_{298^\circ}^\circ = -6950 \text{ cal/mol}.$$

Consequently, such a path for the transformation of aromatic hydrocarbons under the conditions of an oil accumulation is possible when sources of free hydrogen are present. If the entry of simple hydrogen from without is precluded by geologic factors, then its source must be looked for within our system.

Paraffinic hydrocarbons at high temperatures can split off hydrogen to form unsaturated compounds. High temperatures, however, are not characteristic of petroleum accumulations. At low temperatures, however, the splitting off of hydrogen from paraffinic hydrocarbons is accompanied by a drastic increase in free energy. For example, in the reaction, at a temperature of 25°C:

$$C_6H_{14} \rightarrow C_6H_{12} + H_2; \quad \Delta F_{98^\circ}^\circ = +17,090 \text{ cal/mol}.$$

Consequently, such reactions are practically impossible under the conditions of petroleum accumulation and paraffinic hydrocarbons cannot serve as a source of hydrogen for the hydrogenation of aromatic compounds. As far as naphthenic hydrocarbons are concerned, the splitting off of hydrogen from these is again accompanied by the formation of aromatic hydrocarbons, i.e. it represents a reaction opposite to that of the hydrogenation of aromatic hydrocarbons to naphthenes. The sum total of the direct and reverse process is equal to zero. No changes in the system are observed as a result of these opposing processes.

Thus, within our system, there is no source of hydrogen for the hydrogenation of aromatic hydrocarbons and, consequently, the transformation of aromatic hydrocarbons by means of hydrogenation and decyclization is impossible under the conditions of petroleum accumulation.

(b) *Dehydrogenation and condensation*

The transformation of benzene in the reaction

$$2C_6H_6 \rightarrow C_6H_5\!-\!C_6H_5 + H_2; \quad \Delta F^{\circ}_{298^{\circ}} = +2100 \text{ cal/mol}$$

at low temperatures is accompanied by an increase in free energy. The reaction only becames probable at high temperatures that are not characteristic of petroleum accumulations.

Similar relationships also hold for higher molecular-weight aromatic hydrocarbons. Along with this, the examination of values of free energy for some condensed, unreplaced aromatic hydrocarbons permits some interesting conclusions to be drawn (Table 18).

TABLE 18. *Values of Free Energy for Some Condensed, Unsubstituted Aromatic Hydrocarbons*

Compound	Empirical formula	Free energy (cal)	
		Per mol	Per carbon atom
Benzene	C_6H_6	$+29{,}580$	$+4930$
Naphthalene	$C_{10}H_8$	$+47{,}410$	$+4741$
Phenanthrene	$C_{14}H_{10}$	$+63{,}770$	$+4555$
Anthracene	$C_{14}H_{10}$	$+62{,}950$	$+4496$
Pyrene	$C_{16}H_{10}$	$+64{,}250$	$+4015$
Diphenyl	$C_{12}H_{10}$	$+61{,}260$	$+5105$
Diphenylmethane	$C_{13}H_{12}$	$+66{,}190$	$+5092$

From Table 18 it follows that depending on the complexity of the molecule in the sequence benzene → naphthalene → phenanthrene → pyrene, the free energy per atom of carbon decreases from $+4930$ to $+4015$ cal.

Thus, the condensation process for aromatic hydrocarbons in the di-ortho position is quite possible even at 25 °C. At the same time the formation of uncondensed systems of the diphenyl and diphenylmethane type is impossible at low temperatures.

The formation of condensed systems, bonded in the di-ortho position through two carbon atoms, and of unsubstituted cyclic†

---

† "Unsubstituted cyclic" is interpreted to be the meaning of the original Russian term "goloyadernykh" which literally means "holonuclear." [Transl. Ed.]

hydrocarbons by means of ordinary dehydrogenation is impossible. Such a process must involve the preliminary disintegration of an aromatic ring into free radicals accompanied by the formation of the simplest compounds, having a reduced reserve of free energy, in the reaction products.

According to the calculations of N. A. Gruzdeva [2] in the reaction

$$2C_6H_5CH_3 \rightarrow C_{14}H_{10} + 3H_2$$

the change in free energy as a function of temperature is expressed by the equation

$$\Delta F^\circ = 2700 - 40.4\,T$$

and, consequently, the reaction is feasible only at temperatures above 395°C.

At the same time, for the reaction

$$2C_6H_6 \rightarrow C_{10}H_8 + CH_4 + C,$$

$$\Delta F^\circ = -24{,}750 + 2.6T,$$

i.e. the reaction is possible for all temperatures below 679°C.

For the reaction

$$2C_6H_5CH_3 \rightarrow C_{10}H_8 + 2CH_4 + 2C,$$

$$\Delta F^\circ = -25{,}800 - 2.3T,$$

i.e. the reaction is possible at all temperatures and with increasing temperature the probability of the reaction increases. In the reaction for the interaction of benzene and xylene to form anthracene

$$C_6H_6 + C_6H_4(CH_3)_2 \rightarrow C_{14}H_{10} + 3H_2$$

$$\Delta F^\circ = 23{,}800 - 41.2T,$$

from whence, $\Delta F_0 = 0$ at $t = 305°C$.

In view of the known stability of an aromatic ring there is no basis for assuming that it will disintegrate into the simplest compounds (methane and graphite) under the conditions of petroleum accumulation. The transformation of aromatic compounds is possible only through the action of free aliphatic radicals.

Free aliphatic radicals can easily arise in a system from hydrocarbons and will initiate numerous chain reactions [3, 4]. Chain reactions differ in that their occurrence does not require the uninterrupted supply of energy from without, consequently deep transformations of the reacting mixture can be attained by means of the energy of free radicals [5,6].

These discussions naturally deal only with thermodynamically possible reactions having a known energy barrier, which, once overcome, can proceed spontaneously.

The methyl free radical (CH_3), once created, interacts in the liquid phase with a molecule of aromatic hydrocarbon, as has been shown by M. Levin and co-workers [7], to form methylated derivatives of benzene capable of di-ortho condensation.

V. A. Kireev [8] analyzed the known expression for the value of free energy (more accurately, the isobaric–isothermal potential or free energy at constant pressure)

$$\Delta F_0 = \Delta Z = \Delta H - T \cdot \Delta S, \qquad (1)$$

where ΔF_0 is the change in free energy; ΔZ is the isobaric–isothermal potential; ΔH is the change in enthalpy (the thermal effect of the reaction at constant pressure is considered positive when the process is accompanied by heat absorption); ΔS is the change in entropy; T is the absolute temperature of the process.

Any reaction can occur spontaneously only if the process results in a reduction of free energy.

At constant temperature and pressure, a state of equilibrium corresponds to the minimum isobaric potential ΔZ or free energy ΔF^0. Hence, under the given conditions, the reaction can proceed spontaneously only in the case when it is accompanied by a decrease in isobaric potential (free energy at constant pressure). Equation (1) shows that this is aided by a decrease in enthalpy, i.e. $\Delta H < 0$, or increase in entropy, i.e. $\Delta S > 0$, or both together.

In the opinion of V. A. Kireev, the loss of energy (decrease in enthalpy) is basically related to the tendency toward the aggregation of particles (in the broad sense of the word, i.e. in the sense of the general combining of the original particles into larger groups) due to the interaction of particles, while the increase in entropy is basically related to the tendency toward disaggregation caused by the movement of particles.

"Actually, in the simplest processes (consisting of one elementary form of process) the decrease in enthalpy is caused by a tendency toward the liberation of energy due to the mutual drawing together of particles making up the system and their mutual attraction to each other. To these, for example, are related processes involving the combining of atoms or atom groups into molecules, the condensation of vapors, etc. The magnitude of internal energy (and enthalpy) of a system is comprised of the energy of various forms of motion for the particles making up the system.

"The increase in entropy, however, primarily reflects the general tendency to the dissociation of particles or the equalizing of their concentrations as a result of their motion. To these are related, for example, the dissociation of molecules into atoms or atom groups, processes of sublimation or evaporation, the expansion of gas, as well as processes of gas mixing, diffusion in solutions and other processes induced by the movement of particles." [8]

From eqn. (1) it follows that the contribution of the entropy term $T \cdot \Delta S$ increases with increasing temperature. At low temperatures, however, the principal contribution is exerted by the energy factor, the magnitude of the enthalpy, ΔH. Equilibrium will be attained and the processes in the system will terminate when $\Delta F = 0$, i.e. $\Delta H - T \cdot \Delta S = 0$ or $\Delta H = T \cdot \Delta S$.

Equilibrium is attained by two means: on the one hand, by the aggregation of the original particles into larger complexes, which leads to the creation of new bonds and a reduction in enthalpy and, on the other hand, by the dissociation of the original particles into finer ones, which leads to an increase in entropy and the increase of the negative member $-T \cdot \Delta S$.

The relatively low temperature of petroleum accumulations favors the development of the first group of processes, those of aggregation. Thermodynamically suitable to these processes are the aromatic hydrocarbons, while paraffinic hydrocarbons have a tendency toward subdivision. In this regard, there are two principally different paths of development for aromatic and paraffinic hydrocarbons, under conditions of petroleum accumulations, as a result of which the reserve of free energy in both decreases. Aromatic hydrocarbons reduce the level of free energy by means of condensation processes and the loss of hydrogen. Paraffinic hydrocarbons, however, undergo the same process of reduction in energy as a result of hydrogenation processes accompanied by the breaking of carbon–carbon bonds and the creation of lower molecular-weight paraffinic hydrocarbons. Transformation processes for aromatic and paraffinic hydrocarbons are related to each other in time and space in such a manner that aromatic hydrocarbons act as donors, and paraffins as acceptors of hydrogen.

Processes of condensation for aromatic hydrocarbons are demonstrated by M. D. Tilicheev using the following scheme: aromatic hydrocarbons → condensed aromatic hydrocarbons → asphaltenes → carboids. This process, apparently developing according to a chain mechanism, once it begins, continues to the exhaustion of the original products capable of transformation. The yield of carboids can, under known conditions attain significant quantities, as, for example, in the case of fluorene it can reach 66.7 %. The mechanism for the transformation of aromatic hydrocarbons presented above is confirmed in oxidation processes under conditions involving a relative shortage of oxygen at nominal temperatures.

N. I. Chernozhukov and S. E. Krein [10] systematized data on the oxidizability of hydrocarbons and came to the conclusion that the oxidation of aromatic hydrocarbons under mild conditions results in condensation with the formation of tarry matter which complicates the structure. Disaggregation of the original molecules does not occur in this reaction. Oxidation and tar formation proceeds more readily the higher the molecular weight of the original hydrocarbon. In this case oxygen appears as a very active acceptor of hydrogen which it ties up in an extremely stable compound with a very low reserve of free energy, namely water, without permitting the disaggregation of other molecules as a result of the addition of hydrogen. Free radicals formed from the original aromatic hydrocarbons, as a result of the loss of hydrogen, interact with the formation of condensed molecules whose molecular weights are multiples of those of the original molecules. Notwithstanding the significant reserve of free energy, aromatic compounds are quite stable, under usual conditions little inclined to all manner of transformation without the participation of external active reagents. Nominal increases in temperature do little to activate the molecule and processes involving changes in the aromatic nucleus only begin from 700 to 800°. Paraffinic side chains on the aromatic nucleus are less stable and undergo change at relatively low temperatures [10, 11, 12, 13, 14]. Under thermodynamic conditions favorable to aromatic hydrocarbons, the kinetic factor creates obstacles to any form of transformation.

Any transformation of an aromatic hydrocarbon is preceded by a process of destruction of either the C—C or the C—H bonds. Regardless of the path by which the active condition is attained, the number of possible directions along which aromatic hydrocarbon molecules are then transformed is relatively few. In examining these transformations it is convenient to break down the entire class of aromatic hydrocarbons into two groups, unsubstituted† and substituted in the nucleus of the compounds.

In the former (unsubstituted) aromatic hydrocarbons the basic direction of the reaction is the splitting off of hydrogen with the subsequent combination of the radicals formed. In the case of benzene this is accompanied by the formation of diphenyl; in the case of naphthalene, it will be dinaphthyl. M. D. Tilicheev and V. K. Shitikov [15] observed these processes at high temperatures. It is interesting to note that, even with extensive forms of cracking under pressure, it was not possible to discover any compounds among the liquid products with lower boiling points than the original compounds. Hydrogen was the only gaseous product formed by low temperature cracking of phenanthrene and naphthalene. With increasing temperature paraffinic hydrocarbons were also found.

The appearance of paraffinic hydrocarbons in the gaseous reaction products can only be explained by the destructive processes in the aromatic nucleus at very high temperatures. In the course of these processes, the fragments are rapidly saturated with the hydrogen obtained from the original compound. These destructive processes of the aromatic nucleus, however, occupy a secondary position even at high temperatures. The principal mass of the original hydrocarbon changes in the direction of increasing molecular complexity. In the cracking of naphthalene, of the total amount of transformed hydrocarbon, only 4–9 % were subjected to destruction while in the cracking of phenanthrene it was only 2 %.

Alkylbenzenes. The primary reaction for the decomposition of toluene, according to M. D. Tilicheev, consists of the rupture of the $C_{arom.}$—$C_{aliph.}$ bonds and the formation of free methyl and phenyl radicals

$$C_6H_5CH_3 \rightarrow C_6H_5^{\cdot} + CH_3^{\cdot}. \tag{2}$$

† Original Russian term is "goloyadernye" (see footnote on p. 180). [Transl. Ed.].

In the first stages of the process, these free radicals will immediately come in contact with toluene molecules, robbing it of its hydrogen and transforming themselves into saturated molecules. For the energy of activation for such reactions F. O. Rais and K. K. Rais [4] assume a value equal to 20,000 cal, plus a correction for the difference between the energy of the created and ruptured bonds. The lowest value of energy of activation, observed in the course of this, is for the reaction involving the splitting off of a hydrogen atom from the methyl group. In this regard, the probability of this reaction is greater than that for the splitting off of hydrogen from the aromatic nucleus although the latter reaction is not completely excluded.

The first transformation path leads to the formation of a free benzyl radical. The benzyl, encountering the original molecules of toluene, will be transformed into toluene, regenerating a new fraction of the benzyl radical. Consequently, this path will not lead to the development of a chain. The collision of two benzyl radicals will lead to the formation of dibenzyl, i.e. condensation will occur through methylene groups. The chain will break down in this case as well. If, however, the collision between benzyl and a molecule of toluene occurs in such a manner that a methyl phenyl radical will be formed, this path can lead to the subsequent condensation of this radical with a benzyl radical and the formation of anthracene or phenanthrene.

In the cracking of ethyl benzene, P. Ferko [16] observed the formation of 2.2% naphthalene, 2.6% phenanthrene and 0.4% anthracene among the other products of the reaction.

B. L. Moldavskii and L. S. Bezdel' [17] subjected a number of the simplest homologs of benzene to transformation over aluminosilicates at 450°. In the course of this, ethylbenzene, n-propylbenzene, para-methyl, isopropylbenzene and n-butylbenzene yielded about 3% benzene and up to 20% isopropylbenzene. In the latter cases the transformation was reduced to the splitting off of a radical in the form of an olefin, i.e. to the stripping of the nucleus. Similarly, 1,3-isopropyl-toluene yielded 45% toluene and the 1,2-isomer even yielded 67% benzene, while 1,4-tertiary butyltoluene was transformed 100% according to the reaction for the splitting off of the butylgroup, i.e. also yielded toluene.

R. D. Obolentsev and N. N. Gryaznov [18] observed the transformation of isopropyl benzene with an aluminosilicate catalyst at

400–450 °C, in the course of which they noted the formation of propylene and a certain amount of di-isopropylbenzene. The work of K. P. Lavrovskii [19] investigated n-butyl-benzene and isopropyl-benzene with the same results as that of the other workers. Hiven and Hammik [20] found that the more complex the alkyl groups, the easier they are split off at 450°. For ethylbenzene and propyl-benzene the disintegration already becomes the chief reaction. Hansford, Mayers and Sachanen [21] confirmed the data of the preceeding authors in the study of xylene, pseudocumene, methyl-naphthalene and di-ethylbenzene.

Thomas, Hextra, and Pinkston [22] also found that aromatic hydrocarbons in which the radicals contain three or more atoms of carbon de-alkylate most readily of all. Greensfelder et al. [23] showed that the structure of the radicals has great significance. Toluene broke down only to the extent of 1%, ethylbenzene, under the same conditions, to 11%, and propylbenzene to 43%. It is important to note the authors' observation that the resistance to cracking of paraffinic hydrocarbons with carbon atoms numbering between 6 and 24, was found to decrease with increasing molecular weight but that paraffinic hydrocarbons nevertheless are more stable than the corresponding substituted benzenes even though the former have a high molecular weight. Naphthenes occupy an inter-mediate position. G. A. Natanson and M. Ya. Kogan [24], in work-ing with ethylbenzene, obtained benzene and ethylene as well as di-ethylbenzene. Also worthy of mention are the works of Yu. G. Mame-daliev [25], dedicated to the same problems.

There is also a number of works on the transformation of the higher fractions of petroleum into gasoline, but since these works do not provide any information on chemistry and only pursue prac-tical problems, they are omitted in this review. Authors of these works also dealt with high temperatures.

In the cracking of mono-alkylbenzenes, practically no benzene is formed and the newly created aromatic hydrocarbons are represented by high boiling point homologs. The formation of new cyclical compounds probably takes place at the expense of the carbon atoms in the lateral chain and not as a result of the direct combination of benzene nuclei with each other, at least at low temperatures.

It is interesting to note that according to the data of M. D. Tili-cheev [9] the magnitude of the energy of activation in the trans-formation of anthracene is considerably lower than for its isomer

phenanthrene. In this connection the transformation rate for anthracene, under one and the same set of conditions of nominal
temperatures, is 370 times greater than that for the transformation
of phenanthrene. The author is inclined to explain these differences
by the structural peculiarities of these compounds. With this it is
assumed that all three rings of the phenanthrene have an aromatic
character while for anthracene, from the point of view of the formal
alternation of bonds, one ring represents a dehydrobenzene or diene
grouping. These data probably allow one to explain the peculiar
distribution of phenanthrene derivatives in crude oils as compared
to those of anthracene.

If the energy from the break-down of various bonds is taken to
equal the following:

$$C_{arom.}\text{---}C_{arom.} = 97.17 \text{ kcal/mol}$$

$$C_{arom.}\text{---}C_{aliph.} = 79.40 \text{ kcal/mol}$$

$$C_{aliph.}\text{---}C_{aliph.} = 71.14 \text{ kcal/mol}$$

then, obviously, the formation of consolidation products occurs
most readily for those aromatic hydrocarbons in which there is a
$C_{aliph.}$---$C_{aliph.}$ bond. Next in order are hydrocarbons with $C_{arom.}$
---$C_{aliph.}$ bonds and finally those with $C_{arom.}$---$C_{arom.}$ bonds. Rates of
transformation will decrease in the same order. In the light of these
data the facts of the dominant presence of methylated homologs,
mononuclear as well as condensed, of aromatic hydrocarbons in
crude oils, are readily explained.

An examination of data on the thermodynamic properties of
aromatic hydrocarbons, under the conditions for the existence of the
overwhelming majority of petroleum accumulations, confirmed by
available experimental data on their transformation, allows one to
visualize the general picture of the direction of processes for the
formation and change of aromatic hydrocarbons in nature.

Only in rare instances do the initially formed aromatic hydrocarbons represent compounds without replacement in the nucleus.
The separation of the latter from the composition of the complex
original molecule is thermodynamically less beneficial than the
giving off of alkylated molecules. In this connection, unsubstituted†

† Original Russian term is "goloyadernye" (see footnote on p. 180).
[Transl. Ed.]

aromatic hydrocarbons occupy an insignificant place in the composition of the overwhelming majority of natural petroleums. Of basic significance are the alkylated derivatives with short chains. The simple act of intramolecular transformation of a mono-substituted compound, with a long lateral chain, into a poly-substituted one with short chains liberates a considerable amount of energy. Such processes are singular and are observed experimentally.

The mechanism of further transformation of unsubstituted (in the nucleus) and alkylated aromatic hydrocarbons is somewhat different. If the transformation of alkylated hydrocarbons begins with the processes of primary condensation, then the unsubstituted hydrocarbons pass through the alkylation stage beforehand. In this connection, in highly transformed petroleums, one should expect the relative accumulation of unsubstituted aromatic hydrocarbons. The free methyl radicals, formed in the process of transforming paraffinic hydrocarbons, have a relatively small possibility of colliding with an unsubstituted aromatic hydrocarbon molecule to form an alkylated aromatic, since the composition of petroleum includes many more other molecules which, upon collision, will not lead to the desired objective.

Alkylated aromatic hydrocarbons are capable of entering into processes of condensation with the formation of polycyclic systems and the release of hydrogen. Further processes of the complication of condensed systems are accompanied by a reduction in free energy and lead in the end to tars, asphaltenes, and other carbonized products. The latter drop out from the liquid phase system in view of their lack of solubility in the increasing concentration of paraffinic hydrocarbons.

Condensation processes are accompanied by the liberation of hydrogen. The action of hydrogen is ultimately directed towards formation of naphthenic and paraffinic hydrocarbons. The first of these undergo ring clearage with the formation of paraffinic hydrocarbons. The latter, however, gradually subdivide into smaller molecules, ultimately forming methane, the simplest product of mineralization.

The condensation of aromatic hydrocarbons gradually produce more and more carbonized complex polycyclic compounds. The characteristic peculiarity of this process is the absence in their composition of oxygen and other heteroatoms.

2. Polymethylene† hydrocarbons

In terms of the magnitude of free energy, polymethylene (naphthenic) hydrocarbons occupy an intermediate position between aromatic and paraffinic hydrocarbons, staying closer to the latter (Fig. 41). Thus, for example, the value of free energy at standard conditions ($t = 273\,°C$ and $P = 1$ atm) for benzene is equal to +29,580 cal/mol, for cyclohexane + 5910 cal/mol and for hexane +1040 cal/mol [1].

For cyclopentane the value of free energy under the same conditions is +8700 cal/mol, i.e. a value somewhat greater than for cyclohexane. Methylcyclopentane which is isomeric to cyclohexane will have $\Delta F^{\circ}_{298^\circ} = +6760$ cal/mol.

From these data it follows that the processes for the transformation of systems consisting of all three types of hydrocarbons can develop in the direction of change from aromatic to naphthenic and then to paraffinic hydrocarbons. The path from aromatic to naphthenic is impossible in view of the absence of a hydrogen source in our system.

The other conceivable path for creating naphthenes from paraffinic hydrocarbons by means of splitting off hydrogen and further cyclization of a radical at low temperatures is connected with the expenditure of free energy

$$C_6H_{14} \rightarrow C_6H_{12} + H_2$$

$$-1040 \qquad +5910 \qquad 0$$

$$\Delta F^{\circ}_{298^\circ} = 5910 - (-1040) = +6950 \text{ cal/mol.}$$

As was shown earlier [26], with increasing temperature the change in free energy for reaction (2) is expressed by the equation

$$\Delta F^0 = +17,100 - 14.6\,T.$$

Up to a temperature of 1070°K (797°C) the values of ΔF^0 are positive and, consequently, the reaction of cyclization cannot have any practical significance. Only when the temperature exceeds

† Polymethylene is synonymous with cycloparaffin or naphthene. [Transl. Ed.]

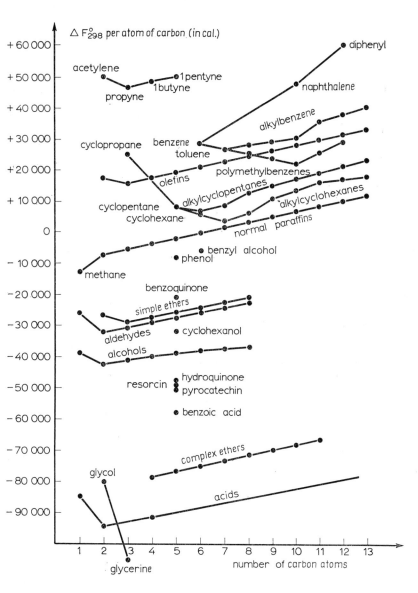

FIG. 41. The free energy of various classes of organic compounds.

1070°K (797°C) does the value of ΔF^0 become negative, i.e. the practical possibility of the reaction arises.

If it is kept in mind that the existence of petroleum accumulations at temperatures higher than 797°C is never observed in nature and contradicts the entire sum of our knowledge of the thermal stability of hydrocarbons, then it should be recognized that the spontaneous cyclization of paraffinic hydrocarbons into naphthenes under natural conditions is a practical impossibility.

It is theoretically possible to imagine a case in which dehydrogenation is accomplished by some external agents, for example, oxygen or sulphur. In that case compounds with a low level of free energy (water or hydrogen sulfide) are formed instead of hydrogen. The free energy balance in the course of this becomes favorable.

$$C_6H_{14} + \, ^1/_2O_2 \rightarrow C_6H_{12} + H_2O$$

$$-1045 \qquad 0 \qquad +5910 \quad -56,690$$

$$\Delta F^{\circ}_{298^{\circ}} = -49,740 \text{ cal/mol.}$$

For the reaction with sulfur $\Delta F^{\circ}_{298^{\circ}} = -1350$ cal/mol. Nevertheless direct experience shows that such processes do not have a place in practice. The action of oxygen does not lead to the formation of cyclic compound from paraffinic hydrocarbons. The process rather occurs in such a manner that during the first stages additional compounds of the peroxide type are formed which further transform into carbon dioxide and water through ketones, acids and hydroxy acid. These facts find a good explanation if one compares the bond energy between different atoms in paraffinic hydrocarbons with each other. The energy required to break the C—C bond comprises 71,100 kcal/mol while for the C—H bond this value is 93,600 kcal/mol [27]. It is easy to see that the atoms of oxygen (or sulphur) attacking the hydrocarbon molecule find it easier to break the C—C rather than the C—H bond. If, however, one takes into account the fact that carbon atoms in the real molecule are surrounded by hydrogen atoms, it is evident that the approach to the C—C bonds is a complicated one. Collisions between a hydrocarbon molecule and the attacking molecule lead in the first place to action on the C—H bond. In the final count this occurrence is limited by the oxygen atom coming in between the atoms of carbon and hydrogen with the formation of peroxide groupings

$$
\begin{array}{cc}
\text{H} \ \ \text{H} \\
| \ \ \ | \\
\text{H—C—C—H} + \text{O} = \text{O} \\
| \ \ \ | \\
\text{H} \ \ \text{H}
\end{array}
\longrightarrow
\begin{array}{cc}
\text{H} \ \ \ \ \ \ \text{H} \\
| \ \ \ \ \ \ \ \ | \\
\text{H—C———C—H} \\
| \ \ \ \ \ \ \ \ | \\
\text{O—OH} \ \ \text{H}
\end{array}
$$

$$
\begin{array}{cc}
\text{H} \ \ \ \ \ \ \ \ \ \ \text{H} \\
| \ \ \ \ \ \ \ \ \ \ \ | \\
\text{H—C—O—O—C—H} \\
| \ \ \ \ \ \ \ \ \ \ \ | \\
\text{H} \ \ \ \ \ \ \ \ \ \ \text{H}
\end{array}
$$

The oxidation theory of A. N. Bakh [28, 29], currently widely accepted, although it recognizes the initial splitting off of the hydrogen atom from the molecule of oxidized matter, does not do so in the form assumed by H. Wieland [30]; not by means of the splitting hydrogen away from a molecule with the formation of olefin compounds, but by means of the dissociation of original molecules into a free hydrogen atom and free organic radical.

As a result of the starting chain oxidation reaction the organic radical $R \cdot$ with oxygen gives a peroxide radical R—OO· which once again joins up with hydrogen to form the stable hydroperoxide R—OO—H. Such a dissociation with the formation of free radicals represents a widespread phenomenon as is seen from numerous recent works dedicated to reactions consisting of the exchange of atoms between molecules. This process has for its basis the processes of thermal movement of molecules. The necessary energy for breaking the bonds between atoms has as its source the kinetic energy of the colliding molecules. The peroxides formed, as first shown by S. Medvedev and E. Alekseeva [31], then further undergo transformation forming ketones as principal products.

$$
\begin{array}{c}
R \\
\diagdown \\
\ \ \ \ \ \ \text{CH—OO—H} \\
\diagup \\
R_2
\end{array}
\rightarrow
\begin{array}{c}
R \\
\diagdown \\
\ \ \ \ \ \ \text{CO} + \text{H}_2\text{O} \\
\diagup \\
R_1
\end{array}
$$

A theory for hydrocarbon oxidation processes based on the chain mechanism was recently presented from an original standpoint by K. I. Ivanov [32]. Academician N. N. Semenov [33] completed the development of the chain theory for the oxidation of hydrocarbons. The data presented in these works indicate the impossibility of the cyclization of paraffinic hydrocarbons as a result of oxidation processes. Thus, neither aromatic nor paraffinic hydrocarbons can be naphthene sources in crude oils.

A. F. Dobryanskii [34] considers that polymethylene cyclical compounds in the posthumous remains of living organisms, during the transformation process of the latter in the mass of sedimentary rock, separate in the form of complex polycyclic compounds containing aromatic and paraffinic structures along with polymethylene nuclei. The author supports this conclusion with data on the group compositions of petroleums and the results of experimental work on the transformation of aromatic and naphthenic hydrocarbons.

It follows from this that the cyclical systems of petroleum are inherited from the matter of living systems and were already formed within a live organism at the expense of a high potential energy—solar energy.

The newest data on the structure of matter in living systems [35, 36] can serve as evidence for this stand. According to this data, cyclical structures are very characteristic of living organisms. Albumins, carbohydrates, lignin, vegetable and animal pigments, vitamins and hormones, terpenes, and tars have groupings of cyclical structures in their composition. Only the fats are composed of open chain compounds. The majority of the compounds enumerated above have a heterocyclic structure. Atoms of oxygen, sulphur or nitrogen enter into the composition of a cyclical compound.

The splitting off of hetero atoms is energetically beneficial since it lowers the reserve of free energy in the system as a result of the release of carbon dioxide, water, hydrogen sulfide or ammonia, i.e. compounds with extremely negative values of free energy. The mechanism of this process is not yet clear but the possibility of it occurring is in accord with the thermodynamic point of view.

Processes for the transformation of naphthenes can be visualized as occurring in two directions. One direction is related to the opening of the hydrocarbon ring and the formation of either an olefin or paraffinic hydrocarbon. The latter can be realized at the expense of an external source of hydrogen. The other direction consists of the loss of hydrogen and the formation of a molecule of aromatic hydrocarbon without disrupting the completeness of the carbon frame.

Let us examine the thermodynamic possibility of these two directions of transformation. The reaction for breaking the ring of a naphthenic hydrocarbon with the formation of a molecule of olefin

$$
\begin{array}{c}
\qquad\; CH_2 \\
H_2C \qquad CH_2 \\
\quad| \qquad\quad | \qquad \rightarrow\; CH_3{-}CH_2{-}CH_2{-}CH_2{-}CH = CH_2 \\
H_2C \qquad CH_2 \\
\qquad\; CH_2
\end{array}
$$

under nominal temperature conditions is accompanied by an increase in free energy. Thus, for example, at 298°K (25°C) the change in free energy comprises $+13,210$ cal/mol, while at a temperature of 400°K (123°C) this change is equal to $+10,940$ cal/mol and becomes a negative value beginning with a temperature of 900°K (623°C). Such temperatures do not occur in petroleum accumulations and, consequently, this path for the transformation of naphthenes is impossible.

The reverse reaction for the cyclization of olefins to naphthenes is quite proper up to a temperature of 900°K (623°C) and at this temperature neither the direct nor the reverse process has any predominance over the other. It is quite probable that this serves to explain the typical absence of olefinic and unsaturated hydrocarbons in petroleums. Unsaturated hydrocarbons formed at some stage of transformation, under the low temperature conditions of crude oil accumulations, will quite rapidly transform into cyclical compounds. This simple act will liberate a considerable amount of free energy and the system will find itself at a lower, i.e. more advantageous, energy level.

The process for the opening of the ring with the breaking of the carbon–carbon bond and the joining of hydrogen from an external source is accompanied by a lowering of the free energy level in the system

$$
C_6H_{12} + H_2 \rightarrow C_6H_{14}
$$

$$
+5910 \qquad 0 \qquad -1040
$$

$$
\Delta F^{\circ}_{298^{\circ}} = -6950 \text{ cal/mol.}
$$

The reaction is possible, as we saw above, right up to a temperature of 797°C. The difficulty lies only in having a source of free hydrogen and overcoming the energy barrier.

A. F. Dobryanskii [34] sees a source of hydrogen in the processes of intrasystem redistribution (disproportionation) of hydrogen.

This process, the universality of which there is no doubt, leads to the appearance in the system of mobile hydrogen atoms. Another source of hydrogen can be seen in the processes for the condensation of aromatic hydrocarbons [34], which is a special case of redistribution processes. The absence of molecular hydrogen in oil field gases indicates that hydrogen atoms remain completely in the system and go wholly into the formation of hydrogenated compounds. Processes for the redistribution of hydrogen are beneficial from the energy point of view as shown above [26] and are well known in practice.

The second direction for the transformation of naphthenes is connected with the process of losing hydrogen

$$C_6H_{12} \rightarrow C_6H_6 + 3H_2$$

and is accompanied by an increase in free energy. For the reaction involving the dehydrogenation of cyclohexane the increase in free energy (in the gaseous state) is 23,399 cal/mol at 25 °C. At a temperature above 550 °K (277°)C the dehydrogenation of cyclohexane is accompanied by a reduction in the level of free energy for the system.

With increasing molecular weight the strength of the bonds between atoms in the organic molecule drops. The strength (breaking energy) of the C—H bond [6] also decreases. While the energy required to break the first C—H bond in methane is equal to 101 kcal, in a normal paraffin with a large number of carbon atoms the energy of the C—H bond in the CH_3 group comprises 93–94 kcal. The energy for removing the H atom from the CH_2 group of such a paraffin is 88 kcal. Breaking of the C—H bond in the tertiary atom of the paraffin hydrocarbon requires the expenditure of 86 kcal.

The energy required to break the C—H bond in ethane is equal to 98 kcal while in acetic aldehyde it requires 80–85 kcal to separate the H atom from the $-C\overset{\displaystyle O}{\underset{\displaystyle H}{\diagup}}$ group. This reduction in energy of the C—H bond is due to the presence of the oxygen atom.

The presence of a double bond in a molecule reduces the energy required to break the C—H bond. Actually, the separation of the H atom from the CH_3 group in propane

$$CH_3-CH_2-CH_3 \rightarrow CH_3-CH = CH_2 + 2(H)$$

requires the expenditure of 95 kcal of energy while the splitting off of the H atom in propylene

$$CH_2 = CH-CH_3 \rightarrow CH_2 = C = CH_2 + 2(H)$$

only requires the expenditure of 77 kcal.

The presence of a benzene ring also reduces the energy required to break the C—H bond in the CH_3 group. Thus in toluene the energy required to break away the H atom from the CH_3 group

$$C_6H_5CH_3 \rightarrow C_6H_5CH_2 - +(H)$$

amounts to 77.5 kcal while in ethane it is 98 kcal. Out of this, in part, comes a curious result. The presence of a large system of connecting bonds which characterize the benzene ring of the phenyl radical acts on the energy required to break the C—H bond in the CH_3 group quantitatively in the same manner as the presence of one double bond in removing an H atom from the CH_3 group in propylene. Because of this, complex organic molecules are less stable and are more subject to various transformations.

Unfortunately, there are as yet no data on the thermodynamic properties of complex molecules and rigid calculation of the probability of these or the other transformations involving them is impossible. Nonetheless, taking into account the data on the strength of bonds between the atoms in organic molecules, it can be maintained that the thermodynamic probability of processes for the redistribution of hydrogen increases with the complexity of the molecule. Within a complex molecule an accumulation of hydrogen will occur in one portion of it at the expense of its loss from others.

The appearance of aromatic structures, bringing with them an increase in the level of free energy in one part of the molecules, is compensated by the appearance of paraffinic structures in the other, leading to a lowering of the free energy level. As a whole the overall reserve of free energy in the system decreases. The latter is characteristic of spontaneous processes. Processes for the redistribution of mass within an individual complex molecule, accompanied by a lowering of the energy level in the system, are more probable than processes between separate neutral molecules. Processes within a molecule require a lower activation energy. Their development is not connected with the probability of colliding with an external molecule and with the necessity for a complete break of the bond between the migrating hydrogen atom and the source carbon atom. It is only necessary to weaken this bond, which is energetically much more profitable. In the course of this the migrating hydrogen atom remains in the field of attraction of the source molecule while being displaced from one part of the molecule to another. The redistribution of hydrogen proceeding to the end, to the formation of methane and graphite by way of end products, is always energetically profitable, regardless of the source hydrocarbon. All hydrocarbons are located higher on the scale than methane or graphite in terms of their free energy reserves and the formation of the latter leads to a lowering of the free energy level in the original system.

The creation of aromatic structures from a portion of the polymethylenes within a complex molecule is quite possible due to the surplus of free energy arising in the processes of the condensation of aromatic structures and the decyclization of a portion of the polymethylene structures. This conclusion is confirmed by the experimental data on processes for the transformation of polymethylenic hydrocarbons. In spite of the close similarity between the chemical properties of paraffinic and naphthenic hydrocarbons there is an essential difference between their transformation processes occurring as a result of thermal activation. While paraffinic hydrocarbons primarily experience transformations in their carbon–carbon bonds, the most vulnerable spot in naphthenes is the carbon–hydrogen bond.

According to Ellis [37] the energy of splitting the carbon–hydrogen bond in cyclohexane equals 94.0 kcal/mol while for hexane this same value is equal to 97.0 kcal/mol and for benzene is 117.0 kcal/mol. Not deprived of significance in this regard is the proposal of Jones [38] that cyclohexanes and hydrogenated naphthalenes preserve their aromatic structure, in one form or another, and that the character of the bond here is basically different from the bond of other cyclic systems with an open carbon chain. This difference is not reflected in the generally accepted method of writing chemical formulae, adopting the unchanging equal value of all four valences of carbon.

The disintegration of cyclohexane with thermal activation is an intermediate process between the disintegration of hexane and benzene, which reflects the intermediate position of cyclohexane very well in terms of its reserve of free energy which lies between these latter two compounds. The disintegration of cyclohexane occurs in such a manner that it first loses two atoms of hydrogen, forming cyclohexene. In turn, the cyclohexene decomposes in two directions with the formation of either benzene or butadiene and acetylene.

Jones and Wheller [39] observed an interesting reaction during vacuum distillation at 350°, involving the formation of an aromatic and a paraffin structure

According to M. D. Tilicheev cycloparaffins fall apart directly into compounds, not into radicals, and after the primary disintegration there is no chain reaction at low pressures. High pressures can cause the appearance of chain compounds.

Cyclopentanes are the most stable of the polymethylene hydrocarbons. In general, thermal decomposition can occur in two directions, e.g.

$$C_5H_{10} \rightarrow C_2H_4 + C_3H_6 \qquad (3)$$

and

$$C_5H_{10} \rightarrow C_5H_8 + H_2. \qquad (4)$$

According to the data of Frey [40], the disintegration of cyclopentane according to reaction (3) proceeds to 60%, and according to reaction (4) to 40%. The hydrogenation reaction proceeds practically to the end, with the formation of a paraffin hydrocarbon.

Cyclohexane. Starting from 490°, upon heating without catalysts, the products are primarily hydrogen, olefins, benzene and ethane [38, 41]. Methyl cyclohexane only gives hydrogen and noticeable amounts of methane.

The catalytic transformation of cyclohexane and its homologs has been studied in greater detail. Depending on the catalysts used, the achieved reactions can involve the breaking of the C—C bond as well as those of dehydrogenation. In known cases, the breaking of the six-member ring leads to the formation of a more stable compound, namely methyl cyclopentane. Nickel at 300°C induces decomposition and dehydrogenation, so does copper at 550°C.

With palladium and platinum, quantitative separation of hydrogen occurs at relatively low temperatures (180–200°). This reaction, discovered by N. D. Zelinskii [42], subsequently achieved analytic significance. With aluminum chloride, cyclohexanes exhibit a very curious behavior. The long lateral chain breaks into a number of short chains which then link up with a ring. From ethyl, propyl, and butylcyclohexane, respectively, dimethyl, trimethyl and tetramethylcyclohexane will be formed [43, 44]. The isomeric reaction occurs at temperatures as low as 120–150°.

Polycyclic naphthenes. The dominant reaction in the thermal or catalytic disintegration of polycyclic naphthenes is dehydrogenation with the formation of aromatic hydrocarbons.

Lieberman [45] showed that alkyl dihydroanthracene readily decomposes when passed over zinc dust, forming anthracene; for the isoamyl derivative, boiling with a reflux condenser will suffice. Wieland [46] catalytically transformed dihydronaphthalene at room temperature into naphthalene and tetrahydronaphthalene (tetralin).

According to Sandgren [47], in the temperature range 560–650° and at pressures between 1 and 30 atm, tetralin undergoes the following reactions:

1. Decomposition into aromatic hydrocarbons with unsaturated lateral chains.
2. Decomposition with breaking of the hydrogenated ring and the formation of aromatic hydrocarbons.
3. Dehydrogenation to naphthalene.
4. Decomposition into methane and carbon.

Under pressure and in the presence of hydrogen, decomposition proceeds in a similar manner with the exception that the products of deep disintegration hydrogenate to methane. The increase in temperature leads to an increase in the reaction rate (but to a different degree than for the reactions indicated above), to a change in the breaking point of the ring, and to a decrease in the number and length of lateral chains in the aromatic hydrocarbons formed. An increase in pressure favors the rupture of C—C bonds and the symmetrical destruction of the molecule as well as an increase in the rate of this process. The use of catalysts increases the degree of disintegration and aids dehydrogenation.

Schraeter [48] in reprocessing tetralin using aluminum chloride at 30–40° discovered 30% newly formed hydrocarbons. Among these were found benzene, octohydrophenanthrene, and octohydroanthracene. The author considers that breaking of the hydrogenated ring occurs in the process with the formation of benzene and an aliphatic free radical. The latter combines with the benzene ring of the original tetralin molecule in the ortho-position with further condensation into saturates of phenanthrene and anthracene. An increase in temperature leads to the formation of even more complex products, for example, $C_{14}H_{16}$, $C_{20}H_{24}$, $C_{20}H_{22}$ and others.

According to A. N. Sakhanov and M. D. Tilicheev [49], under pressure and at 450°, tetralin is 71% converted, experiencing the following transformations:

Breaking of the tetramethylene ring 45%.

Dehydrogenation 34%.

Formation of condensation products 21%.

With increasing temperature and extent of transformation, dehydrogenation begins to take on primary significance. Thus, for example, at 650° the naphthalene yield reaches 75%. Also noteworthy is the formation of significant quantities of coke even at moderate degrees of transformation.

M. D. Tilicheev and V. K. Shitikov [50] found the activation energy for the transformation of tetralin to equal 65,000 cal/mol. Investigation of the thermal disintegration of decalin [50] showed the presence of the following processes:

1. Breaking of one or both rings.
2. Complete or partial dehydrogenation.
3. Condensation or polymerization.
4. Complete disintegration with the formation of carbon, methane and hydrogen.

Transformation products consisted almost completely of aromatic hydrocarbons since the breaking of one ring occurs more often than the breaking of both.

In the presence of hydrogen and under pressure the products of deep transformation, decalin, in contrast to tetralin, was not hydrogenated to methane. Methane, ethane, propane, butane, ethylene, butylene, acetylene and hydrogen were found in the gases. The liquid portion consisted for the main part of C_6 to C_{20} aromatic hydrocarbons, aliphatics, as well as saturated and unsaturated cyclic hydrocarbons.

According to M. D. Tilicheev and V. K. Shitikov [50], about 50% of all of the transformed decalin reacts under pressure by breaking the ring, while only 10–20% of the transformed decalin is subjected

7a TP

to the dehydrogenation reaction. High temperature and low pressure aid the disintegration reaction. Low temperature and high pressure, however, lead to condensation reactions. In the first stages of the transformation of decalin the relative amount of high boiling point polymerization products is considerably greater than that for deeper forms of transformation. Apparently, the high boiling point products first formed eventually decompose into low boiling point compounds to a considerable extent. Compared to tetralin, decalin is dehydrogenated with greater difficulty, which can be explained as being due to the benzene ring of tetralin. The authors present the following values of activation energy of transformation processes for cyclic hydrocarbons.

Cyclopentane	60,000 cal/mol.
Cyclohexane	59,410 cal/mol.
Tetralin	65,000 cal/mol.
Decalin	65,600 cal/mol.

For paraffin hydrocarbons the value of energy of activation equals about 59,000 cal/mol. N. A. Orlov and M. A. Belopol'skii [51], in studying the pyrolysis of perhydrofluorene, obtained cylopentadiene, benzene hydrocarbons, indene and naphthalene at 750°

A. N. Sakhanov et al. [52], in studying the cracking of lubricating oil at 463° and 12 atm, came to the conclusion that the disintegration of naphthenes reduces to the splitting off of lateral chains, isomerization and dehydrogenation.

From an examination of the results of experimental work it follows that the reaction for the transformation of polymethylene hydrocarbons, mononuclear as well as polycyclic, proceed in the following directions when activated by thermal energy:

1. Breaking of carbon rings and splitting off of lateral chains.
2. Hydrogenation and dehydrogenation.
3. Polymerization, condensation and depolymerization.
4. Isomerization.

In each concrete case there can occur either a single type of reaction, any combination of the above or, finally, all of these simultaneously, depending on the external conditions.

All cycloparaffinic hydrocarbons, with the exception of penta- and hexamethylene, preferentially undergo breaking of the carbon-carbon bond. In the case of cyclohexane, the carbon–hydrogen bond breaks easier than the C—C bond. Cyclopentane is the most stable hydrocarbon. Breaking of the ring is accompanied by isomerization with the formation of a compound which is more stable under the given conditions.

Dehydrogenation is the basic reaction for hydrogenated polycyclic hydrocarbons. Homologs of cyclohexane with lateral chains, having more than one carbon atom, are inclined toward isomerization with the formation of methyl groups directly linked with the nucleus out of the lateral chains of methyl groups.

The material presented above, on the thermodynamic and chemical properties of naphthenes, as well as the experimental data, allow the following conclusions to be reached. Naphthenic hydrocarbons occurring in petroleum are not the saturated products of either aromatic or paraffinic hydrocarbons.

On the contrary, the principal parts of both are the products of transformation of naphthenes. A source of polymethylene petroleum hydrocarbons are the cycloparaffinic and heterocyclic structures inherited from the complex molecules in the composition of a living organism. Naphthenic hydrocarbons arise in an orderly manner at a certain stage of development of the organic matter, dispersed in the mass of mineral sediment, as a result of processes involving the splitting off and redistribution of hetero atoms. These processes are the consequence and material reflection of processes for reducing the energy reserves of complex organic molecules synthesized by living organisms at the expense of solar energy.

In contrast to paraffinic and aromatic hydrocarbons, which, under the conditions of petroleum accumulations only change in one characteristic direction, the development and change of naphthenic hydrocarbons proceeds in two directions.

The path for the development of paraffinic hydrocarbons is characterized by desegregation processes tied in with the disappearance of carbon–carbon bonds and their replacement by carbon–hydrogen bonds. Consequently, these processes have for their bases the accumulation of hydrogen about a carbon atom and lead, in the final count, to the formation of methane.

A different path of development is characteristic of aromatic hydrocarbons, representing a direct opposite to the development path of paraffinic hydrocarbons. The change of aromatic hydro-carbons occurs with time in such a manner that the quantity of carbon–carbon bonds increases continuously at the expense of a reduction in the number of carbon–hydrogen bonds. Naturally, such a process assumes the splitting off of hydrogen and ultimately in the formation of graphite, a compound carbonized to a max-imum.

Naphthenes, in view of the peculiarities of their energy state and particular chemical properties, so to speak, combine these two opposing development paths within themselves. On the one hand, naphthenes are capable of losing hydrogen quite readily, forming aromatic structures. On the other hand, under the action of hydro-gen, naphthene rings are inclined to splitting, with the breaking of C—C bonds and the formation of paraffinic chains. Both pro-cesses are, in fact, equally probable, especially in the case of com-plex molecules. The increase in energy level, occurring with the formation of aromatic rings, is compensated within a molecule by a reduction in free energy, which occurs as a result of the opening of polmethylene rings and the formation of paraffinic chains. The formation of one aromatic ring from a hexamethylene ring liberates six atoms of hydrogen, i.e. a quantity sufficient to open three naphthene rings. The energy balance of a hypothetical process, in-cluding the collision of four cyclohexane molecules with the form-ation of one molecule of benzene and three of hexane, only has a free energy deficit of 2.8 kcal.

$$4C_6H_{12} \rightarrow C_6H_6 + 3C_6H_{14}$$

$$4(+5910) + 29,580 + 3(-1040)$$

$$\Delta F^\circ_{298^\circ} = +2820 \text{ cal.}$$

It is natural to assume that with the complication of the original molecule, the energy balance of processes for the redistribution of hydrogen becomes more favorable for the spontaneous occurrence of a process at nominal temperatures. This condition had already been a subject of discussion. Furthermore, experimental data on the transformation of decalin, as well as the thermocatalytic trans-formation of the lube oil fractions of petroleum, confirm this as-sumption. It was shown above that the strength of C—H bonds de-creases with increasing molecular weight of a hydrocarbon. Consequently, any type of process within a complex molecule is thereby facilitated, especially if the monomolecular character (not requiring collisions with other molecules) of these processes is kept in mind.

The redistribution of elements and energy within a complex molecule is to a considerable extent facilitated because of the absence of any necessity for the complete destruction of bonds between the atoms comprising the molecule. The migration of hydrogen atoms can be achieved without the complete destruction of C—H bonds but only at the expense of its partial weakening which, naturally, is energetically less profitable. Numerous examples are known in organic chemistry of the regrouping of atoms within a complex molecule occurring spontaneously, i.e. with the lowering of the free energy level.

The redistribution of elements is closely tied in with the redistribution of energy within a complex molecule in view of the inseparable relationship between mass and energy. In view of the same reasons the probabilities of this process within a molecule is considerably greater than that for the transmission and redistribution of energy within a system of separate, smaller molecules. The spontaneity of this process indicates the occurrence of a reduction in the energy level in a molecule.

In conformance with the views of V. A. Kireev [8] it should be assumed that a reduction in the energy level of a system can either occur through a reduction in enthalpy or an increase in entropy as shown in the expression for free energy

$$\Delta F = \Delta H - T \cdot \Delta S. \qquad (5)$$

Thus for paraffinic hydrocarbons the decrease in the value of ΔF primarily occurs at the expense of the entropy member $T \cdot \Delta S$. This follows from the fact that the disintegration of a large molecule into smaller ones brings about an increase in entropy and, consequently, an increase in the absolute value of the $T \cdot \Delta S$ member. The value ΔH changes little since a decrease in enthalpy is caused by the liberation of energy due to the mutual drawing together of particles making up the system and mutually attracting each other.

For aromatic hydrocarbons, the development of which is characterized by the complication of original particles, the reduction of the thermodynamic potential due to the reasons presented above, primarily proceeds at the expense of a reduction in the enthalpy member ΔH. The change in the entropy member either does not have any significance or, on the contrary, reduces to an increase in the $T \cdot \Delta S$ value at the expense of a reduction in entropy and, because of this, to a change of the minus sign to a plus in eqn. (5).

For naphthenes the reduction of the ΔF value occurs simultaneously at the expense of both a decrease in enthalpy and an increase in entropy which is the reason for the greater lability of this class of hydrocarbons and determines their place as a source of aromatic and paraffinic compounds.

3. Paraffinic hydrocarbons (alkanes)†

Free energies for the formation of alkanes from elements under standard conditions have negative values for all molecules with up to six carbon atoms. With an increase in temperature the values of free energy for these hydrocarbons do increase, although under the conditions for the occurrence of petroleum accumulations, this increase does not lead to any practical consequence only if one disregards the fact that C_4 and C_5 alkanes become unstable with respect to their constituent elements in the course of this.

All paraffinic hydrocarbons, starting with butane, at a temperature of the order of $100\,^\circ C$, have positive values of free energy and, consequently, are thermodynamically unstable and inclined toward change into lower molecular-weight groups as well as carbon and hydrogen.

It follows from this that for a system composed of paraffinic hydrocarbons the general tendency of the change is toward transformation leading to a decrease in the content of high molecular-weight hydrocarbons and an increase in the content of low molecular-weight hydrocarbons.

† In the first approximation one should exclude from consideration the question of the effect of numerous groups of petroleum compounds on the equilibrium state of alkanes. Such an assumption, apparently, will not significantly effect the qualitative course of our reasoning. H.A.Wilson [53] showed that the presence in the original mixture of other classes of hydrocarbons, close to alkanes in their physical properties, does not effect their equilibrium state leading to a reduction in the content of high molecular-weight hydrocarbons and an increase in low molecular-weight members.

Keeping in mind the relatively chemically inert nature of alkanes one can consider that the rates of these transformations will, in general, be nominal compared to the transformation rates of cyclic compounds with a greater reactive capability.

Due to the small changes in the value of free energy in reactions for the disintegration of alkanes, there will be considerable quantities of original hydrocarbons in the system at the moment that equilibrium is attained. Equilibrium will be established very slowly.

The definite requirement for spontaneous processes will be satisfied by processes related to the formation of alkanes with a lowering of the reserve of free energy of methane and ethane, for example

$$C_nH_{2n+2} \to CH_4 + C + C_{n-2}H_{2n-2}\dagger \tag{6}$$

$$2C_nH_{2n+2} \to CH_3\!-\!CH_3 + C_{2(n-1)}H_{4n-2}. \tag{7}$$

To a considerably lesser degree these will be satisfied by processes leading to the formation of saturated and an ethylenic hydrocarbon

$$C_nH_{2n+2} \to C_{\frac{n}{2}}H_{2\left(\frac{n}{2}\right)+2} + C_{\frac{n}{2}}H_{2\left(\frac{n}{2}\right)}. \tag{8}$$

In this case the reserve of free energy in the end products of the reaction is greater than in the original. Thus processes of the enlargement of alkanes will predominantly occur either along the line of the splitting off of methane and hydrogen with the formation of a new alkane, containing two less carbon atoms, or with the formation of ethane and a new alkane having a carbon chain of $(m + n - 2)$ carbon atoms. Here m and n are the numbers of carbon atoms in the molecules of the original alkanes.

Francis [54] first indicated that it is thermodynamically impossible to obtain higher alkanes from lower ones directly with the exception of those cases when lighter hydrocarbons can be formed simultaneously at least in equivalent quantities.

Reaction (6) is always accompanied by a lowering of the level of free energy while for reaction (7) the change in free energy is close to zero. For example, in the reaction

$$2C_{10}H_{22} \to CH_3\!-\!CH_3 + C_{18}H_{38}$$

† The formation of a carbonized residue is alway observed even with low temperature, thermocatalytic transformation of alkanes.

at a temperature of 400 °K

$$\Delta F^{\circ}_{400^{\circ}K} = 2(+32,010) - \{(-3,447) - (+67,840)\} = +373 \text{ cal.}$$

For the reaction

$$2C_{15}H_{32} \rightarrow C_2H_6 + C_{28}H_{58}$$

under the same conditions

$$\Delta F^{\circ}_{400^{\circ}K} = 2(+54,410) - \{(-3,437) - (+112,632)\} = +365 \text{ cal.}$$

At the same time for a reaction with the splitting off of methane and carbonized matter, for example,

$$C_{10}H_{22} \rightarrow C_8H_{18} + CH_4 + C$$

$$\Delta F^{\circ}_{400^{\circ}K} = \{(+23,060) + (-10,048)\} - (+32,010) = -18,998 \text{ cal.}$$

and for the reaction

$$C_{15}H_{32} \rightarrow C_{13}H_{28} + CH_4 + C$$

$$\Delta F^{\circ}_{400^{\circ}K} = \{(45,450) + (-10,048)\} - (+54,410) = -19,008 \text{ cal.}$$

This situation allows one to maintain that in the series of condensation reactions, everything else being equal, type (6) reactions leading to the formation of alkanes with a lower molecular weight than the original will be of primary significance.

The type (7) reaction has a secondary significance and the presence of newly formed heavy alkanes in the reactive mixture will only occur in the initial and intermediate stages of the process of petroleum change. During these transformation stages there exist cyclic compounds lade n with energy capable of the most important transformations. With the exhaustion of the basic mass of these compounds having a cyclic nature, the group most susceptible to transformation becomes the high molecular weight alkanes which are close to naphthenes in terms of their reserve of free energy. Their disintegration, according to eqn. (6), will be compensated to a certain extent by those that are newly formed according to eqn. (7). Heavy alkanes first appear in relatively significant quantities in the composition of petroleum at the start of the last stages of metamorphism when the primary masses of naphthenes became cyclized and formed significant quantities of alkanes having an intermediate molecular weight. The presence of high molecular-weight alkanes in the composition of a mixture in equilibrium will be in effect until the reserves of alkanes having an intermediate molecular weight are exhausted. In an active system the changes primarily occur at the expense of intermediate and high molecular weight alkanes. The amount of the former decreases, being replenished only by means of the decyclization of naphthenes:

naphthenes → intermediate molecular weight alkanes.

The amount of the latter likewise diminishes but not concurrently and is replenished by means of reaction (7). With decreasing reserves of naphthenes capable of reactions, the replenishing of the reserves of intermediate molecular weight alkanes is retarded while the reaction rates for the transformation of the latter are still quite high.

Such a relationship between the rates of disintegration and regeneration leads to the fact that, during the progressive stages of metamorphism, a decrease in the content of intermediate molecular-weight alkanes will generally occur. The relative and absolute content of light alkanes increases in the process and the content of heavy hydrocarbons (petroleum waxes) will, to a certain extent, be preserved or increased.

The decyclization of replaced naphthenes leads to the formation of iso-type alkanes having intermediate molecular weights. Their transformation according to reaction (7) leads to the generation of high molecular-weight alkanes likewise having an iso-structure, for example

$$2CH_3-\underset{CH_3}{\overset{CH_3}{\diagup}}\bigcirc-CH_3 \xrightarrow{+6H_2}$$

$$\xrightarrow{+6H_2} 2CH_3-\underset{CH_3}{\overset{|}{CH}}-\underset{CH_3}{\overset{|}{CH}}-\underset{CH_3}{\overset{|}{CH}}-CH_2-CH_2-CH_3 \longrightarrow$$

$$\longrightarrow 2CH_3-CH_3 +$$

$$+ CH_3-\underset{CH_3}{\overset{|}{CH}}-\underset{CH_3}{\overset{|}{CH}}-\underset{CH_3}{\overset{|}{CH}}-CH_2-CH_2-\underset{CH_3}{\overset{|}{CH}}-\underset{CH_3}{\overset{|}{CH}}-\underset{CH_3}{\overset{|}{CH}}-CH_3.$$

Alkanes having an iso-type of structure have a somewhat lower reserve of free energy compared to the normal-type. However, the transition of alkanes from iso- to normal-types by the splitting off of lateral chains is energetically beneficial since it is tied in with the enlargement of molecules and will occur spontaneously. The return path for the transformation is not too probable if there is no source of energy having a high potential. Consequently, the presence of high molecular weight, iso-type alkanes (ceresins) in petroleum attests to the fact that the system is generally at earlier stages of development than a petroleum containing only normal alkanes of high molecular weight (waxes). The second type of petroleum is more highly transformed than the first.

Let us examine the fate of high molecular-weight paraffinic hydrocarbons. From the point of view of a material and energy balance one would think that processes for transformation into low molecular-weight compounds should be accompanied by processes involving the formation of those that are poor in hydrogen and hence carbonized. Such could be aromatic hydrocarbons with a

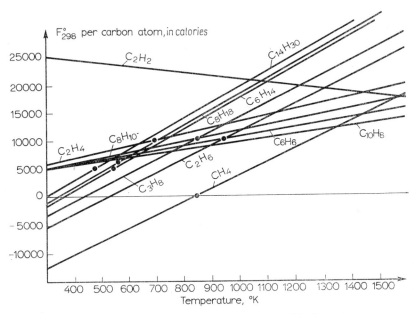

Fig. 42. Change in free energy of various classes of hydrocarbons as a function of temperature.

structure gradually increasing in complexity right up to highly carbonized compounds of the graphite type.

Relationships for the change in free energy as a function of temperature for various classes of hydrocarbons are presented in Fig. 42.

The change in free energy with temperature for various hydrocarbons occurs in a non-uniform manner as calculated for one and the same temperature interval. Thus, for example, in increasing the temperature by 100° the free energy of paraffinic hydrocarbons increases approximately by 2500 cal per carbon atom. At the same time increasing the temperature by 100° leads to an increase in the free energy for hexamethylene hydrocarbons of 2300 cal per carbon atom and, for pentamethylene compounds, of 2200 cal per carbon atom. The free energy of ethylenic and aromatic hydrocarbons increases even less. For the former this increase comprises 1000 and for the latter only 800 cal per carbon atom. The performance of acetylene with increasing temperature calls attention to itself. For this hydrocarbon an increase in temperature leads, not to an increase, but rather to a decrease in free energy, comprising 800 cal per carbon atom for each 100°.

This leads to the fact that, depending on the increase in temperature, the differences between the values of free energy for individual classes of hydrocarbons are minimized and the stability relationships between the various classes take on a different character. If, at temperatures up to 500°K, hydrocarbons of the paraffinic order are more stable, then, at this temperature, the free energy level of eicosane ($C_{20}H_{42}$) becomes equal to the corresponding value for benzene, i.e. at 500°K eicosane no longer has any advantage over benzene, in the thermodynamic sense, and the probability of the existence of one or the other is the same. A further increase in temperature makes the existence of benzene more probable than that of eicosane. Since computations of free energy are made in terms of one carbon atom, when these values are equal at $t = 500°K$, the transition of carbon atoms from a state where their bonds are characteristic of eicosane to a state characteristic of benzene does not bring about any change in energy level of the system and, in this manner, there arises the possibility of equilibrium between eicosane and benzene. Paraffinic hydrocarbons having a higher molecular weight than eicosane naturally attain this equilibrium state at a lower temperature. If one keeps in mind that the value of free energy pertaining to one carbon atom drops in the sequence benzene → naphthalene → anthracene (phenanthrene) → pyrene from 4930 cal, for benzene to 4015 cal for pyrene, then the equilibrium between high molecular-weight hydrocarbons of the paraffinic order and complex condensed systems of aromatic hydrocarbons can be attained at lower temperatures than for benzene. Along with this, if one considers the possibility of hydrogenation, by hydrogen given off in the reconstruction of paraffinic into aromatic hydrocarbons, of fragments of the original molecule into light hydrocarbons, the total energy effect of the reaction will be even more favorable for processes of aromatization.

From these same data comes the explanation for the peculiar thermal stability of aromatic hydrocarbons. Starting with a temperature of 500–550°K, the free energy of all the simplest hydrocarbons of the polymethylene order and high molecular-weight paraffinic hydrocarbons exceeds the free energy of benzene and, consequently, at high temperatures the existence of aromatic hydrocarbons is more likely than that of all others with the exception of acetylene.

It is interesting to call attention to the situation that the same level of free energy, computed per carbon atom, for ethylenic and paraffinic hydrocarbons is attained at much higher temperatures than for benzene. Thus, for example, for methane and ethylene this temperature is close to 1600°K, for eicosane and ethylene about 720°K, at the same time for benzene and methane, as already reported earlier, the temperature for energy equilibrium is equal to 1300°K. It is 520°K for benzene and eicosane. In this regard, with increasing temperature, the free energies per carbon atom for paraffinic and aromatic hydrocarbons will become equal before those for paraffinic and ethylenic hydrocarbons. With this it is important to keep in mind that the energy equilibrium, at relatively low temperatures, between paraffinic and aromatic hydrocarbons is established only in the case of the paraffinic hydrocarbon having a high molecular weight. Equilibrium for low molecular weight paraffinic hydrocarbons is established at considerably higher temperatures.

Additional confirmation for the conclusion as to the existence of a direct genetic relationship between paraffinic and aromatic hydrocarbons can be found in the condition that, in the temperature range from 300 to 1700°K, the free energy of ethylene per carbon atom is always higher than that of benzene. The occurrence of carbon in the form of ethylene in that case is less likely than in the form of benzene.

In this manner the transition from paraffinic to aromatic hydrocarbons is not tied to the necessary passage through the ethylenic hydrocarbon stage. On the contrary, from the energy point of view, the transition from paraffinic to ethylenic hydrocarbons is unavoidably tied in with passing through a level of energy of the carbon atom characteristic for the aromatic order of hydrocarbons.

The absence of derivatives of the cyclopentane and cyclohexane order in the products of thermocatalytic transformation of high molecular weight, paraffinic hydrocarbons is explained by the fact that at the temperatures of thermocatalysis (400–500 °K) the free energy level for cyclomethylenes of the simplest type is higher than for paraffinic hydrocarbons and the transition from the latter to the former is thermodynamically unprofitable.

In our thermodynamic analysis we deliberately investigated the least profitable, in the energy sense, case of hydrocarbon transformation, namely that for one with a low molecular weight, eicosane ($C_{20}H_{42}$), into benzene, the simplest representative of aromatic hydrocarbons. The transformation of hydrocarbons with a higher molecular weight than eicosane into homologs of benzene and even more so into alkylated aromatic hydrocarbons having a condensed structure will occur at lower temperatures in view of the fact that the value of free energy per carbon atom increases with increasing molecular weight of the paraffinic hydrocarbons and decreases for aromatic hydrocarbons. In view of this the point of intersection for the lines expressing the relationship for free energies is displaced in the direction of lower temperatures, i.e. equilibrium between these can be realized at lower temperatures.

The transformation of alkanes at elevated temperatures, as well as under various conditions of pressure and catalytic effects of numerous materials, is widely covered in the literature. Alkanes up to C_8 were covered in an especially detailed manner. The transformations of high molecular-weight alkanes are investigated in a considerably fewer works, as are the intermediate molecular-weight alkanes (C_8—C_{16}).

It was established that methane is the most stable hydrocarbon and that the thermal stability of alkanes drops with increasing molecular weight. Catalysts (primarily metals, metal chlorides and oxides, aluminosilicates) lower the temperature for the start of disintegration of alkanes. Thermal disintegration of alkanes occurs primarily at the C—C bond, with breaking of the C—H bond occuring to a much lesser degree. This is explained by the fact that the energy for breaking the C—C bond in alkanes is 71.1 kcal while for the C—H bond this value is about 22.5 kcal greater, being equal to 96.3 kcal. The probability for breaking one C—C bond or another in alkanes is the same but with increasing molecular weight of the alkane the bonds in the central portion of the molecule are broken preferentially. Non-catalytic disintegration of alkanes in the vapor phase occurs with the formation of a molecule of alkane and one of alkene, each having approximately the same molecular weight.

Along with the formation of molecules having a lower molecular weight during the thermal disintegration of alkanes, especially in the presence of catalysts, the formation of high boiling point products with increased molecular weight is also observed. High molecular weight paraffins (waxes) [55, 56] are present among these products.

Alkanes having an iso-structure are less stable and are more susceptible to thermal transformation with the formation of hydrocarbons having a normal type of structure. H. A. Wilson [53] theoretically investigated the equilibrium of alkanes and came to the conclusion that the low temperature disintegration of these yields alkanes of higher or lower molecular weight than the original by way of a principal product. Wilson indicates that if the high boiling point fractions of petroleum are subjected to heat at a sufficiently high temperature, then a rapid buildup of readily volatile and high boiling point components will be observed in the reactive mixture. With time this process will slow down and an equilibrium state is reached for each specific temperature and pressure. The rate of decomposition and establishment of equilibrium increases with increasing temperature. Since the mixtures obtained in the course of thermal reaction primarily consist of alkanes, the equilibrium state must be a definite equilibrium between the alkanes present in abundance.

Wilson checked his theoretical results by experimental means and obtained good correlation between the two. Some of the more recent work [57, 58, 59] established that low temperature transformation of the hydrocarbons in the oil fractions in the presence of aluminosilicates leads to establishment of equilibrium in a relatively short time. In the composition of an equilibrium mixture there are original hydrocarbons as well as higher and lower boiling point fractions. No unsaturated compounds were discovered among the reaction products. With increasing depth of the process in a reactive mixture, a decrease in the content of intermediate molecular-weight alkanes and an increase in more volatile and heavier products is observed. High pressures of the order of 200 atm oppose the reactions for the decomposition of alkanes and lead to the formation of products having a higher molecular weight as a result of alkylation reactions.

K. Schneider and M. Frolich [60] showed that reactions of the type (6) as, for example, in the case of propane

$$2C_3H_8 \rightarrow C_2H_6 + C_4H_{10}$$

take place for a whole number of alkanes. It is interesting to note that although these reactions at first glance appear to be bimolecular, their rate is nevertheless quite accurately expressed by the equation for monomolecular reactions. This situation attests to the radical mechanism of the reaction

$$CH_3{-}CH_2{-}CH_3 \rightarrow CH_3{-}CH_2^{\cdot} + CH_3^{\cdot} \tag{9}$$

$$\left.\begin{aligned}
CH_3CH_2^{\cdot} + CH_3^{\cdot} &\rightarrow CH_3{-}CH_2{-}CH_3 \\
CH_3^{\cdot} + CH_3^{\cdot} &\rightarrow CH_3{-}CH_3 \\
CH_3{-}CH_2^{\cdot} + CH_3{-}CH_2^{\cdot} &\rightarrow CH_3CH_2CH_2CH_3
\end{aligned}\right\} \tag{10}$$

The second stage of the process, the grouping of radicals amongst each other in different combinations, proceeds at an unexpectedly rate of speed higher than that for the stage of the disintegration of the original molecule into free radicals, and in view of this is not reflected in the overall balance of time for the total process.

According to the data of Calingaert [61], in the disintegration of pentane at 600°, the chain breaks at the central carbon atom with the formation of ethyl and propyl radicals. Next, one of these radicals becomes saturated with hydrogen at the expense of the other. The reaction proceeds in the following manner: 55% of the original pentane forms ethane and propylene, 25% of the original pentane is transformed into propane and ethylene, while a large portion of the remainder decomposes into methane and butylene. Isopentane decomposes with the formation of methane and isobutylene as well as ethane and propylene. In the latter case ethane is always formed, i.e. hydrogenation of the ethyl radical occurs.

Reactions for the alkylation of paraffinic hydrocarbons by olefins occur at low temperatures, elevated pressures and in the presence of catalysts. As a result, alkanes with lower and higher molecular weights and boiling point temperatures [53] are formed along with the compounds having the anticipated molecular weight. A reduction in temperature and elevation of pressure favors these reactions. The alkylation reactions are reversible with respect to the reactions for the decomposition of alkanes

$$C_{n-m}H_{2(n-m)} + C_mH_{2m+2} \rightleftarrows C_nH_{2n+2}.$$

The isomerization of normal alkanes into products having an iso-structure occurs at elevated temperatures (300–400°) and in the presence of catalysts (zinc chloride, aluminum chloride, molybdenum sulfide, etc.). According to B. L. Moldavskii [62], the isomerization of butane into isobutane is a reversible reaction. With increasing temperature the equilibrium is shifted in the direction of the formation of normal butane.

On the basis of presented experimental data it can be considered established that intermediate molecular-weight alkanes, under known conditions, are susceptible to redistribution (disproportionation) processes of mass as confirmed by the theoretical understanding of the transformation paths for alkanes. As a result of these processes we have formed, on one side, the products with a higher molecular weight and, on the other, the low molecular-weight alkanes

$$2C_nH_{2n+2} \rightleftarrows C_{n-1}H_{2(n-1)+2} + C_{n+1}H_{2(n+1)+2}.$$

Reactions for the conversion of intermediate molecular-weight alkanes are in equilibrium and the equilibrium state depends on the temperature and pressure. The rate for establishing equilibrium is low at low temperatures and increases either with increased temperature or with the action of catalysts. An increase in the rate of a primary reaction is not attained with unlimited temperature increases. There is some optimum temperature which, when exceeded, leads to the development of secondary reactions involving the disintegration of the formed high molecular-weight alkane. Average temperatures and pressures aid the reactions for the conversion of intermediate molecular weight alkanes and obstruct reactions for the decomposition of high molecular-weight alkanes.

Experimental data on the synthesis of high molecular-weight hydrocarbons from a mixture of carbon monoxide and hydrogen shows that the process occurs under conditions of low and average pressures and nominal temperatures of the order of 300° in the presence of catalysts [63]. The synthesis proceeds with the release of substantial heat at the expense of the creation of water and requires the most meticulous cooling to prevent local overheating. An increase in temperature above the optimum value leads to the predominant creation of low molecular-weight alkanes right up to methane:

at low temperatures

$$n CO + m H_2 \rightarrow CH_3-(CH_2)_n-CH_3 + n H_2O,$$

at high temperatures

$$CO + 3H_2 \rightarrow CH_4 + H_2O.$$

It is quite probable that the formation of methane at elevated temperatures has as its basis the decomposition of the initially formed complex alkane into methylene radicals. The latter hydrogenate completely in the presence of excess hydrogen to form methane.

The formation of high molecular-weight from low molecular-weight alkanes was observed with the reaction on the latter of quanta of high intensity light ray energy [64, 65, 66] and with thermal cracking [67]. The basis for these processes lies in the activation of the original molecule at the expense of external sources of high potential energy, while the redistribution of the mass of intermediate molecular-weight alkanes has as its basis the internal energy reserve of the molecule, the reserve of free energy.

The formation of a molecule with a large reserve of free energy occurs at the expense of the paralleling process for the formation of a molecule with a reduced reserve. A process occurs involving the redistribution (disproportionation) of energy, accompanied by the irreversible loss of some portion of the initial reserve in the form of heat, in accordance with the second law of thermodynamics.

On the basis of the material presented above it is possible to come to the following conclusions:

1. Alkanes, with the exception of methane, are not the end products of metamorphism but are capable of further spontaneous transformation.

2. Graphite and methane are the end products of alkane change, being compounds with the least reserve of free energy under reducing conditions.

3. On their way to becoming methane and graphite the alkanes pass through a number of intermediate stages characterized each time by a lower reserve of free energy for the system in general and a decreasing average molecular weight.

4. The disintegration of alkanes can occur in two ways: (a) by the splitting off of methane and carbon with the formation of an alkane having two less carbon atoms, and (b) by the splitting off of a molecule of ethane from two molecules of the original hydrocarbons and the formation of an alkane having an increased molecular-weight. The latter process leads to the appearance of solid hydrocarbons having a normal (paraffin) and iso-structure (ceresin) in the composition of petroleum. Splitting into olefin and alkane having a lower molecular weight is thermodynamically less likely under the temperature conditions encountered in oil fields.

5. The process of change in paraffinic hydrocarbons leads to a decrease in the content of alkanes having an intermediate molecular weight in the system and to an increase (absolute and relative) in the content of low molecular-weight alkanes. With this, high molecular-weight alkanes having a branch type or normal structure are formed in the system during the initial and intermediate stages of transformation. In the final stages of transformation the high molecular-weight paraffins disappear once again. ·

6. Thermodynamic analysis indicates the possibility in principle of transformation of high molecular-weight paraffinic hydrocarbons at relatively low temperatures, approximately starting with eicosane, into aromatic hydrocarbons. Experimental data on the thermocatalytic transformation of the higher paraffinic hydrocarbons in the waxes and ceresins of petroleum confirm this conclusion. It follows from here that one of the possible paths for the transformation of solid petroleum hydrocarbons in nature is that which involves their transformation into aromatic hydrocarbons.

7. The appearance of iso-structure type of alkanes (ceresins) pre-

cedes the appearance of alkanes having a normal structure (waxes). The latter are primarily transformation products of higher molecular-weight hydrocarbons with an iso-structure.

8. The depth and rate for the transformation of an original system, corresponding to the law of mass action, directly depends on the completeness and rate of removal of volatile products of transformation (low molecular-weight hydrocarbons) from the system. Incomplete and gradual removal of volatile products leads to a slowing down of the transformation rate for the system as a whole and, consequently, to a lower depth of transformation during a given time.

9. With increasing depth of transformation the rate of change for petroleum decreases more and more, all other conditions being equal.

BIBLIOGRAPHY

1. KOROBOV, V. V. and FROST, A. V. *Free Energies of Organic Compounds*, Izd. V. Kh. O. Im. Mendeleeva, March 1949.
2. GRUZDEVA, N. A. *Zh. prikl. Khimii*, **25**, No. 9, 989 (1952).
3. UOTERS, U. *Chemistry of Free Radicals*, I. L., 1948.
4. RAIS, F. O. and RAIS, K. K. *Free Aliphatic Radicals*, ONTI 1937.
5. SEMENOV, N. N. *Tsepnye Reaktsii (Chain Reactions)*, Goskhimizdat, 1934.
6. SEMENOV, N. N. *Some Problems in Chemical Kinetics and Reactive Capability*, Izd. AN SSSR, 1954.
7. LEVIN, M., STEIN, BERG I. and SCHWARTZ, M. J. *J. Am. Chem. Soc.*, **76**, 3439 (1954).
8. KIREEV, V. A. *Kurs Fizicheskoi Khimii (Course in Physical Chemistry)*, Goskhimizdat, 1951.
9. KIREEV, V. A. *Usp. Khimii*, **33**, Issue 8, 921 (1954).
10. CHERNOZHUKOV, N. I. and KREIN, S. E. *Okislyaemost' Mineral'nykh Masel (Oxidizability of Mineral Oils)*, Third edition, Gostoptekhizdat, 1955.
11. DOBRYANSKII, A. F. *Scientific Bases of Crude Oil Cracking*, ONTI, 1935.
12. EGLOFF, G. E., et al. *Decomposition and Polymerization of Hydrocarbons*, ONTI, Khimteorizdat, Summer (1935).
13. SAKHANEN, A. N. *Pererabotka Nefti (Reprocessing of Crude Oil)*, Gostoptekhizdat, 1947.
14. *Crude Oils Handbook, Chemical and Physical Properties*, Chief Editors B. T. Brooks and A. E. Dunstan, "Science of Petroleum" Series, Vol. V, Part 1, O.U.P., 1950.
15. TILICHEEV, M. D. and SHITIKOV, V. K. *Neft. Khoz.*, No. 1, 51 (1937).
16. FERKO, P. *Ber.* **20**, 660 (1887).
17. MOLDAVSKII, B. L. and BEZDEL', L. S. *Zh. Obshchei Khimii*, **16**, No. 10, 1633 (1946).
18. OBOLENTSEV, R. D. and GRYAZNOV, N. N. *Dokl. Akad. Nauk SSSR*, **73**, No. 1, 121 (1950).

19. LAVROVSKII, K.P., FISH, YU.L. and NAIMUSHIN, N.N. *Trudy Inst-ta Nefti Akad. Nauk SSSR*, Vol. II, p. 101 (1952).
20. HIVEN, P. and HAMMIK, D. *J. Soc. Chem., Lond.* 1779 (1949).
21. SACHANEN, HANSFORD and MAYERS, *Ind. Eng. Chem.* **37**, No. 7 (1945).
22. THOMAS, HEXTRA and PINKSTON, *J. Am. Chem. Soc.* **66**, 1684 (1944).
23. GREENSFELDER, WOOG and GOOD, *Ind. Eng. Chem.* **17**, No. 12, 1163 (1945).
24. NATANSON, G.A. and KOGAN, M.YA. *Zh. Obshchei Khimii*, **16**, 1639 (1946).
25. MAMEDALIEV, YU.G. *Izv. Akad. Nauk SSSR, Otdel Khim. Nauk*, No. 2, 197 (1947).
26. DOBRYANSKII, A.F. and ANDREEV, P.F. *Izv. Akad. Nauk Estonskoi SSR*, **3**, No. 2, 193 (1954).
27. SYRKIN, YA.K. and DYATKINA, M.E. *Khimicheskaya Svyaz i Stroenie Molekul (Chemical Bonds and Molecular Structure)*, Goskhimizdat, 1956.
28. BAKH, A.N. *Zh. Russk. Fiz. – Khim. Obshchestva*, **29**, 373 (1897).
29. BAKH, A.N. *Ibid.*, **44**, Appendix 1–79 (1912).
30. WEILAND, H. *Ber.* **46**, 3864 (1913).
31. MEDVEDEV, S. and ALEKSEEVA, E. *Zh. Obshchei Khimii*, **1**, 1193 (1931).
32. IVANOV, K.I. *Promezhutochn. Produkty i Promezhut. Reaktsii Avtookisleniya Uglevodorodov (Intermediate Products and Reactions of Hydrocarbon Auto-oxidation)*, Gostoptekhizdat, 1949.
33. SEMENOV, N.N. Development of the chain theory for the oxidation of hydro-carbons, *Sbornik "Problemy Okisleniya Uglevodorodov"*, Izd. Akad. Nauk SSSR, 1954.
34. DOBRYANSKII, A.F. *Geokhimiya Nefti (Geochemistry of Crude Oil)*, Gostop-tekhizdat, 1948.
35. ZELINSKII, N.D. *Izbran. Trudy*, Vol. II, Izd. Akad. Nauk USSR, 1941.
36. DEMYANOVSKII, S.YA. *Kurs Organicheskoi i Biologicheskoi Khimii (Course in Organic and Biological Chemistry)*, Izd. "Sov. Nauka", 1952.
37. ELLIS, K. *Phys. Rev.* (2), **33**, 27 (1929).
38. JONES, J. *J. Am. Chem. Soc.* **107**, 1582 (1915).
39. JONES, J. and WHELLER, H. *J. Am. Chem. Soc.* **105**, 2562 (1914).
40. FREY, F.E. *Ind. Eng. Chem.* **26**, 198 (1934).
41. FROLICH, G., SIMAREL, K. and WHITE, *Ind. Eng. Chem.* **22**, 240 (1930).
42. ZELINSKII, N.D. *Ber.* **44**, 3121 (1911).
43. GRIGNARD, G. and STRATFORD, H. *Comptes rend.* **178**, 2149 (1924).
44. STRATFORD, H. *Ann. comb. liq.* **4**, 317 (1929).
45. LIEBERMAN, J. *Ann.* **122**, 78 (1882).
46. WIELAND, H. *Ber.* **46**, 484 (1912).
47. SANDGREN, S. *Ann. comb. liq.* **5**, 35 (1930).
48. SCHRAETER, K. *Brenn. Chem.* **1**, 39 (1920).
49. SAKHANOV, A.N. and TILICHEEV, M.D. *Ber.* **62**, 658 (1929).
50. TILICHEEV, M.D. and SHITIKOV, V.K. *Zh. Obshch. Khimii*, **9**, No. 2, 1087 (1939).
51. ORLOV, N.A. and BELOPOL'SKII, M.A. *Ber.* **62**, 1226 (1929).
52. SAKHANOV, A.N., *et al. Ber.* **62**, 670 (1929).
53. WILSON, H.A. *Proc. Roy. Soc., Lond.* **116** A, No. 775, 501 (1927).
54. FRANCIS, F. *Ind. Eng. Chem.* **20**, 277 (1928).
55. WILSON, H.A. *Proc. Roy. Soc., Lond.* **116** A, No. 775, 501 (1927).

56. SAKHANEN, A. N. *Pererabotka Nefti (Reprocessing of Crude Oil)*, Gostop-tekhizdat, 1947.
57. DOBRYANSKII, A. F. and BOGOMOLOV, A. I. *Zh. prikl. Khimii*, **22,** No. 10, 1124 (1949).
58. DOBRYANSKII, A. F. and GAVRILOV, B. G. *Nauchn. Bull. LGU,* No. 23, 13 (1949).
59. GALINSKAYA-RIVLIN, G. YA. Avtoreferat Kandidatskoi Dissertatsii (Ph. D. Thesis), LGU, 1949.
60. SCHNEIDER, K. and FROLICH, M. *Ind. Eng. Chem.* **23,** 1405 (1931).
61. CALINGAERT, F. *J. Am. Chem. Soc.* **52,** 1262 (1930).
62. MOLDAVSKII, B. L., *et al. Dokl. Akad. Nauk SSSR*, **23,** 919 (1939).
63. RAPPOPORT, I. B. *Iskusstvennoe Zhidkoe Toplivo (Synthetic Liquid Fuel)*, Part II, Gostoptekhizdat, 1950.
64. LIND, K. and BARDWELL, H. *J. Am. Chem. Soc.* **48,** 2335 (1926).
65. KEMULA, W. *Roczniki Chem.* **10,** 213 (1930).
66. LIND, K. and HOCKLER, M. *J. Am. Chem. Soc.* **52,** 4450 (1930).
67. FISCHER, F. *Brenn. Chem.* **9,** 309 (1928).

CHAPTER V

OXIDATIVE TRANSFORMATIONS
OF PETROLEUM IN NATURE†

A. CONDITIONS OF PETROLEUM OXIDATION IN NATURE

The geochemical changes of petroleum, as described in other sections of this book, comprise essentially thermocatalytic transformations resulting in relative paraffinization of petroleum accompanied by the formation of substances of high carbon content. Along with these, under certain conditions, goes the development of processes of opposite character, principally oxidation. Whereas transformation of petroleum is accompanied by subsidence and metamorphism (broadly) of the reservoir rocks, the oxidation of petroleum is related to geotectonic oscillatory movements of positive sign (of course, not just any movements, but those with sufficient amplitude) and occurs along with hypergenic changes of the reservoir rocks. The significance and scale of magnitude of petroleum oxidation must be recognized as quite substantial, considering not only the main body of commercially significant liquid petroleum deposits existing at the present time, but also all the remains of deposits already destroyed by the action of surface factors and all those of which no traces have been left by such factors.

Whereas transformations of petroleum theoretically may take place anywhere, the oxidation of petroleum is possible only under certain conditions, in the presence of definite oxidizing agents.

† The first section of this chapter was prepared by geologist A. A. Kartsev, the second one by chemist P. F. Andreev. The editor decided to combine both sections in a single chapter, though the two authors do not quite agree with each other on certain subjects. A. A. Kartsev is treating the problem of petroleum oxidation principally from the viewpoint of geology while P. F. Andreev deals with it from the chemical viewpoint. Both authors bring forward such important arguments in favor of their opinions that it would be inexpedient to arbitrarily combine their viewpoints on a subject which at present lacks as yet a solid basis of accurately determined and experimentally proven facts. [The editor.]

The oxidation of petroleum in nature may occur either with free molecular oxygen (aerobic oxidation) or at the expense of bound oxygen and certain other compounds (anaerobic oxidation). Aerobic oxidation, in turn, may be divided into oxidation with atmospheric oxygen and oxidation with oxygen present in solution in underground waters. Anaerobic oxidation may be divided, first of all, according to the nature of the compound in which the oxygen is bound and, secondly, according to whether the process is biochemical or abiochemical.

In accordance with the above classification of natural oxidation of petroleum, the following geochemical zones of petroleum oxidation may be separated: (1) zone of oxidation with atmospheric air, (2) zone of oxidation with dissolved oxygen, (3) anaerobic biochemical oxidation zone, and (4) anaerobic abiochemical oxidation zone.† Each succeeding zone embraces progressively deeper layers of the earth's crust.

The characteristics of each zone shall now be discussed.

1. Zone of oxidation by atmospheric air

This zone corresponds to the "aeration zone" known in hydrogeology, i.e. the portion of the lithosphere, situated above the ground water table, where the pores and cavities in the rocks are partially filled with air (termed soil air and subsoil air). The thickness of this zone ranges from 0 to about 220 m, reaching usually dozens and dozens of meters.

According to available data, the oxygen content in soil and subsoil air ranges from 5 to 18%, i.e. substantially less than in the atmosphere [1].

The petroleum in the aeration zone is present principally in the form of asphaltic-kir‡ beds. Liquid oil deposits of commercial importance are virtually absent in the aeration zone.

The oxidation of petroleum in the aeration zone is accompanied by volatilization of light constituents, which leaves a significant impression on the chemical characteristics of the oxidation

† The existence of this zone is denied by most researchers, and the existence of the third zone is not universally recognized.

‡ "Kir" is inspissated petroleum, a natural product resulting from combined evaporation and oxidation of petroleum due to aerial exposure. [Transl. Ed.]

products. The typical products of transformation of petroleum in this zone are kirs.

Microbiological processes are likewise operative in oxidation of petroleum in this zone.

2. Zone of oxidation by dissolved oxygen

The upper boundary of the zone corresponds to the lower boundary of the zone discussed above, i.e. to the surface of the water table. The lower boundary, defined by the disappearance of dissolved oxygen, is not sharply delineated. At successively lower levels in the lithosphere the amount of dissolved oxygen diminishes and at a depth of several hundred meters (as a maximum) it disappears completely, being consumed by the oxidation of organic substances scattered throughout the rocks and being fixed by various minerals.

The changes in composition of dissolved gases with depth occur in the following sequence: the oxygen–nitrogen gases are gradually succeeded by carbon dioxide–nitrogen, nitrogen–carbon dioxide and purely nitrogen gases, and finally by hydrocarbon–nitrogen gases.

Unfortunately, not enough data are available on the oxygen content of underground waters. It is often virtually impossible to distinguish between cases where oxygen is actually present from those in which oxygen entered the sample during sampling.

It is quite obvious that the ultimate depths at which dissolved oxygen is encountered may vary depending on hydrogeological conditions, mobility of underground waters, and distance from their source of supply of meteoric waters.

The results of special investigations conducted by A. I. Germanov indicate that dissolved oxygen is encountered in artesian waters under free water exchange conditions at depths down to 500–600 m and possibly even lower, in quantities ranging from a few hundredths to 4–5 mg/l and that its spread depends also on how rich the rocks are in sulfides and organic matter [2].

Oxygen is a "forbidden" gas for petroleum deposits and the waters adjacent thereto. Absence of oxygen in oil-bearing formations depends, as a rule, not on the petroleum itself but on the action of the components of rocks; in very deep layers the oxygen is absent even where there is no oil.

Oil in commercial quantities is only rarely encountered in the dissolved oxygen distribution zone. Though accurate data are not available, it is possible to cite some commercial deposits of liquid petroleum present apparently in the dissolved oxygen occurrence zone or in direct contact with that zone. Such deposits include in the first place the deposits in exposed formations, i.e. in formations outcropping into the open air so that air is in direct proximity to the deposit. These deposits are shielded either by seepage waters or by asphalt-kir formations. The first ones may be classified as belonging to the "hydraulically shielded" type of deposits and are encountered in the Mirzaani and Binagady oil fields. The second may be termed "geochemically shielded" or "self-shielded" deposits: the shielding is due to geochemical processes in the deposit itself (one portion of the deposit, having lost its liquid consistency, acts as a shield with respect to the other portion of the deposit which has retained its liquid consistency). Examples of "self-shielded" deposits are McKittrick, Shubany, and others.†

The hydraulically shielded deposits in exposed formations are evidently supplied with oxygen by the shielding intrusive waters (of the groundwater type, i.e. without pressure). The existence of commercial deposits of liquid petroleum under these conditions over an extended period of time does not appear to be possible and even their short-term presence is not fully understood. Some researchers explain it through formation of an asphalt-type protective "crust" at the contact surface between the oil and the water shield, so that as a consequence such deposits should be regarded as identical in principle with deposits of the "self-shielded" type.

In conditions of oxidation of oil with dissolved oxygen, an important factor (more important than in the aeration zone) appear to be biochemical processes—the activity of aerobic hydrocarbons bacteria. The distribution of these bacteria under natural conditions was studied primarily in connection with their utilization as indicators in prospecting for oil. Among the aerobic hydrocarbon bacteria under natural conditions, mostly the methane oxidation bacteria and the propane oxidation bacteria have been studied. The methane oxidation bacteria, classified as the *Methanomonas methanica* genus, are widely distributed in ground waters and connate waters. Data are available on their ability to assimilate certain other hydrocarbons besides methane [4]. Propane oxidation bac-

† A special case involves deposits where the asphalt-kir seal and the liquid oil have each originated at a different age (Changyrtash) [3].

teria, classified according to E. N. Bokova [4] in the *Mycobacterium rubrum* var. *bacterium* species, are utilized as the most characteristic indicator organism in prospecting for oil. They are also capable of consuming heavier hydrocarbons. The majority of *Mycobacterium rubrum* varieties utilize only molecular oxygen and are not capable of existing on the oxygen of sulfates and nitrates.

The bacteria capable of oxidizing gaseous and liquid hydrocarbons such as pentane, hexane, heptane, etc., are apparently quite variegated, but their occurrence in underground waters and rocks has only been slightly studied. The species *Bac. aliphaticum liquefaciens* has been established. Among them are facultative anaerobes capable of utilizing the fixed oxygen of nitrates.

The overall effect of the action of aerobic hydrocarbon bacteria upon petroleum under the conditions existing in nature remains largely obscure.

It should be taken into consideration that the overall result of the transformation of petroleum in the zone of dissolved oxygen will be affected also by processes of selective solution and entrainment of certain component parts of the oil by circulating waters.

A typical product of the zone of dissolved oxygen appear to be true asphalts. Unfortunately, the chemical diagnostics of asphalts and kirs is as yet insufficiently developed.

Possibly the consequence of aerobic oxidation of petroleum may be a loss of saturated hydrocarbons by the oils (Naftalan, Kara, Okha, etc., crudes).

3. Anaerobic biochemical oxidation zone

The upper limit zone of anaerobic biochemical oxidation partly overlaps into the preceding zone, but fundamentally it should begin where macro-concentrations of free oxygen are no longer present. The lower boundary of this zone theoretically depends on the physicochemical limits of the active life of microorganisms and on the disappearance of reducible oxygenated substances if the succeeding zone be absent (see below). The limits of the development of bacteria, according to the available data, are defined by temperature (above 80–90 °C) and by the high salinity and acidic character of waters, which inevitably appear in the deep portions of the earth's crust.

The thickness of the zone of anaerobic biochemical oxidation, according to certain data, may be very great. Live bacteria have been found at depths substantially in excess of 2000 m [5]. On the basis of the accepted average geothermal gradient of 33 °C/1000 m, it may be calculated that the lower limit of the spread of bacteria should be at depths of the order of 2000–3000 m.

The problem of the bacterial population of oil-bearing strata has been raised long ago. However, many of the details relating to it, even the fundamental ones, still have not been unequivocally established. For this reason some of the researchers at the present time continue to deny the existence of bacterial population in oil-bearing formations up to the instant of penetration by the drill [6]. The origin as well as the possibility of microbial life in oil-bearing formations remain largely obscure.

The lack of full assurance about the autochthonous nature of bacteria found in oil-bearing formations tapped by wells (the possibility of introducing the bacteria during drilling operations is quite obvious) and the entirely obscure origin of the stratum bacteria if they be autochthonous, are the reasons for the quite peculiar situation prevailing in the status of the microbiology of petroleum deposits and the associated problems of anaerobic oxidation of oil.

In view of the importance of this subject, it is necessary to discuss in more detail the basic data on the microbiology of petroleum deposits.

In the past few years a number of reviews on the microbiology of petroleum deposits have been published [5, 7, 8, 9]. Originally the bacteria in oil-bearing formations, as is known, were discovered in 1926 simultaneously but independently by T. L. Ginzburg-Karagicheva [10] and E. Bastin [11]. Since that time microbiological investigations have been made on a large number of samples of oils, waters and rocks from oil-bearing formations (Caucasus, Ural–Volga, Emba, California, Mid-Continent, Pennsylvania, etc.). In most of the oil-bearing formations the presence of bacteria was detected. However, the noted American geomicrobiology specialist C. ZoBell pointed out as early as 1946 that there is never any assurance that the bacteria had not been carried into the connate waters during the drilling operations and yet at the same time there is no reason why it should be assumed that this is actually the case [12, pp. 92, 99].

The most widely distributed bacteria in oil-bearing strata are the desulfatizing bacteria (sulfate-reducing or "desulfurizing" bacteria) *Vibrio desulfuricans* and *V. thermodesulfuricans*. They constitute the main mass of bacteria. Among other groups of bacteria there were found denitrifying bacteria, bacteria which cause protein decomposition, butyric acid fermentation bacteria, bacteria active in the anaerobic fermentation of cellulose, and some others. Though the presence of sulfate-reducing and denitrifying bacteria and the predominance of the sulfate-reducers may be fully explained, an explanation must still be found for the development of the other groups mentioned above. Generally, the specificity of the nourishment of bacteria in petroleum deposits remains unexplained. It may be assumed that, for instance, the bacteria which decompose proteins are nurtured on relics of other bacteria. No explanation is available for the presence of bacterial forms capable of decomposing cellulose.

In the distribution of bacteria throughout the cross-section of petroleum deposits, a series of relationships have been noted. In some deposits it was established that bacteria are found in oil-bearing strata but are absent in oil-free portions of the strata. In the opinion of L. D. Shturm, this feature may be utilized in investigating the oil-bearing prospects of the strata of new areas being surveyed [8].

According to V. A. Ekzertsev's data, the oil-free rocks have a very scant bacterial population which in quite a few cases cannot be determined by direct count under the microscope. Up to 35 million bacteria per 1 g of rock has been calculated in such cases, compared with up to 105 million in oil-bearing rocks.

It is established that the existence of sulfate-reducing bacteria is paralleled by absence of sulfates and presence of hydrogen sulfide in the waters, the presence of carbon dioxide, and non-paraffinic nature of the oils [13]. L. D. Shturm found these bacteria in all of the hydrogen sulfide-bearing waters of the Second Baku [14]. In the Devonian of the Second Baku hardly any bacteria were found [15]. At the same time there is practically no hydrogen sulfide, but the sulfates are likewise absent. In the Devonian of the Volga–Ural oil-bearing region, bacteria were found at Radaevka and Yablonovyi Ovrag where the connate waters are relatively less mineralized and apparently are more mobile [16].

The dependence of physiology and morphology of stratum bacteria on geological and chemical conditions of their occurrence is a matter of great interest. L. D. Shturm has established that the sulfate-reducing bacteria occur almost exclusively in waters, while in rocks a significant distribution of denitrifying and ammonifying bacteria is noted. This relationship should be associated with the complete absence of nitrates in underground waters at profound depths and the retention of small quantities of nitrates in rocks, even of ancient age.

In hydrogen sulfide-bearing waters the elongated curvilinear forms predominate, whereas in waters free from hydrogen sulfide principally cocci, oval forms, and rod-shaped bacteria occur [7].

In limestones of the Upper Carboniferous (Ural–Volga region) chiefly vibrios were encountered while in Verey clays the rod-shaped and in Tournaisian dolomites the thread-like forms were found.

Also very interesting are the established facts of morphological and physiological differences between bacteria recovered from deep wells and bacteria occurring on the surface of the ground, and the differences between bacteria from formations of different age. Thus, according to L. D. Shturm, the sulfate-reducers from waters of Paleozoic deposits are morphologically different from those occurring in contemporary basins and in tertiary formations, the former being more elongated and stretched forms, namely *Desulfovibrio desulfuricans* var. *granularis* [17].

According to a report by Z. I. Kuznetsova and G. A. Mogilevskii, the sulfate-reducing bacteria from oil-bearing formations can be cultivated in a medium with heptane as the only source of carbonaceous nutrition in contrast to sulfate-reducers of ground surface origin, which do not possess such ability [18].

The above-mentioned items—facts indicating a broad capacity of the bacteria to adaptation under subsurface conditions, the wide scope of their geochemical activity (accumulation of gases, etc.), the differences between underground bacteria and surface bacteria—suggest that autochthonous and even practically endemic bacteria do exist in oil-bearing formations.

Yet it is necessary to point out a series of circumstances which, along with the previously cited impossibility of precluding the contamination of earth strata during drilling, compel a careful approach to the final solution of the problem.

In the first place it is necessary to recall that bacteria are known to propagate very rapidly and undergo very rapid morphological-physiological changes. As a consequence of this feature, even a short period of residence in the underground could be sufficient for attaining the observed variety of their forms and their distribution in accordance with geological-chemical conditions.

Secondly, there is the undeniable fact that extensive drilling of oil-bearing formations had taken place in the majority of deposits where large-scale results of geochemical action of bacteria were noted. In this connection, the observations made by V. M. Nikolaev (in Grozny fields) are of interest [19]. He noted that the sulfate content of waters gradually disappears during the producing operations. This leads to his conclusion that bacterial reduction of sulfates takes place only during the working of the deposit, but not before. V. M. Nikolaev's observations in idle wells have shown that complete disappearance of sulfates formerly present in concentrations of 0.28 g/l takes place in a water column about 400 m high within 25 days. Sharp variations in the sulfate content of waters during the producing operations were observed also in the Sulu-tepe-Chakhnaglyar deposit.

Thus the geochemical action of bacteria in the oil-bearing formation apparently may be manifested very rapidly. It is quite possible that the bacteria which penetrated into the formation through the first discovery wells may have multiplied and spread within a period of several years at a rate enabling them to exert a substantial influence upon the geochemistry of the formation.

If the bacteria are accepted as autochthonous in oil-bearing formations, an explanation of their origin is met with considerable difficulties. Conservation of bacteria in oil-bearing sediments from the time the latter were buried is, generally speaking, scarcely probable. The absence of oil accumulations in the reservoirs in the initial stages of their existence implies a virtual absence of nutrition sources for the bacteria. A later penetration of bacteria into the petroleum deposits from the surface should in most cases encounter the same barrier—the lack of food.

From the viewpoint of petroleum oxidation the bacteria are visualized as intermediaries in the process. Oxidation of petroleum in the anaerobic geochemical zone evidently depends on the presence of reducible oxygenated substances and on other conditions for bacterial activity, such as temperature and chemical properties of the medium.

In contrast to the two zones discussed above, the anaerobic biochemical oxidation zone contains a very large number of commercial deposits of liquid petroleum. The extent of oxidation undoubtedly varies sharply in different portions of this zone. Generally, the extent of anaerobic oxidation of oils under natural conditions remains a much debatable subject.

The characteristic products of anaerobic biochemical oxidation of oil are still almost unknown. Some researchers believe that they are the asphalt-like products formed at the water-oil interface under certain conditions, i.e. sour crudes or, on the basis of certain data, the heavy crudes depleted of alkanes.

A number of deposits were found to include zones with extra heavy, sometimes non-fluid oils at the water–oil contact surface. The existence of such zones is evidently an obstacle to oxidation of oil in other portions of the deposit. Therefore the spread of the oxidation process throughout the entire deposit appears hardly probable.

The possibility of complete destruction of large accumulations of liquid oil merely by the action of oxidation factors in the anaerobic zone remains a debatable problems, as well as the possibility of the formation of "genuine" asphalt accumulations in its place.

It appears especially desirable to discuss the available information on the occurrence of aerobic bacteria in commercial oil-producing formations. In 1936 A. A. Maliyants and E. A. Reinfel'd discovered that waters of the Surakhany oil field contained purple sulfur bacteria which oxidize hydrogen sulfide to sulfates [20]. These organisms gave a pink color to the water. The quantity of bacteria was related to the content of naphthenates in the water. As suggested by V. I. Vernadskii and B. L. Isachenko, the purple sulfur bacteria may utilize micro concentrations of molecular oxygen formed in the breakdown of water molecules under the action of radioactive elements [21]. The presence of such micro concentrations of oxygen in the anaerobic zone is not excluded, but they could hardly be cited as a source in explaining the existence of large amounts of sulfur bacteria detected in the Kirmakin series of the Apsheron Peninsula (hundreds of tons of pink water were obtained from wells). It is rather probable that these bacteria were utilizing the fixed oxygen of naphthenates, i.e. they were facultative anaerobes.

Generally, the question of sulfur bacteria in oil-bearing formations continues to be quite vague and the cases cited above are rather puzzling.

4. Zone of anaerobic abiochemical oxidation

The existence of anaerobic abiochemical oxidation of petroleum in nature is rejected by many, if not by the majority of researchers. There are few facts to support the existence of such a zone. As an indirect confirmation of reactions taking place between oils and sulfates without the participation of organisms, the cases of absence of sulfates in waters at high temperature may be cited. For instance on the Apsheron Peninsula, as pointed out by D. V. Zhabrev, no sulfates are present in waters which are in contact with oil deposits; they are absent even in formations where the temperature reaches 100 °C; yet at a sufficient distance from the oil deposits, in the same formations, the waters contain sulfates [22].

The upper boundary of the abiochemical zone is defined by the lower limit (in depth) of bacterial activity, while the lower boundary of abiochemical oxidation of oil should theoretically be the region where the solubility limit of sulfates in underground brines is reached.† In the virtual absence of flow and with virtually sulfate-free underground waters (brines) in the platform portions, it seems that such zones should generally not exist at all, because on platforms the disappearance of bacterial oxidation conditions coincides with the disappearance of conditions for the oxidation of petroleum in general. The development of an abiochemical zone may be expected only in deep geosynclinal basins where the waters can be relatively mobile, slightly mineralized, and contain an appreciable amount of sulfates even at depths of the order of 3 km. No results of oxidation of oil in the abiochemical zone are known at all.

A comparison of the above data for all of the zones leads to the conclusion that the conditions for petroleum oxidation grow progressively more unfavorable as each succeeding zone is reached, until they entirely disappear. Petroleum deposits exist under conditions characteristic of the anaerobic zones. In the course of positive (upward) tectonic oscillatory movements the oil deposit may traverse all of the zones, starting with the fourth one and terminating with the first, so that it is subjected each time to more severe oxidation conditions. Obviously the overwhelming majority of the presently existing commercial deposits of liquid petroleum never passed

† Theoretically, at still greater depths a fifth zone should exist in which there is no oil oxidation at all.

beyond the confines of anaerobic zones. Yet again, as follows from the above, the questions of conditions and products of oil oxidation in anaerobic zones are to a considerable extent open to discussion.

B. THERMODYNAMIC AND CHEMICAL DATA ON OXIDATION OF PETROLEUM IN NATURE

The interaction of any organic compounds with oxygen, including hydrocarbons, is a spontaneous process since it is accompanied by a very substantial decrease in the free energy level of the system. Thus, for example, the reaction of methane with oxygen to form carbon dioxide and water causes a reduction in the free energy of the system by 219.72 kcal/mol, and the oxidation of benzene to carbon dioxide and water lowers the free energy level of the system by 761.57 kcal/mol. Incomplete oxidation of hydrocarbons to aldehydes, ketones and acids is likewise accompanied by a substantial decrease in the free energy of the system.

Certain data reported by G. Parks and G. Huffman [1] on the change in free energy resulting from the introduction of oxygen into the organic molecule are cited in Table 19.

TABLE 19

Structural change	Change in free energy (kcal/mol)
Substitution of H by an OH group to form a primary monohydric alcohol	−34.0
Substitution of H by an OH group to form a secondary monohydric alcohol	−37.0
Substitution of H by an OH group to form a phenol	−41.0
Substitution of H by an OH group to form a poly-hydroxy compound	
(a) for a primary OH group	−34.0
(b) for a secondary OH group	−37.0
Introduction of an —O— linkage in the chain with the formation of an ether	−20.0
Substitution of 2H by oxygen to form an aldehyde	−20.0
Substitution of 2H by oxygen to form a ketone	−30.0
Substitution of H by a COOH group to form an acid	−83.2
Introduction of the —COO— group into the hydrocarbon chain to form an ester	−70.0

The large negative values of free energy change in oxidation reactions are evidence of the fact that such reactions proceed to completion, provided a sufficient amount of oxidizing agent is available.

This leads to the conclusion that the reactions inverse to oxidation, i.e. those involving the removal of oxygen from the oxidized molecule in the elemental state are non-conforming reactions and will not take place with influx of a high energy potential from the outside. On the other hand, the splitting off of oxygen in the form of water or carbon dioxide from the oxidized molecule with the formation of a hydrocarbon in certain cases may prove to be thermodynamically consistent because it will be accompanied by a reduction of free energy [1].

Hydrocarbon oxidation processes are irreversible processes and, once started, continue practically to completion until the available supplies of hydrocarbon or oxidizing agent have been exhausted. In comparison with the oxidation products, i.e. carbon dioxide and water, any organic substance is at higher free energy level and consequently the transition from the reduced to the oxidized state is a spontaneous process which does not demand any input of energy from the outside and moreover is accompanied by a large decrease in free energy level.

When there is not enough oxidant in the system or the oxidation process occurs under relatively mild conditions, a certain amount of the consumed oxygen will not be converted to carbon dioxide or water but remains in the fixed state, resulting in oxygenated organic compounds. The other portion of oxygen will be utilized for the formation of fully oxygenated compounds which are CO_2 and H_2O formed through conversions of oxygenated compounds originating in the initial stages. This course of the oxidation process indicates that it takes place in stages and that intermediate compounds are formed which tend to be unstable under the conditions of the process.

1. Mechanism and kinetics of oxidation processes

In the preceding section we established that oxidation processes are highly favored processes from the energy viewpoint, with a high degree of probability for their full completion. In this connection we are confronted with the question of how is it possible that, under actual conditions on the earth's surface, a great variety of organic compounds persist in large quantities for an extended period of time. Why is it that in the atmosphere, which contains 21% by volume of elementary oxygen, living organisms composed of organic compounds can exist?

Answers to these questions are provided by chemical kinetics.

Any chemical reaction depends essentially on the fact that as a result of interaction of initial molecules, a reconstruction of the system of bonds between atoms takes place. The old bonds disappear and are replaced by new ones. The quantity of initial atoms remains unchanged, but the number and arrangement of the bonds between atoms undergoes more or less of a change by virtue of the chemical reaction. It is known that the formation of each new bond is accompanied by liberation of energy, and the rupture of an existing one requires a consumption of energy. The chemical reaction would consequently proceed spontaneously only if the amount of energy necessary for breaking the bonds which existed before the reaction is less than the amount of energy liberated in the formation of new bonds.

Furthermore, if an outside source of energy at high potential is supplied to the previously existing system, i.e. if there is available a source of energy and a suitable mechanism for its transfer from the source to the system, then the system may experience reactions associated with reconstruction of the existing system of bonds in a manner such as to replace the previously existing bonds with new ones which are characterized by reduced values of disruption energy.

In the pertinent reactions of oxidation of organic compounds, at least three different processes may be distinguished.

1. Oxidation with molecular oxygen under conditions of exposure to daylight, i.e. at relatively low temperature and a partial oxygen pressure corresponding to its content in the air.

2. Oxidation with various substances capable of splitting off oxygen under definite conditions. In this case the oxidation will take place with atomic oxygen.

3. Biochemical oxidation with the oxygen available in compounds incapable of splitting off oxygen under ordinary conditions.

2. Oxidation with molecular oxygen (autoxidation)

The generally accepted current theory of oxidation by reaction with molecular oxygen is the peroxide theory evolved by A. N. Bakh [2] and K. Engler [3]. The status of this theory was significantly enhanced by N. N. Semenov's concept of chain reactions [4, 5].

The basis of this theory is the concept that the oxygen molecule reacts as a whole, without undergoing a preliminary splitting into atoms by complete rupture of the $O=O$ bond. Only one bond is broken and the free radical —O—O— is formed. From the chemical and thermochemical viewpoint the $O=O$ molecule does not display any biradical properties and appears highly stable. The rupture energy of two $O=O$ bonds in the oxygen molecule is equal to 117 kcal, while the rupture energy of one $O=O$ bond in the peroxide (H_2O_2) is about 50 kcal. The apparent ease with which O_2 enters certain reactions is not due to activity of the oxygen molecule as such, but to the characteristics of radical chain reactions, i.e. the properties of the O atom and —O—O— radical. When conditions for the development of a chain reaction are absent, the O_2 molecule proves to be completely inert. With hydrogen, the O_2 molecule reacts only in accordance with the chain mechanism, but the direct reaction of H_2 and O_2 molecules does not occur to any appreciable extent. The magnitude of the activation barrier of the direct reaction is at least 50 kcal, which is typical for reactions of conventional saturated molecules and which is higher by one order of magnitude than the activation energy of the reaction of radicals with saturated molecules.

According to N. N. Semenov [5], the relative ease of oxidation of complex hydrocarbons and other organic compounds (particularly in the liquid phase) at a temperature of about 100–150°C is due to primary chain generation processes.

$$RH + O=O \rightarrow R^{\cdot} + HO_2^{\cdot}.$$

Since in complex hydrocarbons the breaking away of an H atom requires considerably less energy than in the case of a hydrogen molecule (108 kcal) and frequently may be as low as 80–90 kcal, the activation energy of such reactions will probably be equal to about 40 kcal. With such activation energies the process would take place at low velocity even at temperatures close to room temperature.

At the present time it may be regarded as firmly established that free atoms and radicals are the main factors in the mechanism of chain reactions, including autoxidation reactions. Owing to their high activity, they easily participate in chemical interactions with saturated molecules, always generating new free atoms or radicals. Periodic regeneration of radicals during the process of chemical interaction constitutes the basis for the chain mechanism of reactions.

The free radical formed as a result of the reaction of an oxygen molecule with the hydrocarbon molecule reacts with another oxygen molecule to form secondary peroxide radicals

$$R^{\cdot} + O_2 \rightarrow ROO^{\cdot}.$$

The peroxide radical, in turn, on reacting with another hydrocarbon molecule, is converted to a peroxide and provides a new oxidation site

$$ROO^{\cdot} + R_1H \rightarrow ROOH + R_1^{\cdot}$$

thus contributing to the development of the oxidation chain.

It may be readily seen that with such an oxidation course even small amounts of activating energy are capable of converting substantial amounts of a hydrocarbon. In the case of thermal activation, only a small rise in temperatures would be sufficient to cause development of chain oxidation and give substantial results.

The oxidation of saturated hydrocarbons may be expressed by the following scheme.

1. Formation of an active site

$$RCH_2CH_3 + O_2 \rightarrow RC^{\cdot}HCH_3 - HO_2^{\cdot}.$$

2. Formation of a peroxide radical

$$R\,C^{\cdot}HCH_3 + O_2 \rightarrow (CH_3)-\overset{\displaystyle R}{\underset{\displaystyle |}{C}}H-O-O^{\cdot}.$$

3. Development of the chain with regeneration of the hydrocarbon radical

$$(CH_3)-\underset{\displaystyle R}{\underset{\displaystyle |}{C}}H-O-O^{\cdot} + RCH_2CH_3 \rightarrow (CH_3)-\underset{\displaystyle R}{\underset{\displaystyle |}{C}}H-O-O-H + RC^{\cdot}HCH_3$$

and so on.

The peroxide formed is unstable and may either undergo a breakdown with the formation of new free radicals of the type (CH_3)—CH—O· and OH· (degenerative branching) or it may react with another oxygen molecule to give bivalent peroxides which are extremely liable to undergo decomposition reactions with rupture of C—C bonds and the formation of an acid and a ketone

$$RCH_2CH_2\underset{\underset{\text{H}}{|}}{\overset{\overset{\text{CH}_3}{|}}{C}}—CH_3 + O_2 \rightarrow RCH_2CH_2—\underset{\underset{\text{OO—H}}{|}}{\overset{\overset{\text{CH}_3}{|}}{C}}—CH_3 + O_2 \rightarrow$$

$$\rightarrow RCH_2—\underset{\underset{\text{OOH}}{|}}{CH}—\underset{\underset{\text{OOH}}{|}}{\overset{\overset{\text{CH}_3}{|}}{C}}—CH_3 \rightarrow R—CH_2—\overset{\overset{\text{OH}}{\diagup}}{C}{=}O + (CH_2)_3C{=}O.$$

The most important idea in the theory of chain conversions is that as soon as a primary radical has appeared in a system that is capable of chemical conversion, it rapidly reacts with a molecule to generate a new radical which, reacting again, generates another radical. Thus alternating, these radicals readily create a long chain of conversions. This chain is broken only when free valency disappears, i.e. when two radicals from different chains upon collision will form a molecule by virtue of mutual saturation of valencies.

Since the concentration of radicals is low as compared with concentration of molecules and the reactive capacity is high, this as a rule favors reactions involving long chains of conversions.

The oxygen is incorporated into the hydrocarbon molecule in the majority of cases at the C—H bond rather than the C—C bond, though the energy of rupture of the C—H bond is greater than that of the C—C bond. The reason for this, as explained by N. N. Semenov [5], is that the C—C bonds are shielded from external influence by hydrogen atoms: to push apart these hydrogen atoms, the attacking molecules would expend so much extra energy that the overall effect of the process, despite the relative ease of rupturing the C—C bond, would be unfavorable and the process of C—H bond rupture would be more likely to take place.

According to data by K. I. Ivanov [6], the most vulnerable point for oxygen attack in normal paraffinic hydrocarbons is the secondary α-carbon atom and in isoparaffinic hydrocarbons the tertiary carbon atom followed by the secondary α-carbon atom. In naphthenic hydrocarbons having aliphatic substituents the oxygen is added at the C—H bond of the tertiary ring carbon atom linked to the side chain. In aliphatic-aromatic hydrocarbons the C—H bond is ruptured at the secondary carbon atom linked to the aromatic radical. Naphthenic-aromatic hydrocarbons are subject to attack by the oxygen molecule at the carbon atom of the naphthenic ring closest to the aromatic nucleus. It is remarkable that in olefins the first bond to react is not the double bond C=C, but the C—H bond of the carbon atom situated in direct proximity to the double bond.

The nature of products formed in oxidation depends much on the structure of the initial hydrocarbons molecule.

A common feature for hydrocarbons of all types is the presence of compounds such as CO_2, H_2O, CO, and formic and acetic acids among the oxidation products, indicating a profound oxidative decomposition of the initial hydrocarbon molecules. In addition, more complex products were likewise found in the oxidation products of hydrocarbons of different types.

The Bakh–Engler peroxide theory of autoxidation has been generally accepted, but not immediately after its publication and only after a prolonged and involved struggle against other opinions about oxidation processes.

Among the rejected and erroneous opinions, Wieland's dehydrogenation theory of autoxidation is worthy of mention [7]. In accordance with this theory, the cause of autoxidation is not activation of oxygen but decrease in the strength of the C—H bond in the molecule of organic substance as a result of action of oxygen or catalyst. The decrease in C—H bond strength is so great that it leads to complete breaking away of hydrogen atoms from the molecule with the formation of an unsaturated compound. The role of oxygen is limited to taking hydrogen away from and regenerating the catalyst. The mechanism of oxygen action, according to Wieland, may be twofold. In the first case the oxygen molecule, being an unsaturated molecule, is added to the organic bond formed. In the other case the oxygen combines with the hydrogen atoms.

Wieland himself realized that this theory does not provide a complete explanation of the mechanism involved in oxidation processes.

The point is that Wieland's dehydrogenation theory was used as a basis for certain erroneous concepts which formed the foundation of the hypothesis of the oxidative cyclization of paraffinic hydrocarbons [8]. According to this hypothesis, oxidation of paraffinic hydrocarbons is accompanied by the formation of unsaturated hydrocarbons of the ethylenic series. These unsaturated hydrocarbons, in turn, undergo spontaneous rearrangement with the formation of cyclic compounds, i.e. naphthenes

$$R-(CH_2)_4-CH_2-CH_3 + \tfrac{1}{2}O_2 \rightarrow$$

$$\rightarrow R-(CH_2)_4-CH=CH_2 \rightarrow \begin{array}{c} CH_2 \\ \diagup \diagdown \\ H_2C \quad CH-R \\ | \qquad | \\ H_2C \quad CH_2 \\ \diagdown \diagup \\ CH_2 \end{array} + H_2O$$

Thus, as a result of oxidation, the saturated aliphatic hydrocarbons are supposed to be converted to products which include naphthenes. Oxidative dehydrogenation of the latter leads to the formation of aromatic hydrocarbons.

Experimental data on the autoxidation of saturated and unsaturated compounds furnished no confirmation of Wieland's theory. In every instance, the formation of unsaturated and cyclic compounds was not noted, but the formation of peroxides was observed.

In this connection, considerations relating to oxidative cyclization of saturated aliphatic hydrocarbons carry hardly any conviction because they are based on the supposition that unsaturated compounds are formed as intermediates in the oxidation of saturated aliphatic hydrocarbons; this has not been proved by experiments and belongs in the realm of speculation.

Hydrocarbon oxidation rates have been studied on many occasions under the most diversified conditions. The initial stage of the oxidation under controlled moderate temperature conditions is characterized by absence of visible changes in the system, though the absorption of oxygen is well defined. The duration of this stage greatly varies for different systems of hydrocarbons. In this respect an important factor is the external conditions under which the process is conducted. An increase in temperature, as well as an increase in partial pressure of oxygen, serve to reduce the induction period. A very important factor is the presence of catalytically active substances in the system, including those present in the system from the start. Very important also is the degree of purity of the hydrocarbons. It has been repeatedly demonstrated [9, 10] that resinous substances act as antioxidants. The mechanism of such inhibitory action of resinous substances is still largely obscure. In general, it seems probable that resinous substances (especially the heterocyclic compounds in the resins) are preferentially attacked by oxygen, thus protecting the main body of hydrocarbons against oxidation. Apparently, the increased size of the molecule and the presence of hetero atoms in it causes a decrease in the activation energy of the oxidation reaction. This by no means excludes the possibility of explaining the protective action of resinous substances in a manner similar to the theory of antioxidant action of polyhydric phenols proposed by Mouren and Dufreisse [11, 12], because there are reasons to believe that phenolic hydroxyl groups may be present in the molecules of resinous substances.

At the conclusion of the induction period the interaction of hydrocarbon molecules with hydrogen proceeds at an accelerated rate. This stage of the process is accompanied by liberation of heat and intensive formation of peroxides. The simultaneous breakdown of peroxides and further oxidation of the breakdown products causes a rise in acidity and saponification number.

In the third stage of the process varying amounts of condensation products, which are insoluble in the main body of hydrocarbons, are formed; the quantity of such products depends on the type of hydrocarbons originally present. The process gradually slows down and its exothermic effect is superseded by an endothermic one, resulting in a slower formation rate of primary oxidation products and retardation of the process as a whole. This stage of oxidation involves the formation of the bulk of low molecular-weight acids through splitting of the previously formed higher molecular-weight oxidation products.

The kinetics of hydrocarbon oxidation in the presence of resinous substances is likewise characterized by an induction period, a vigorous reaction period, and an attenuation of the latter with time. In this case, according to data by A. N. Sakhanov and N. A. Vasil'ev [13], the oxidation proceeds in a manner such that at first oxygen reacts with aromatic hydrocarbons and sulfur compounds to convert them into resinous substances which undergo oxidative condensation to form asphaltenes. Further oxidative consolidation of asphaltenes leads to the formation of insoluble carbonized products—the carbenes. As time goes on, the hydrocarbon oxidation reaction tends towards accumulation of drastic polycondensation products, i.e. carbenes and carboids. Along with them, the amount of volatile oxidation products likewise increases, as shown by the decrease in amount of residue after oxidation. With rise in temperature the velocity of oxidation processes greatly increases, and progressively more carbenes and carboids are accumulated in the precipitates, being the condensation products of asphaltenes and hydroxy acids. The nature of products resulting from oxidation is a function of composition and structure of the initial system of hydrocarbons.

Let us discuss the oxidation processes and the composition of oxidation products for the different series of hydrocarbons.

(a) Saturated aliphatic hydrocarbons

The saturated aliphatic hydrocarbons are fairly inert to the action of oxidizing agents at moderate temperatures. Even strong oxidants such as nitric and chromic acids or permanganate practically do not attack the saturated aliphatic hydrocarbons at room temperature. Molecular oxygen behaves in a similar manner towards these hydrocarbons.

Nevertheless even a relatively slight rise in temperature sharply activates the paraffin molecule and renders it capable of profound oxidation processes.

Most of the published papers dealing with the oxidation of low molecular-weight saturated aliphatic hydrocarbons are restricted to vapor phase oxidation processes and, vice versa, the oxidation of high molecular-weight aliphatics has been investigated chiefly in the liquid phase. Considering that with greater complexity of the molecule the strength of C—C and C—H bonds diminishes, it is apparent that the data on oxidation of high molecular-weight paraffins, obtained for liquid phase oxidation, cannot strictly be applied to low molecular-weight hydrocarbons without the use of substantial corrections which would make allowance for the fact that the latter are oxidized in the liquid phase at reduced rates and may prove to be appreciably more stable than hydrocarbons of other types.

A. N. Bashkirov and Ya. B. Chertkov [14] have established with the oxidation of n-octadecane and n-tridecane as examples, that the oxidation process in the presence of catalysts takes place with the formation of oxygenated compounds containing a small number of carbon atoms in the molecule. They state that the cleaving of carbon atoms from the initial molecule occurs in a series of steps. On the other hand, in other papers it is demonstrated that the splitting of the paraffin hydrocarbon molecule proceeds not only along the bond at the terminal carbon atom, but predominantly in the middle of the chain with the formation of acids containing an appreciably smaller number of carbon atoms in the molecule, than the initial hydrocarbon [15, 16].

The primary products of the oxidation of saturated aliphatic hydrocarbons are hydroperoxides. Further action of the oxidizing agent is directed principally upon such hydroperoxides to form divalent peroxide groups in a single molecule. The instability of the hydrocarbon molecule burdened by peroxide groups leads to its rapid decomposition with rupture of the carbon bond and the formation of oxidized products having a smaller number of carbon atoms. The oxidation products were found to contain in addition to carbon dioxide and water, acids, alcohols, aldehydes, ketones, hydroxy acids, etc. It is worthy of note that oxidative condensation products, i.e. resins and asphaltenes, are formed in minimum amounts.

Saturated aliphatic hydrocarbons having a branched chain of carbon atoms are generally more readily oxidized than hydrocarbons having a tertiary carbon atom. On the other hand, hydrocarbons having a quaternary carbon atom are unusually resistant to oxidation, a fact which must be particularly borne in mind in discussing the processes of petroleum oxidation under natural conditions. A study of the oxidation of saturated aliphatic hydrocarbons of normal and iso structures, conducted by S. E. Krein [17] has shown that oxygen absorption by hydrocarbons and the quantity of free and combined acidic products in the oxidized compounds rise with increase in the number of side chains in the molecule. Furthermore, the tendency to oxidation increases with increase in the number of side chains, rather than with the number of chains in general or their length. There is no exact proportionality between the number of side chains and the oxidation tendency of hydrocarbons. The greater the number of side chains, the greater the deviation from proportionality towards higher values.

Based on research by S.E. Krein [18] and A.D. Petrov [19] it may be concluded that stability of hydrocarbons varies with the position of the quaternary hydrocarbon atom in the chain. The highest stability against oxidation is shown by hydrocarbons in which the quaternary carbon atom is at the end of the chain.

It is easily seen that the development of oxidation processes in a system of saturated aliphatic hydrocarbons will lead chiefly to disappearance of branched chain compounds from the mixture and accumulation of saturated aliphatic hydrocarbons of normal structure in the residue. At the same time, other conditions being equal, oxidation will occur initially in the relatively high molecular-weight portion of the saturated aliphatic hydrocarbons having predominantly a branched structure.

Thus we have shown, by the evidence cited above, the incompetence of the hypothesis of oxidative cyclization of saturated aliphatic hydrocarbons. As additional proof of this conclusion may be cited the fact that if the system contains only saturated aliphatic hydrocarbons, no appreciable tar formation is noted in oxidation. The latter would have been very substantial, as discussed further herein below, if the oxidation of paraffins were accompanied by formation of cycloparaffins, because cyclic hydrocarbons and primarily the aromatics are precisely the cause of tar formation during oxidation.

(b) Naphthenic hydrocarbons

Unsubstituted naphthenes react with oxygen to form initially peroxide compounds. According to data of N.I. Chernozhukov and S.E. Krein [20], treatment of cyclohexane in the liquid phase with oxygen at a temperature of 81 °C and 15 atm pressure for a period of 6 hr resulted in oxidation of 3.6% of the initial material. Among the oxidation products were found free and combined acids and resinous substances. Under approximately, the same conditions, methylcyclohexane was 13.7% oxidized to form a substantial amount of acids, including volatile acids, and also 3.6% resinous substances.

Introduction of an alkyl radical into the cyclohexane molecule increases the tendency to oxidation; substituted naphthenes are more rapidly and profoundly oxidized than unsubstituted ones. Still more readily oxidizable are naphthenes having fused rings. Thus, for example, decalin at 150 °C over a period of 3 hr gives 32.2 % of oxidation products containing free and combined acids, hydroxy acids, neutral oxygenated compounds, and ether-soluble resinous substances. The oxidation of decalin causes principally cleavage of polymethylene rings with the formation of relatively low molecular-weight products. At the same time, there is noted a negligible amount of partial dehydrogenation of the naphthene rings with the formation of phenols. No aromatic hydrocarbons have been found among the oxidation products of naphthenes. The tendency to dehydrogenation in oxidation increases with rise in the number of condensed rings in the molecule of naphthenic hydrocarbon. The condensation products obtained in oxidation of decalin appear to be chiefly substances resulting from condensation of the primary oxidation products, principally hydroxy acids.

In reactions of substituted naphthenes the ring rupture occurs predominantly at the point of attachment of side chains. The major factor responsible for reducing the resistance of polymethylene rings is attributed to alkyl radicals. The closer the substituents are to one another, the lower the resistance of the polymethylene ring [21]. A. E. Favorskii [22] has established that when two substituents are present on the same carbon atom in the polymethylene ring, the compound proves to be very unstable and susceptible to ring rupture.

The role of substituents in the molecule of a naphthenic hydrocarbon is limited to their effect on the resistance of the ring. Depending on the nature of the substituent (chain length, normal or iso structure), the stability of the ring may vary to a greater or lesser extent. The greater the bond strength of the tertiary carbon atom with the substituent radical, the lower the strength of the ring and the greater the ease with which it will break down on oxidation.

With rise in temperature of the oxidation process, a progressively larger amount of oxygen is used up for the formation of more severe oxidation products and the quantity of low molecular-weight acid products is correspondingly reduced.

Naphthenic hydrocarbons separated from lubricating oil fractions of petroleum, according to data by N. I. Chernozhukov and S. E. Krein [20], proved to have the same capacity to oxidation as the individual naphthenes. It was also demonstrated that removal of solid hydrocarbons from naphthenic-paraffinic fractions by the adsorption method and subsequent oxidation of the resulting relatively pure naphthenic hydrocarbons gives results which are essentially similar to those previously obtained with naphthenic-paraffinic hydrocarbon fractions.

These data serve as a basis for the conclusion that with respect to their tendency to oxidation, the paraffin hydrocarbons, including the high molecular-weight varieties, possess no advantage over naphthenes and that the oxidation of mixtures of such hydrocarbons proceeds in the same way as the oxidation of individual compounds.

The oxidation of naphthenic hydrocarbons occurs principally at the point where the side chain is attached or at the contact site of the rings in condensed systems. This course of the process may be explained by greater tendency of the tertiary carbon atom to oxidation, as readily illustrated in the particular case when tertiary atoms are present in the ring or the side chain.

The principal products resulting from oxidation of naphthenes in a layer of substantial thickness at moderate temperatures consist of acids and hydroxy acids. Oxidative condensation products, mainly resins and a negligible amount of asphaltenes, are formed under these conditions as a consequence of secondary condensation processes from ketones, hydroxy acids, etc. The quantity of condensation products is not large as compared with that of the acidic portion.

(c) Aromatic hydrocarbons

A paramount influence on the processes of oxidation of aromatic hydrocarbons and on the nature of resulting products is exerted by the presence of alkyl side chains and their structural features.

Unsubstituted aromatic hydrocarbons. Under ordinary conditions of temperature and oxygen pressure the unsubstituted hydrocarbons are resistant to oxidizing action, benzene being the most difficult to oxidize. With increase in number of rings in the complex molecule, its tendency to oxidation rises. According to data of N. I. Chernozhukov and S. E. Krein [20], anthracene is the most readily oxidizable in the series benzene → naphthalene → phenanthrene → anthracene. At 250°C and 15 atm air pressure for a period of 6 hr, anthracene was oxidized to the extent of 24.6% compared with

13.4% of phenanthrene. On the other hand, naphthalene remained entirely unchanged after 3 hr at a temperature of 150°C and 15 atm air pressure. Anthracene has a higher tendency to oxidation presumably because one of its nuclei is, in effect, non-aromatic. The action of oxygen on such hydrocarbons is directed chiefly toward the C—H bonds with the formation of miscellaneous condensation products. Acid products resulting from rupture of C—C bonds are formed in minor amount. For example, in the oxidation of anthracene 7 times as much condensation products as acid products are formed, and 8 times as much in the case of phenanthrene. The acidic portion of the products consists of high molecular-weight phenols. The saponifiable portion contains reaction products of phenols with acids, and a substantial portion comprises neutral oxygenated products which during analysis are accounted for partly as resins and partly as "unsaponifiable" matter.

Alkylsubstituted aromatic hydrocarbons. The introduction of an alkyl radical into the aromatic nucleus brings a substantial increase in the oxidation tendency of the molecule. Benzene underwent no appreciable change in oxidation experiments conducted at 210°C by Schrader [23], whereas toluene under the same conditions gave appreciable amounts of oxidation products.

The oxidation tendency of aromatic hydrocarbons rises with increase in number of side chains [24], as indicated by quantities of acids formed as oxidation products of various aromatics:

Hydrocarbon	Accumulation of acids, %
Benzene	0
Toluene	12.0
o-Xylene	25.5
m-Xylene	31.0
p-Xylene	37.0
p-Cymene	25.0
Mesitylene	56.7
Ethylbenzene	43.0

In the oxidation of alkylaromatic hydrocarbons, the first structures subject to oxidation are aliphatic side chains. This is fully consistent with data on the amount of energy required for rupturing the C—C and C—H bonds in aromatic and saturated aliphatic hydrocarbons.

The chain length of the substituent radical is an important factor. The longer the aliphatic chain, the greater the ease with which the hydrocarbon is oxidized. Moreover, with increasing length of the alkyl chain, there is a rise in the content of acids in the reaction products while the quantity of condensation products (resins) diminishes quite sharply. Available data [20] show that in the oxidation of propylbenzene 3 % resins are formed, whereas oxidation of decylbenzene leads to formation of mere traces of resinous substances. These observations are explained by the authors who suggest that primary oxidation of side chains produce exclusively acid products having no tendency to condensation. After the entire reserves of aliphatic groups have been used up, the action of oxygen is directed against the aromatic nucleus. The formation of resins occurs chiefly via the action of oxygen upon the C—H bond in the aromatic nucleus to give phenols and polyphenols which are very prone to undergo subsequent condensation processes with the formation of resinous substances.

An investigation of the kinetics of oxidizing aromatic and alkylaromatic compounds has demonstrated that the increase in yield of oxidation products is not directly proportional to temperature but tends to approach a certain limit. The reason is that the autoxidation process in the case of hydrocarbons is also a negative autocatalytic process because some of the oxidation products (resins, phenols, etc.) inhibit further oxidation.

Naphthenic-aromatic hydrocarbons have a strong tendency to oxidation reactions. The addition of oxygen to tetralin occurs at the naphthenic rather than at the aromatic nucleus with the formation of hydroperoxide, rupture of the naphthenic ring, and formation of o-carboxylic acid.

In the oxidation of tetralin the process is directed not only toward formation of acid products, but also toward formation of condensation products. In regard to type of products formed in oxidation, the naphthenic-aromatic compounds occupy an intermediate position between unsubstituted aromatic compounds and naphthenes. Their aromatic nature is evidenced by the greater tendency of such hydrocarbons to give condensation products as a result of oxidative condensation, and their naphthenic nature is manifested by an equally high tendency to form acid products.

In the oxidation process the polymethylene rings are partially broken and oxidized with the formation of acid products. The aromatic rings, as well as various primary oxidation products of the polymethylene nuclei, undergo condensation to form resins and asphaltenes.

An increased complexity of the molecule, asymmetry of its structure, and the presence of a tertiary carbon atom all contribute to reducing the resistance of the compound to oxidative action.

The oxidation of narrow fractions of aromatic hydrocarbons separated from different crudes has shown [20] that, with rise in boiling point of the fraction, all of the aromatic hydrocarbons, regardless of their origin, are progressively more liable to oxidation reactions. On the basis of a study of oxidation processes, the authors feel justified in formulating conclusions on the structure of initial fractions of petroleum to the effect that aromatic fractions from Balakhany crude oil range in first place with respect to development of side chains, followed by hydrocarbons from Grozny non-paraffinic crude and finally by hydrocarbons from Grozny paraffinic crude.

(d) Oxidation of mixtures of hydrocarbons

On the basis of their own research and an analysis of references from the literature, N. I. Chernozhukov and S. E. Krein [20] arrived at the conclusion that in the oxidation of mixtures of unsubstituted aromatic hydrocarbons and naphthenes, the oxidizability of the latter is reduced. The aromatic hydrocarbons as such participate in oxidation processes and their content in the mixture diminishes after oxidation. In contrast, naphthenic hydrocarbons induce the oxidation of aromatics. A sort of averaging of the oxidation tendency of aromatic and naphthenic hydrocarbons takes place when they are co-present in the mixture being oxidized. An important point is that aromatic hydrocarbons, when present in a mixture together with naphthenes, are oxidized more readily than the naphthenes themselves. The effectiveness of the antioxidant action of aromatic hydrocarbons with respect to naphthenes increases at a rate which is not quite proportional to the rise in their concentration, but lags slightly behind it.

In the oxidation of mixtures of naphthenic hydrocarbons and aromatics having side chains, it was found that the latter in low concentrations practically do not reduce the oxidizability of naphthenic hydrocarbons and in certain cases even increase the total percentage of oxidation products. Upon increase in concentration of alkylaromatics to 20–30% or more, a substantial increase in inhibiting effect is noted. In the oxidation of such mixtures the acidity is low and precipitates are formed. Resin formation is likewise diminished. Naphthalene homologs are more effective as inhibitors in the autoxidation of alkylated naphthenes than are benzene homologs.

Oxidation of mixtures of naphthenes and naphthenic-aromatic hydrocarbons has shown that the formation of acid products and resins is sharply reduced in comparison with those in the oxidation of naphthenes alone and that a certain quantity of precipitates are present, which were not obtained in the oxidation of naphthenes. The precipitates formed in the oxidation of such mixtures consist chiefly of asphaltenes and hydroxy acids, or asphaltenes and more complex products of oxidative condensation.

Mixtures of naphthenic hydrocarbons with paraffins and isoparaffins are oxidized essentially by the additive rule for the components of the mixture. Mixtures of naphthenic, paraffinic, and isoparaffinic hydrocarbons with aromatic hydrocarbons having long chains and present in low concentrations (up to 10–20%) in the mixture are oxidized practically the same way as in the absence of aromatics. Unsubstituted aromatic hydrocarbons and hydrocarbons of the di- and tri-phenylmethane type, if present together with naphthenes and paraffins, sharply inhibit oxidation of the latter. Aromatic hydrocarbons having alkyl side chains inhibit the oxidation of naphthenic and paraffinic hydrocarbons only in concentrations of 20% and higher. Naphthenic-aromatic hydrocarbons such as tetralin and octahydroanthracene reduce the oxidation of naphthenic and paraffinic hydrocarbons as far as the formation of acid products and resins is concerned and, on the contrary, they favor the formation of appreciable amounts of severe condensation products. It is assumed that the antioxidant action of aromatic hydrocarbons depends essentially on the formation of phenols, naphthols, etc. It has been demonstrated also that the naphthenic-paraffinic hydrocarbon fractions recovered from the oils of different crudes are close to each other with respect to susceptibility to the action of aromatic hydrocarbons, which is a confirmation of the established relationships.

In concluding this review of the available literature references pertaining to oxidizability of different types of hydrocarbons and their mixtures, it may be stated that all hydrocarbons to a greater or lesser extent are subject to the oxidizing action of molecular oxygen. The highest tendency to oxidation processes is manifested not by high molecular-weight paraffins, as has been noted for some reason in certain papers, but by naphthenic-aromatic hydrocarbons. An increased tendency to oxidation is specific for all hydrocarbons containing a tertiary carbon atom in their structure. Compounds of symmetrical structure of all series are resistant with respect to oxidizing action. Depending on the structure of their carbon skeleton and the bonding energies between carbon atoms, the different types of hydrocarbons tend to form different products as a result of oxidation processes. A tendency to form resinous products is characteristic for hydrocarbons having strong C—C bonds and relatively less stable C—H bonds, as, for example, aromatic hydrocarbons.

Corresponding to the magnitude of the energy required for bond rupture, the oxidizing action in the case of saturated aliphatic hydrocarbons is directed in the long run to the C—C bonds, followed by rupture of the bonds and the formation of acid products. Condensation products are formed in negligible amount because the processes involve oxidative disaggregation of the initial molecule having unstable C—C bonds. On the contrary, for the aromatic molecule with its characteristic relatively weak C—H bond, the attack by the oxygen molecule is indeed directed toward the C—H bond and finally causes its rupture, thus creating the possibility for the development of aggregation processes by virtue of newly formed C—C bonds instead of the formerly existing C—H bonds.

The aggregation and disaggregation processes under reducing conditions from the thermodynamic viewpoint have been discussed previously. At that time we came to the conclusion that aggregation processes are characteristic for compounds of the aromatic series and that disaggregation processes are typical for compounds of the saturated aliphatic series. For naphthenes, however, both paths of development are possible. In the first-mentioned case, the aggregation process of aromatic compounds has as its basis the process of lowering the free energy level of the system through reduction of the magnitude of the heat content (enthalpy) of the system, which exceeds the rise in free energy through reduction of entropy in the aggregation process. For disaggregation processes, particularly in the case of saturated aliphatic hydrocarbons, both the enthalpy and the entropy factors operate in the same direction, towards reducing the free energy level of the system. The replacement of the C—C bond of the saturated aliphatic hydrocarbon by the C—H bond causes a liberation of energy, while at the same time the splitting of the initial molecule into two smaller ones results in an increase in the energy of the system, thus lowering still further the free energy level of the initial system.

On examining the oxidation processes as a whole, it is readily realized that the mechanism of the action of oxygen on the different types of hydrocarbons, from the viewpoint of thermodynamics, boils down to simplifying and accelerating the regular processes of reducing the free energy level. This accelerating action is based on the fact that the process of interaction between oxygen and the hydrocarbon molecule has lower (as compared to those in processes in a reducing medium) values of activation energy, which tends to accelerate the processes of C—C bond rupture in the case of saturated aliphatic hydrocarbons and C—H bond rupture in the case of aromatics. The CO_2 and H_2O molecules formed along with the others are effective in further lowering the energy level of the reacting system. The change in molecules will proceed in the same regular direction as for transformations under reducing conditions: saturated aliphatic molecules will tend to disaggregate and aromatics to aggregate. All of these processes will of course take place only if the external conditions (elevated temperature, high partial pressures and excess of oxygen) do not give rise to more drastic processes resulting in replacement of all C—C and C—H bonds in the organic molecule by C—O and H—O bonds, i.e. to formation of carbon dioxide and water. Molecular oxygen under moderate conditions of temperature, pressure and concentration acts as a catalyst stimulating the processes of disproportionation of the elements of the hydrocarbon system. These processes in the case of some molecules result in disaggregation of the initial system of C—C bonds and with other molecules, on the contrary, cause an aggregation of the system of C—C bonds.

Oxygen acts as a hydrogen acceptor in aggregation processes and as a structural breakdown agent in processes of disaggregation of organic molecules. These contrary processes of aggregation and disaggregation occur in a reducing environment, but at a slower rate owing to relatively high activation energies. Oxygen is a unique initiator of mass disproportionation processes, not unlike the initiators of chain polymerization processes. In small quantities and under relatively mild conditions the oxygen mobilizes only the interior opportunities of the system with respect to disproportionation processes. The consumption of oxygen in the process takes place predominantly by way of its combining with the low molecular-weight portion of the reaction products, and only a minor part of reacted oxygen is combined with high molecular-weight substances which are the other terminal members of the overall process. The more drastic the process conditions, the smaller is the portion of oxygen that combines with them.

Complete oxidation to carbon dioxide and water represents the ultimate case of disproportionation of the hydrocarbon molecule. All of the previously existing C—C and C—H bonds are broken, with the carbon atoms concentrating in the form of CO_2 at one pole and the hydrogen atoms at the other pole. The difference from disproportionation processes in a reducing medium lies in that disproportionation processes in the oxidizing medium are complicated by interaction of oxygen with low molecular-weight fragments of saturated aliphatic hydrocarbon molecules to form oxygenated products including acids, alcohols, aldehydes and ketones, which, of course, does not occur in a reducing medium. In the latter case the fragments of the saturated aliphatic hydrocarbon molecule are saturated by hydrogen split from aromatic hydrocarbon molecules.

3. Effect of external conditions on the course of oxidation processes

The experimental data discussed above pertained to oxidation of hydrocarbons with molecular oxygen at relatively low temperature and various partial pressures. These processes take place when petroleum encounters conditions close to those existing in the surface zone of the earth's crust. Such cases are relatively infrequent and may be pertinent only in the solution of problems relating to investigations of petroleum occurrences, carried out for the purpose of prospecting.

Of more direct significance to the problem of petroleum transformation under natural conditions are the hypothetical processes of petroleum oxidation in subterranean deposits. The reality of such processes is recognized by some researchers and rejected by others. The reasoning used by supporters of subterranean oxidation of petroleum is based principally on an erroneous interpretation of the characteristic composition of petroleum. It is granted that the presence of asphaltic and resinous substances in petroleum, as well as the higher specific gravity associated therewith and the low content of light fractions, are indications of underground oxidation processes which have occurred (or are occurring). Additional reasons cited in support of the existence of subterranean oxidation processes are data on the presence of microflora in the depths of some petroleum deposits and hydrogeological considerations about the "degree of exposure" of the petroleum deposit. In most of the case the latter argument cannot be proved owing to difficulties in solving the problems of migration of underground waters and complete lack of knowledge as to the scope of this process under natural conditions.

The considerations against the possibility of subterranean anaerobic oxidation of petroleum by atmospheric oxygen dissolved in underground waters in the majority of known deposits were formulated by A. F. Dobryanskii [26], and at the present time the probability of such a process of petroleum oxidation in nature may be regarded as being of no practical significance. A. F. Dobryanskii's arguments quoted above may be amplified by some very recent data relating particularly to the discovery of petroleum deposits in which the oil is in contact with slightly mineralized waters very probably of surface origin, and yet the oil shows no traces of oxidation. There are still other facts at hand, but they are hardly capable of adding anything to A. F. Dobryanskii's framework of evidence against the possibility of subterranean aerobic oxidation.

In the realm of organic chemistry many different substances are known to have an oxidizing action on hydrocarbons under certain conditions, for example, higher oxides of lead, manganese and chromium, hydrogen peroxide, and others. However, in spite of their fairly high activity under certain conditions, such oxidants for obvious reasons cannot be taken into consideration in processes of petroleum alteration in nature.

The supporters of oxidative transformations of petroleum in nature have put forward a new and, in their opinion, an actually existing process of anaerobic oxidation of petroleum in subsurface environments which involves the combined oxygen in certain salts of sulfuric and nitric acids. An indispensable ingredient for these processes is supposed to be the activity of certain specific micro-organisms at the oil-water contact in the reservoir.

Let us discuss this variant of the oxidation hypothesis [27, 28] in some detail. This appears necessary and timely because of the recent tendency to resort to microbiological mechanisms in explaining quite a number of obscure problems in the geochemistry of petroleum. This type of approach to the subject furnished interesting possibilities. It turned out that a number of complex, still obscure and often contradictory phenomena and facts may be explained in a very simple way. You need merely cite the microbial factor. This is done, for instance, by certain authors in explaining the cyclization of petroleum at higher levels in the section [28]. Some converse relationships encountered in nature are likewise explained by the microbial factor. An expression of such ideas in their highly categorical form can be found in A. L. Kozlov's articles [27, 29].

A reader who is not too familiar with the fine points of organic chemistry, microbiology, and geochemistry may find these articles quite reliable and convincing. True, microbes are generally known to exist, so why should they not take care of converting the types of petroleum present in nature. All the more since the chemistry of microbiological processes is largely unknown and many new discoveries may be expected in microbiology. Such an approach to the subject allows one to avoid complex experimental research and merely to wait for new discoveries in the field of microbiology. The unknown is explained by the unknown.

Let us discuss, on the basis of established facts, the reasoning put forth by supporters of the hypothesis of microbial oxidation of petroleum under subsurface conditions. The backers of this hypothesis accept as indisputable truth the presence of sulfate-reducing bacteria in the oil-bearing formation. Some of them render this stipulation more precise and state that the habitat of the microflora is the oil–water contact surface. Usually, the research by T. L. Ginzburg-Karagicheva [30] is cited.

How much documentary value does this research have as an item of scientific evidence? From the viewpoint of procedure in recovering the microbiological samples it appears very convincing. Every possible precaution was taken to prevent contamination of samples by microflora from the outside. T. L. Ginzburg-Karagicheva had sterilized even the string on which the sterile flask for recovery of liquid was lowered from the surface into the opened well. With such magic manipulations forming part of this study, one important factor was overlooked: namely, that before recovering the sample of water or oil it is first necessary to drill the well and that the conditions in drilling oil wells are known to be far from sterile. The introduction of microflora from the surface into the well being drilled may be regarded as a certainty. Moreover, the microorganisms recovered from samples of drilling waters proved to be strikingly similar to those existing at the surface.

Sulfate-reducing bacteria are capable of existing within a fairly wide range of temperatures and water salinities, and any possible substantial differences in the rate of reduction of sulfates between microbes originating on the surface and "underground" are of no consequence. The well is not drilled within a single day, and the microorganisms introduced from the surface have enough time for adapting themselves to the new, gradually changing conditions. The adaptability of microorganisms to external conditions of habitation is a well-known fact in microbiology. There have been reports that samples taken from different wells in the same oil field showed different results. In samples taken from some wells the microspira† is absent, but it occurs in others. This fact is cited as proof that microflora could not be introduced from the surface when drilling the well. However, no allowance is made for the history of the well before the instant of taking the water and oil samples from it. A case can be easily visualized, where a well reaching the crest has been flowing clean oil. The stream of water-free oil sterilized the entire pipeline system in the oil field. Naturally, even if the well would be producing water afterward, the microbiologist will fail to find the microspira in a sample of the emulsified oil. A case of this sort may be regarded rather as evidence that the earth formations are sterile. On the other hand, a well that has been sunk into the oil–water contact zone will always show the presence of microflora in the oil–water mixture. This would be the microflora entrained from the surface and which, possibly, had adapted itself to some extent to the new living conditions and spread along the oil–water interface.

Thus the documentary value of experiments with the separation

† Microspira *(Microspira desulfuricars)* is an archaic synonym for **Desulfovibrio desulfuricans**, the accepted designation for sufate-reducing bacteria. [Transl. Ed.]

of microflora from borehole waters of oil wells is extremely limited. No direct proof of the existence of microflora in the body of petroleum deposits is available as yet.

The microflora in petroleum deposits, prior to human intervention, cannot exist for the following additional reasons. In the literature, two different explanations are given for the presence of microflora at the contact between oil and water. According to the first one, the microflora is regarded as being a relict form which has survived until the present from the time of deposition of the sediment. Another opinion holds that microflora is carried into the depths of petroleum formations together with surface waters.

These are very few who are in favor of the first explanation. It is obviously erroneous. In order to live and develop, the microspira needs sulfates and a source of organic carbon, nitrogen and phosphorus. The reservoir rocks contain almost no organic material at all before the arrival of petroleum from pelites. Even when sulfates are present, the absence of organic material would result in rapid disappearance of microflora in sandstones or carbonate rocks. It must be borne in mind that sulfate-reducing bacteria do not produce spore forms and consequently would be unable to exist until the present time in a state of anabiosis [31]. Furthermore, based on the teachings of the development of organic life, it is difficult to visualize how the microspiras could have gotten along from Devonian to our present times without a change. Anyway, no direct proof is available for the absence of evolutionary development of microorganisms.

As to the possibility of the microflora being carried into the sites of petroleum deposits by surface waters, such a viewpoint appears to be quite probable at first glance. Yet, it, too, turns out to be in direct contradiction with the facts.

To begin with, by no means is every petroleum deposit in communication with the earth's surface. On the contrary, the overwhelming majority of petroleum deposits are characterized by the stagnant state of the waters or are located in a zone of hindered water exchange [32]. The rate at which sulfates are introduced with the waters into the oil–water contact zone is quite comparable with the rate of oxygen supply, as discussed above. The microspira, whose habitat is the oil–water interface, clearly will not have enough sulfates for any appreciable oxidizing action upon the petroleum. It is known that with closer approach to a petroleum deposit the sulfate content in subsurface waters progressively decreases. The waters in petroleum deposits as a rule do not contain any sulfates. This fact was proposed for use as an indication in prospecting for oil [33].

The microspira which reached the water–oil contact surface must perish because of lack of oxygen. Actually, death will occur much sooner. The surface waters carrying sulfates and microflora require a long period of time to reach the petroleum deposit. To reach oil-bearing formations at an average depth of 1000 m, for example in the Northern Caucasus, the surface waters have to travel along a path at least 1500 m long. Even if the propagation rate of the intruding waters along the bed of the same order of magnitude as the flow rate of liquid toward the bottom of a well, which is about 5 m per month [32], the time required for travel through this path would be at least 300 months or 25 years. Considering that the bed had been thoroughly flushed and all of the organic material therein was consumed long ago by the preceding colonies of microflora, it is clear that the colony of microorganisms now entering the bed from the surface has very little chance to reach the carbon and nitrogen source of the petroleum deposit. The source of phosphorus to be assimilated is likewise not clear.

The sulfate-reducing bacteria are strictly anaerobic. Surface waters carrying the oxygen are, in the initial stages of their movement through the bed, an unfavorable medium for the active life of these bacteria. The major part of the microspirae perishes along the first few meters of the water travel.

Let us repeat again that, according to data by B. L. Isachenko [31], the sulfate-reducing bacteria have no spore forms.

The sum total of these facts indicates that there is no possibility of the microflora being entrained by surface waters into the body of a petroleum deposit. As a consequence, these data serve also as a confirmation of the sterile state of the subsurface prior to human intervention. No buried microflora exists in the body of a petroleum deposit, nor is it carried in from the surface. The microflora is carried into the depths during the drilling of wells.

The literature contains reports on crude oils being progressively heavier in the direction from the crest toward the depressed sides of the fold in anticline type deposits. Supporters of the oxidation hypothesis explain this by bacterial oxidation processes at the water–oil contact surface. Could this be true? Is there not another reason for this effect? Let us forget for a while about our arguments for sterility of the depths of a petroleum deposit and discuss the mechanism of the action of sulfate-reducing bacteria upon petroleum hydrocarbons. A careful analysis of the facts known in microbiology will convince us that all petroleum hydrocarbons, without exception, are suitable as a nutritive medium for microorganisms. V.O.Tauson [34] points out that different species of bacteria are capable of assimilating all petroleum hydrocarbons, without exception. Even phenol, a most powerful poison, in low concentrations is utilized as food by bacteria.

The decomposition of crude oil in such processes goes on until its complete annihilation and conversion into carbon dioxide and water.

Let us now consider certain physicochemical aspects of the life activity of microflora under the conditions within a petroleum reservoir.

Microorganisms, as is well known, may live and develop their activity exclusively in an aqueous medium only. Absence of water or a lack thereof inevitably results in the death of these beings. For this reason the oil–water contact surface is universally recognized as the place of residence of microbes under the conditions prevailing in an oil-bearing formation. Naturally, it is assumed that the microbes live in the water adjacent to the oil, rather than in oil adjacent to the water. In such case the source of nutrition for the microorganisms would be the organic compounds dissolved in water. Consequently, any sparingly water-soluble organic substances could not constitute a basic source of nutrition for the bacteria. The latter would assimilate only those substances which are present in predominant amount in aqueous solution.

Furthermore, it is known that among the large variety of hydrocarbons present in petroleum the most soluble are aromatic hydrocarbons, especially those of low molecular weight. Saturated aliphatic hydrocarbons have a much lower solubility compared with the former. Available data [35] indicate that the solubility of benzene in water is 0.7 g/l while the solubility of hexane is 0.13 g/l. A similar relationship is valid also for higher molecular-weight hydrocarbons of the same series, but the difference in solubility for high molecular-weight compounds is still greater than for the lighter molecules.

From these data it follows that the principal hydrocarbon components in aqueous solutions in petroleum deposits will be aromatic compounds rather than saturated aliphatic ones.

A still higher solubility is shown by oxygenated compounds, particularly those of an acidic nature, such as naphthenic acids, phenols, fatty acids, hydroxy acids, etc.

Thus the basic source of nutrition for microorganisms at the water–oil contact surface consists largely of oxygenated and perhaps also sulfur and nitrogen compounds. Lesser amounts of low molecular-weight aromatic hydrocarbons are likewise available. Finally, hydrocarbons of the saturated aliphatic and naphthenic series are present in insignificant amount. Among saturated aliphatic hydrocarbons, high molecular-weight paraffins are entirely absent because their solubility in water and especially in brines is equal to zero.

The active life of microflora at the water–oil contact surface would cause transformations of exactly these hydrocarbons and hetero compounds, which are dissolved in the waters in contact with the oil. After transformation of all of the dissolved compounds, new portions of the same compounds would subsequently arrive from the principal body of petroleum in accordance with diffusion laws. Thus the principal body of petroleum would become relatively depleted in hetero compounds and aromatic compounds while being enriched in aliphatic and naphthenic hydrocarbons. Among the aliphatic hydrocarbons, mostly the high molecular-weight compounds will tend to accumulate because their solubility in water is nil. The latter compounds will be protected from destruction by the microflora precisely because of the presence of other types of hydrocarbons and hetero compounds in the system.

As will be explained later, the principal direction in which microorganisms act upon hydrocarbons is that of their complete destruction to carbon dioxide and water. Moreover, at certain stages it may be expected, theoretically at least, to find also products of incomplete assimilation in the form of miscellaneous oxygenated compounds. Yet all of such incompletely assimilated hydrocarbon residues, being oxygenated compounds, are appreciably more soluble in water than in oil and consequently would have no tendency to go over from the aqueous medium back into the oil and will remain in aqueous solution. Microbiological experiments [36] show that this is exactly the case. A loss is observed in the bulk of the petroleum, while the aqueous medium becomes enriched in soluble products, the quantity of the latter constituting a minor portion of the disintegrated petroleum.

Thus the considerations concerning the selective disintegration of high molecular-weight aliphatic hydrocarbons by the microflora inhabiting the water-oil contact surface are not in agreement with available experimental data and must be dismissed as not being in accord with the facts.

Let us once more forget temporarily our previous arguments for the sterility of the depths of a petroleum deposit prior to intervention by man. Suppose that at the water–oil contact surface there exists an ample microflora which successfully flourishes in its life activities. Let us examine the data available in the literature on processes relating to the action of some microorganisms upon petroleum and to the nature of products formed thereby.

The literature dealing with bacterial action upon hydrocarbons is quite large. Several reviews are available, one of the more recent ones being the Russian review article by L. K. Osnitskaya [37]. A characteristic feature of all of the published material on this subject is that it deals to a very limited extent with the nature of intermediate and final products of bacterial transformation of petroleum.

Some of the papers relate to specific microbiological questions, as, for example, the extensive work by C. E. ZoBell, C. Grant and H. Haas [38] who consider whether sea water and marine bottom deposits contain any specific microflora capable of oxidizing hydrocarbons under aerobic conditions. Naturally, such literature has no direct relation to solving the problem of transformation of petroleum under conditions existing in petroleum deposits and consequently it shall not be discussed here. Another group of papers is devoted to bacterial transformation of hydrocarbons but discusses microorganisms which so far have not been recovered from petroleum nor from rocks and waters of petroleum deposits. These papers are of no interest to us.

From all of these papers which have no relationship with our problem, it is possible to draw the conclusion formulated in 1942 by R. Stone, M. Fenske and G. White [39] that under favorable conditions there may almost always be found microorganisms which are capable of disintegrating any petroleum hydrocarbon, including even asphaltic and resinous substances.

Research relating to destruction of hydrocarbons separated from borehole waters in oil fields, particularly by the action of anaerobic sulfate-reducing bacteria, has been rather scarce. It includes in first place the original work by V.O.Tauson [40] who observed, under anaerobic conditions, the destruction of Dossor petroleum and solar† and cylinder oils, which consist predominantly of naphthenes. In another paper, V. O. Tauson and I. Ya. Veselov [41] reported the destruction of aromatic hydrocarbons and even vegetable resins by sulfate-reducing bacteria under anaerobic conditions.

L. K. Osnitskaya [42] has established that mixed culture of microbes recovered from Taman oil-saturated soil will actively destroy naphthenic acids. L. Buchnell and H. Haas [43] have found that in the oxidation of kerosene, gasoline and oils by microorganisms recovered from the bottom of petroleum storage tanks or oil wells, a rise in the boiling temperature of the residue is noted. The authors explain this as being the result of hydrocarbon dehydrogenation processes which occur in bacterial oxidation and which are followed by polymerization of the unsaturated compounds thus formed. The oxidation of hydrocarbons, as reported by the authors, proceeded in their experiments all the way to carbon dioxide and water.

The authors' explanations may be disputed on a number of points. The rise in boiling point of the residue after oxidation by microbes cannot be explained by dehydrogenation processes if only because Wieland's dehydrogenation theory of oxidative processes proved to be incompetent, as discussed earlier, and must be rejected at this time.

Furthermore, though insisting that unsaturated compounds are really present in the microbial oxidation products, the authors report that they did not find any intermediate compounds besides the final products, i.e. carbon dioxide and water, among the oxidation products. Such would not be the case if dehydrogenation processes had been going on, resulting in the formation of unsaturated hydrocarbons. There can be no doubt but that at least traces of unsaturated compounds would have been found in the oxidation products.

Among the more recent papers, the investigations of I. L. Appert and M. Louis [36] and those of F. Bennet and M. Louis [44] are to be noted. These authors subjected crude oils to the action of microorganisms under aerobic conditions. Upon examination of the

† Solar oil is a 300–400°C petroleum fraction, which occupies a position intermediate to the kerosene and gas oil fractions. [Transl. Ed.]

oxidation products it was established that the resin content increases and the content of asphaltenes remains almost constant. The content of oils is higher. The naphthene content diminishes, particularly in the initial phase when the resin content rises. Subsequently, the resin content drops while the naphthene content rises, probably at the expense of the resins present. The authors come to the conclusion that bacterial disintegration of petroleum is much inferior in regard to intensity, compared with destruction of hydrocarbons by oxidation with air.

In all of the investigations it is pointed out that oxidation of hydrocarbons proceeds in the overwhelming majority of cases to carbon dioxide and water. Intermediate products, which have been found in a few and somewhat doubtful instances, consist of oxygenated compounds such as acids, ketones, etc.

No special experiments to study the selective action of microorganisms upon different types of hydrocarbons have been reported in the literature. This question for the time being remains open, although on the basis of indirect reasoning some researchers believe that saturated hydrocarbons are more susceptible to microbial oxidation than the hydrocarbons of other series. Such judgments are presumably due to the fact that oxidation products of saturated hydrocarbons may be determined more easily than the oxidation products of other hydrocarbon varieties.

Substantial evidence, backed by theoretical computations, indicates that oxygenated compounds tend to succumb much more readily to attack by microbes, than the hydrocarbons themselves [45, 46]. Higher aliphatic acids, alcohols, fats, waxes, and resins are oxidized by microorganisms. The higher the number of oxidized carbon atoms in the molecule, the more accessible becomes the substance to further microbial action.

The reaction velocity of the oxidation of aromatic hydrocarbons is approximately within the same range as that of saturated hydrocarbons [37]. Their oxidation usually proceeds to the end, i.e. to carbon dioxide and water. Aromatic hydrocarbons having alkyl side chains are oxidized more easily than unsubstituted ones. Intermediate products of the oxidation were found to consist of aromatic acids up to benzoic acid, as well as phenol.

Thus the admittedly incomplete study of the process of microbial oxidation of petroleum under anaerobic conditions leads us to conclude that the final products of this process are principally carbon dioxide and water along with a certain amount of water-soluble substances. No other intermediate or final products have been discovered, except for the protoplasm of microorganisms developed through partial assimilation of the petroleum matter.

Despite the scant and fragmentary data on the microbial oxidation of hydrocarbons, the latter processes and the processes of oxidation with molecular oxygen have many features in common.

In the former and in the latter case the attack is directed primarily against that particular bond in the molecule, whose rupture energy is lowest. For saturated hydrocarbons such a bond is the C—C bond and for aromatic hydrocarbons it is the C—H bond. Naphthenes in this respect occupy an intermediate position and for them the probability of oxidative rupture of the C—C bond or the C—H bond is approximately equal.

Consequently, depending on the composition of the hydrocarbon mixture subjected to oxidation, the bacterial action will be directed first toward transformation of compounds having the least energy of bond rupture among those present in the system. Such compounds, in the case of petroleum, may prove to be not the high molecular-weight paraffins at all, but compounds of other series. It is probable that the first ones to be oxidized will be the oxygenated compounds or, broadly, hetero compounds that are non-toxic to microorganisms. Following these will be those compounds having a tertiary carbon atom or a carbon atom at the double bond or a secondary carbon atom, such as substituted aromatic or naphthenic hydrocarbons, naphthenic-aromatic, branched aliphatic compounds, etc. Only after the available reserves of such molecules have been depleted will the straight-chain high molecular-weight paraffins be attacked, followed in order of their bond strength by alkyl substituted low molecular-weight monocyclic aromatic and naphthenic compounds with short side chains and with a limited number of such chains in the molecule. The last ones to be destroyed will be the low molecular-weight paraffins and cycloparaffins having no nuclear substituents.

It is important to bear in mind that products of the oxidative disintegration of aliphatic hydrocarbons do not accumulate in the mixture being oxidized, but migrate in the form of water-soluble oxygenated compounds into the aqueous phase inhabited by the microorganisms or disappear without any trace as they are completely oxidized to carbon dioxide and water.

Aromatic hydrocarbons, however, give partly as their oxidative transformation products, water-insoluble resinous substances which go over into the hydrocarbon phase and thus are accumulated in residual products. Part of the aromatics are completely disintegrated to CO_2 and H_2O. The mechanism of the formation of resinous substances along with oxidative condensation of complex aromatic and naphthenic molecules is supposed to proceed via an intermediate stage consisting of oxygenated products such as aldehydes, ketones and phenols, which are formed during the destruction of the initial molecule and which give rise to resins in the condensation process with liberation of water. Part of the oxygen atoms may be retained in the resin molecules.

Naphthenic hydrocarbons, occupying an intermediate position between aromatic and aliphatic hydrocarbons with respect to strength of their bonds, undergo oxidative transformations both via disaggregation to form water-soluble acid products as well as via aggregation which leads to the formation of complex resinous substances. It may be expected that resins of oxidative origin formed from naphthenic hydrocarbons will differ from resins originating from aromatics by an increased content of hydrogen and oxygen and will closely resemble the resinous substances of primary origin, which are indigenous to the initial stages in the transformation of parent petroleum material.

The qualitative resemblance between microbial oxidation processes and oxidation with molecular oxygen tends to suggest that microorganisms do not necessarily have a selective affinity for high molecular-weight paraffinic hydrocarbons, as has been previously assumed by many researchers. Microorganisms utilize preferentially those organic molecules which are more accessible to them in regard to magnitude of bond energy between atoms in the molecule and to solubility in the aqueous medium inhabited by the microbes, regardless of whether or not such molecules are indeed straight-chain paraffins. They may prove to be in the majority of cases not high molecular-weight paraffins at all, but other organic compounds containing energy bonds of reduced stability between atoms. The "selectivity" of the action of microorganisms is defined by the composition of the initial mixture of organic compounds. In some particular case the least stable may prove to be the bonds present in oxygen-bearing molecules, in another case the aliphatic-aromatic hydrocarbons, in a third case the isoparaffins, and in some cases the transformation may occur in substituted or even in unsubstituted polycyclic naphthenes. The relative water solubilities of the representatives of various types of compounds are likewise very important. As noted above, the attack will be directed preferentially toward compounds having the highest solubility, despite the presence of other compounds with lesser energy of bond rupture but insoluble in water. The composition of salts present in the medium appears to be also an important factor with respect to its effect on the solubility of the different organic molecules.

The resemblance between microbial oxidation processes and oxidation with molecular oxygen is further demonstrated by the fact that a sufficient excess of the oxidizing agent in combination with favourable external conditions in both instances causes complete oxidation of the initial system of organic molecules to form carbon dioxide and water, along with a certain amount of the components of the microorganisms themselves (in the case of bacterial oxidation).

The difference between the two oxidation processes consists only in the rates at which they proceed. Oxidation with molecular oxygen proceeds as a rule much more rapidly than oxidation with the aid of anaerobic bacteria. This difference, from the viewpoint of energy relationships in the process, is believed to be due to the microorganism's need to draw the oxygen required for the reaction from the stable salts of sulfuric acid. The rupture of $S=O$ bonds involves a substantial expenditure of energy of a high potential and, considered in its entirety, the process of oxidation by means of sulfates is less profitable from the energy viewpoint than oxidation with molecular oxygen. The activation energy of the process of $S=O$ bond rupture is not known but, judging from the strength of these bonds, it should be considerably higher than in the process of oxidation with molecular oxygen. The low intensity of biogenic oxidation processes is reflected in their sluggish rate.

In anaerobic oxidation processes the microorganisms function as a unique catalyst for the process of oxygen transfer from the sulfate molecule to the organic molecule to be oxidized, which decreases the activation energy of the process of $S=O$ bond rupture. In this respect, life participates as a stimulant for chemical processes of a type which otherwise would not take place at all or would do so only at extremely slow rates.

To extend further the analogy between biogenic and abiogenic oxidation processes of organic compounds, it is quite evident that in microbial oxidation the same processes of mass disproportionation are operative as in oxidation with molecular oxygen.

The slowest of the processes of disproportionation of elements is the disproportionation in a reducing environment. Under these conditions the process extends over a protracted period of time, even on the geological time scale, and never proceeds to full completion because of the relatively small decrease in the available free energy of the system.

Rather more rapid is the process of disproportionation under the action of microorganisms in an anaerobic environment. At the same time the nature of the products formed will be somewhat different from those formed in the process occurring in an oxygen-free medium. These differences have been discussed earlier.

Finally, the quickest and the most likely to fully accomplish the objective is the process of disproportionation by the action of molecular oxygen or, still better, through the agency of other, more drastically acting oxidants.

Whereas disproportionation processes in a reducing environment require for reasonably effective performance either elevated temperatures or extended periods of time at low temperatures, in the presence of oxygen the process is accomplished within a short time and at more moderate temperatures. Oxidation processes involve a most complete separation of carbon atoms from hydrogen atoms, and the resulting free valencies of carbon and hydrogen atoms are not correspondingly, resaturated by valencies of carbon and hydrogen atoms, but are engaged in processes of forming the new C—O and H—O bonds which are more favourable from the energy viewpoint. However, the process as such remains the same, as bonds with a low rupture energy are replaced by high energy bonds. If the system includes atoms with which the formation of bonds appears to be of greater advantage from the energy viewpoint than the formation of C—C and C—H bonds, then such energy-gaining bonds will be preferentially formed to replace the C—C and C—H bonds which are less favored in that particular environment.

Returning to the question of microbial oxidation of petroleum in an anaerobic environment, it is evident that even if, for the moment, a possibility of effective action of microorganisms be admitted, the result of such action would prove to be entirely different from what is expected by the backers of the oxidation hypothesis of petroleum transformation in nature. For example, the disappearance ex-

clusively of high molecular-weight and generally paraffinic hydrocarbons need not necessarily take place, even in case of intensive
development of microflora in the body of the oil-bearing formation.
These compounds are disintegrated only after the system has been
denuded of other compounds that are more accessible to microbial
action and thereafter of hydrocarbons having tertiary and secondary carbon atoms. Transformations will occur first in complex
high molecular-weight aromatic, cycloparaffinic and isoparaffinic
hydrocarbons, particularly cycloparaffins with a large number of
aliphatic side chains.

Moreover, oxidative transformations will not be accompanied
by cyclization of open-chain compounds; if there were no cycloparaffins in the system right from the start, none will be present
in the system after oxidation.

The final products of microbial oxidation of petroleum are carbon dioxide and water. Intermediate stages of the process will be
characterized by successively decreasing amounts of hydrocarbons
having tertiary carbon atoms, specifically naphthenic-aromatic,
substituted aromatic and naphthenic, and isoparaffinic hydrocarbons. There will be a decreasing content of compounds having
hetero atoms (of oxygen, sulfur, and nitrogen), and instead of them
there will be formed complex hetero atomic molecules of the resinous type which are immune to microbial action. The relative
content of aliphatic hydrocarbons, particularly of low molecular
weights, will rise unless they will have an opportunity to escape by
physical means from the initial system.

A certain portion of aromatic hydrocarbons will be converted by
oxidative condensation to resinous substances and another portion
will be broken down to water-soluble compounds and finally to
carbon dioxide and water. Naphthenes will be converted partly to
resinous substances and partly to low molecular-weight oxygenated
compounds, down to CO_2 and H_2O.

With progressive development of the process in the system there
will be an accumulation of the most stable compounds: hydrocarbons of symmetrical structure free from tertiary and secondary
carbon atoms, resinous compounds of complex structure which cannot be assimilated by microorganisms, unsubstituted cycloparaffins,
normal paraffins, etc.

It is quite evident that such systems resulting from incomplete
assimilation of petroleum matter by microorganisms are very simi-

lar to systems formed as a result of normal disproportionation processes in a mass of molecules under reducing conditions.

In both instances the initial system tends to assume a state of the least reserve of free energy, and the mechanism of this movement of matter will actually be the same: the earliest reactions will be the transformation of the most labile molecules that have the least amount of bond rupture energy between their atoms and consequently possess the highest free energy value.

CONCLUSIONS

1. The change from a reducing environment in petroleum systems to an oxidative one raises the intensity of the processes of disproportionation of elements at the expense of decreasing the activation energy of the process, but does not tend to change the direction of the process.

2. The mechanism of the action of various oxidants, including also microorganisms, on petroleum appears to be essentially the same and gives identical results. The action of oxidants is directed at first to compounds which contain bonds having the least amount of rupture energy. These bonds are likewise the target in disproportionation processes under reducing conditions.

3. The difference between the processes of oxidation with inorganic oxidants and microbial oxidation lies in the different velocities of these processes. Microbial oxidation processes, particularly under anaerobic conditions, take place at a reduced rate as compared with the processes of oxidation by inorganic oxidants.

4. The difference between the processes of disproportionation in reductive and in oxidative conditions lies in that the former give as final products methane and graphite, along with carbon dioxide, water, hydrogen sulfide, ammonia, and nitrogen, while under oxidative conditions the final products consist exclusively of carbon dioxide, water, nitrogen, and sulfur.

BIBLIOGRAPHY

For Section A

1. KARTSEV, A.A., TABASARANSKII, Z.A., SUBBOTA, M.I. and MOGILEVSKII, G.A. *Geochemical Methods of Exploring and Prospecting for Oil and Gas Deposits*, Gostoptekhizdat, 1954.

2. GERMANOV, A.I. Oxygen in underground waters and its geochemical significance, *Izv. Akad. Nauk SSSR, Ser. geol.* No. 6 (1955).
3. KARTSEV, A.A. and TABASARANSKII, Z.A. The problem of genesis of petroleum deposits in Eastern Fergana, *Sov. Geologiya*, in press.
4. BOKOVA, E.N. *Izv. GUGF*, No. 3, Gosgeolizdat, 1947.
5. BEERSTECHER, E. *Petroleum Microbiology*, Houston, 1954.
6. ANDREEV, P.F. *Trudy VNIGRI*, No. 83 (*Geologicheskii Sbornik*, No. 1). Lengostoptekhizdat, 1955.
7. SHTURM, L.D. *Mikrobiologiya*, **19**, No. 1 (1950).
8. SHTURM, L.D. *Trudy Inst. Nefti Akad. Nauk SSSR*, **1**, No. 2 (1950).
9. GINZBURG-KARAGICHEVA, T.L. *Trudy VNIGRI*, No. 4 (1954).
10. GINZBURG-KARAGICHEVA, T.L. *Azerb. Neft. Khoz.* Nos. 6–7 (1926).
11. BASTIN, E. *Bull. Am. Ass. Petr. Geol.* **10**, No. 12 (1926).
12. ZOBELL, C.E. *Marine Microbiology*, Waltham, 1946.
13. KOLESNIK, E.A. *Trudy VNIGRI*, No. 83 (*Geologicheskii Sbornik*, No. 1), Lengostoptekhizdat, 1955.
14. SHTURM, L.D. *Sbornik "Pamyati akad. I.M. Gubkina"*, Akad. Nauk SSSR, 1951.
15. KOLESNIK, E.A. *Trudy VNIGRI*, No. 82, Lengostoptekhizdat, 1955.
16. MAIMIN, Z.L. *Trudy VNIGRI*, No. 82, Lengostoptekhizdat, 1955.
17. SHTURM, L.D. *Trudy Inst. Mikrobiologii Akad. Nauk SSSR*, No. 2 (1952).
18. KUZNETSOVA, Z.I. and MOGILEVSKII, G.A. *Izvest. VGF*, Gosgeolizdat, 1946.
19. NIKOLAEV, V.M. *Reduction of Sulfates and Geological Conditions for Preservation and Disintegration of Petroleum Deposits in the Terek-Sunzha Oil-Bearing Region*, Grozny, 1949.
20. MALYSHEK, V.T., MALIYANTS, A.A. and REINFEL'D, E.A. *Azerb. Neft. Khoz.*, Nos. 7–8 (1935).
21. ISACHENKO, B.L. *Selected Works*, vol. 2, Publ. by Akad. Nauk SSSR, 1951.
22. ZHABREV, D.V. and KHATSKEVICH, N.I. *Neft. Khoz.*, No. 12, 1951.

For Section B

1. PARKS, G. and HUFFMAN, G. *Free Energies of Some Organic Compounds*, ONTI, 1936. (Original English Edition—New York, 1932.)
2. BAKH, A.N. *Zh. Russk. Fiz.-Khim. Obshch.* **29** (1897).
3. ENGLER, K. *Ber.* **30**, 1669 (1897).
4. SEMENOV, N.N. *Chain Reactions*, Goskhimizdat, 1934.
5. SEMENOV, N.N. Development of the chain theory of the oxidation of hydrocarbons, *Sbornik "Problemy Okisleniya Uglevodorodov"*, Publ. by Akad. Nauk SSSR, 1954.
6. IVANOV, K.I. *Intermediate Products and Intermediate Reactions of Hydrocarbon Autooxidation*, Gostoptekhizdat, 1949.
7. WIELAND, *Über den Verlauf der Oxidationsvorgänge*, Stuttgart, 1933.
8. USPENSKII, V.A., RADCHENKO, O.A. Geochemistry of bitumen, *Petroleum Field Geologist's Handbook*, First edition, Lengostoptekhizdat, 1952.
9. TYCHININ, B.G. and BUTKOV, N. *Neft. i Slants. Khoz.*, No. 8, 341 (1924).
10. TYCHININ, B.G. and BUTKOV, N. *Neft. i Slants. Khoz.*, No. 1, 38 (1925).
11. MOUREN and DUFREISSE, *Comptes Rend.* **174**, 258 (1922).
12. MOUREN and DUFREISSE, *J. Chem. Ind.* **32**, 819 (1928).

13. SAKHANOV, A. N. and VASIL'EV, N. A. *Chemical Composition of Crude Oils*, GNTI, 1931, p. 283.
14. BASHKIROV, A. N. and CHERTKOV, YA. B. *Dokl. Akad. Nauk SSSR* **78**, No. 3, 473 (1951).
15. TSYSKOVSKII, V. K. *Preparation of Synthetic Acids by Oxidation of Kerosene Fractions*, Gostoptekhizdat, 1954.
16. WIETZEL, *Fette und Seifen*, **42**, 21 (1939).
17. KREIN, S. E. *Sbornik "Additives to Lubricating Oils"*, Gostoptekhizdat, 1946, p. 120.
18. CHERNOZHUKOV, N. I., KREIN, S. E. and LOSIKOV, B. V. *Chemistry of Oils*, Gostoptekhizdat, 1951.
19. PETROV, A. D. *Chemistry of Motor Fuels*, Publ. by Akad. Nauk SSSR, 1953.
20. CHERNOZHUKOV, N. I. and KREIN, S. E. *Oxidizability of Mineral Oils*, Third edition, Gostoptekhizdat, 1955.
21. USPENSKII, S. P. *Izv. Inst. Chistykh Reaktivov*, No. I, II, 1922.
22. FAVORSKII, A. E. *Zh. Russk. Fiz.-Khim. Obshch.* **50**, 55 (1918).
23. SCHRADER, C. *Ges. Abhandl. z. Kenntnis der Kohle*, **4**, 322 (cited from item 20).
24. CIAMICIAN, SILBER. *Ber.* **45**, 38 (1912); **46**, 417 (1913).
25. SEMENOV, N. N. *Some Problems of Chemical Kinetics and Reactivity*, Publ. by Akad. Nauk SSSR, 1954.
26. DOBRYANSKII, A. F. *Geochemistry of Petroleum*, Gostoptekhizdat, 1948.
27. KOZLOV, A. L. *Proceedings of Scientific Geological Conference on Petroleum, Ozokerite and Natural Gas*, publ. by Akad. Nauk Ukrain. SSSR, Kiev, 1949.
28. USPENSKII, V. A. and RADCHENKO, O. A. *The Problem of Genesis of Different Types of Crudes*, Lengostoptekhizdat, 1947.
29. KOZLOV, A. L. *Problems of Geochemistry of Natural Gases*, Gostoptekhizdat, 1950.
30. GINZBURG-KARAGICHEVA, T. L. *Microbiological Essays*, ONTI, 1932.
31. ISACHENKO, B. L. *Selected Works*, **2**, Publ. by Akad. Nauk SSSR, 1951.
32. SULIN, V. A. *Hydrogeology of Petroleum Deposits*, Gostoptekhizdat, 1948.
33. LEVINSON, V. E. and UTSHTEIN, N. G. *Sbornik "Geochemistry of Petroleum Deposits"*, ONTI, Aznefteizdat, Baku, 1934.
34. TAUSON, V. O. *Great Deeds by Little Creatures*. Publ. by Akad. Nauk SSSR, 1948.
35. *Chemist's Handbook*. Goskhimizdat, 1948.
36. APPERT, I. L. and LOUIS, M. *Rev. Inst. Franç. du Petr.* **10**, No. 5, 337 (1955).
37. OSNITSKAYA, L. K. *Mikrobiologiya*, **15**, No. 3, 249 (1946).
38. ZOBELL, C. E., GRANT, C. and HAAS, H. I. *Bull. Am. Ass. Petr. Geol.* **27**, No. 9, I (1945).
39. STONE, R., FENSKE, M. R. and WHITE, G. *Bacter.* **44**, No. 2 (1942).
40. TAUSON, V. O. On the bacterial oxidation of petroleum, *Neft. Khoz.* No. 2, 220 (1928).
41. TAUSON, V. O. and VESELOV, I. YA. *Mikrobiologiya*, **3**, No. 3 (1934).
42. OSNITSKAYA, L. K. *Dokl. Akad. Nauk SSSR*, **58**, No. 1, 139 (1947).
43. BUCHNELL, L. and HAAS, H. J. *Bacter.* **41**, 653 (1941).
44. BENNET, F. and LOUIS, M. *Rev. Inst. Franç. du Petr.* **10**, No. 5 (1955).
45. TAUSON, V. O. *Mikrobiologiya*, **1**, No. 1 (1932).
46. TAUSON, V. O. *Priroda*, No. 6 (1934).

CHAPTER VI

SIGNIFICANCE OF CLAYS IN THE FORMATION AND CONVERSION OF PETROLEUM IN THE EARTH'S CRUST

A. EVOLUTION OF IDEAS ABOUT THE CATALYTIC PROCESSES OF FORMATION AND CONVERSION OF PETROLEUM

The concept of the catalytic effect of various mineral substances in accelerating reactions involving the transformation of organic residues into petroleum arose a considerable time ago. Ochsenius associated the formation of petroleum with the action of solutions of magnesium and aluminum salts on the fatty substance of marine fauna and flora residues [54, 55]. This idea was substantially strengthened and gained acceptance after the studies successfully carried out by Gustavson [12] on the action of aluminum chloride upon ethylenic hydrocarbons and crude oil fractions. Gustavson proved that unsaturated hydrocarbons are polymerized by the action of aluminum halides to form high molecular-weight saturated compounds similar to hydrocarbons present in lubricating oils.† Heusler [46] and later Zaloziecki [60] were the first to express in a more definite form the notion that mineral substances participate in petroleum genesis processes. It was understood to be a catalytic action of rocks upon organic matter, the meaning being the same as expressed later by Künkler [50].

An especially strong influence upon the development of ideas relating to the role and significance of catalytic processes in the

† Currently, this reaction is used in industrial manufacture of synthetic lubricating oils from ethylene in the presence of anhydrous aluminum chloride "SS"-oils).

formation of petroleum was exerted by the investigations made by V. N. Ipat'ev [21] and by the classic work of Sabatier and his collaborators on the catalytic conversion of miscellaneous organic compounds by the salts and oxides of heavy metals. Of particular interest in this respect appears to be the research of Sabatier and Senderens [52] and also of Sabatier and Mailhe [53] on the conversion of alcohols, esters, and fatty acids by the above-mentioned catalysts. This research has demonstrated that fatty acids are split most easily in the presence of thorium oxide and not quite as easily in the presence of aluminum oxide and clay. The conversion of acids takes place at a temperature of 340–400 °C to form ketones, while alcohols are dehydrated to olefins. In the decomposition of esters, usually ketones (from the acyl radical) and ethylenic hydrocarbons (from the alcohol) are formed. In this connection the research by V. E. Tishchenko [30] should be cited, who as early as 1901 used alumina for the alcohol dehydration reaction.

The next stage in the development of organic chemistry is characterized by a broad development of catalytic reactions and their application in the chemical technology of various industries. Among the large variety of catalysts used, increasing attention was drawn to natural aluminosilicates. In this connection, special reference is made to research by V. N. Ipat'ev on the polymerizing action of clay catalysts upon ethylenic hydrocarbons, published in 1911. This research essentially served as a foundation for the study of the currently well-known reactions of isomerization and hydrogen enrichment or depletion by aluminosilicate catalysts, inasmuch as the reaction products obtained from ethylene were found to contain saturated aliphatic hydrocarbons in addition to polymers.

At about the same period appeared the studies of Ubbelohde and Woronin who, in 1911, investigated the catalytic action of clays on the conversion of petroleum [59]. On heating a petroleum fraction together with clay at a temperature of 180–450 °C, its catalytic effect on the cracking reactions of high molecular-weight petroleum hydrocarbons was noted.

Research on the catalytic conversion of Lycopodium spores in the presence of a decolorizing clay† as catalytic agent was published by Graefe [45]. Upon distillation of Lycopodium spores in the

† In the literature it is frequently referred to as "Fuller's earth", "Floridin", "Terrana", etc.

presence of clay he obtained a mixture of hydrocarbons similar in composition to the oil from Scottish shales. On the basis of his investigations the author came to the conclusion that the mineral portion of the shale substance (clay) acts as a catalytic agent in the breakdown of bituminous constituents during distillation of shale.

The investigations by Hviid [47] relating to conversion of oleic acid in the presence of acidic clay must also be noted. He has demonstrated that on heating an acid together with clay, a decomposition of the acid takes place with the formation of liquid hydrocarbons and gaseous products, which in the absence of clay are not formed at all or are formed only in limited amounts and at elevated temperature.

This series of studies includes also the research by Severin on the conversion of oleic and stearic acid in the presence of various catalytic agents [43]. The author used kieselguhr, decolorizing clay and quartz as catalysts. The above-mentioned reactants were heated over a period of three hours at a temperature of 400°C and higher. A reduction in acid number of the oleic and stearic acid was noted, as well as a decrease in their molecular weight. After saponification, hydrocarbons of varying fractional composition and molecular weight were obtained from the reaction products. The author's conclusions seem rather strange to us, as he maintains that quartz sand has a stronger catalytic action than the decolorizing clay which is known to be a clay of the montmorillonite type. Severin's research, in comparison to investigations by others at that time, is outstanding with respect to the scope and thoroughness in analyzing the products obtained. The hydrocarbons separated from the conversion products were fractionated and their elemental composition and specific gravity were determined.

Highly significant in the study of polymerization of unsaturated hydrocarbons over natural aluminosilicates are the papers by L.G.Gurvich and S.V.Lebedev. In the article entitled "Notes on Adsorption" published in 1912, L.G.Gurvich reported that a natural clay (Floridin) is capable of causing polymerization of amylene to diamylene even at room temperature [14]. Upon mixing amylene with Floridin at ordinary temperature, 15% of the amylene is converted to diamylene within 2 hr, and after 15 hr the conversion yields 85% amylene. First in experiments with individual unsaturated hydrocarbons and then with petroleum products, L.G.Gurvich demonstrated that the process of interaction between clay and unsaturated hydrocarbons is not merely a physical manifestation but is accompanied by profound chemical rearrangement of unsaturated molecules. This has been clearly illustrated in particular by the decolorizing of petroleum distillates with Floridin, whereby highly modified resinous components were separated. The author studied the adsorptive capacity and catalytic properties of a large variety of porous materials, such as animal char, infusorial earth, alumina, and decolorizing clay (Floridin), and showed that the latter occupies a special position among them in regard to adsorptive capacity as well as to polymerizing action. He suggested that adsorption in this connection is not strictly a physical process but is rather associated with "remanent chemical affinity", i.e. it is a physico-chemical process. Shortly thereafter S. V. Lebedev and his associates [23, 24] began an investigation of the catalytic properties of aluminosilicates, specifically Floridin. In a whole series of studies, S. V. Lebedev investigated in detail the reactions of polymerization and depolymerization of olefins of different structure in the presence of decolorizing clay at various temperatures. It was established that clay, depending on reaction temperature, may act as a catalyst in the polymerization of unsaturated molecules or as a catalyst in the reverse process of depolymerization of polymeric forms. S. V. Lebedev demonstrated that clay is also a catalyst for isomerization and for hydrogen disproportionation. The depolymerization of tri-isobutylene gives over 65% di-isobutylene and 27% isobutylene. Along with depolymerization, there occurs also a hydrogen disproportionation reaction between the isobutylene molecules with the result that isobutane is formed.

The research by L. G. Gurvich and S. V. Lebedev is of interest also because it indicates that olefin isomerization and polymerization reactions may be regarded as being effective at any stage of conversion of organic matter, provided such reactions take place at substantial velocity in the presence of clays at ordinary and even below-zero temperatures.

Thus, prior to 1915, the world literature had already accumulated a substantial amount of experimental and theoretical material relating to conversion of different organic compounds over a large variety of catalysts, including natural aluminosilicates. With this as a basis, Engler [44] succeeded in formulating in a more concrete form the idea about the role of catalytic processes in the genesis of petroleum. In his fundamental book under the title *Das Erdöl*, a special section is devoted to the role of catalysis in the genesis of petroleum. Engler collected and systematically arranged the scattered material and reached a number of highly interesting conclusions relating to the role and the position of catalytic processes in the transformation of organic remnants into petroleum. Specifically, it was he who first posed the problem of the different trend of catalytic processes which occur under pressure and the effect of such processes on the genesis of different types of crude oils.

The idea about the transformation of organic matter into petroleum with the participation of catalysts, repeatedly expressed in different variations by different authors, was further developed in the 1920's by N. D. Zelinskii in his studies [20]. On contacting anhydrous aluminum chloride with cholesterol, fatty acids, resin acids, bees-wax, and betulin, he obtained substances resembling petroleum hydrocarbons in outward appearance and composition. The author's statement on this subject was as follows: "The chemist thus becomes capable of converting natural organic material into combustible petroleum oils, and it may be stated that depending on the composition and structure of the natural substances, their decomposition yields a certain mixture of petroleum hydrocarbons including all of the typical representative petroleum hydrocarbons but in different quantitative proportions."

N. D. Zelinskii carried out his experiments with anhydrous aluminum chloride which, as is well known, is absent in natural environments. However, as discovered later on, the mechanism of catalytic action of anhydrous aluminum chloride upon organic substances resembles to a large extent the action of aluminosilicates. The geochemical ideas about the significance of catalytic reactions in the earth's crust during oil and gas genesis processes have been developed by A. V. Frost. Based on the work of his predecessors including V. N. Ipat'ev, L. G. Gurvich, S. V. Lebedev and others, he demonstrated that reactions catalyzed by anhydrous aluminum chloride may proceed likewise in the presence of various natural clays. He showed that in the presence of clays under moderate temperature conditions of the order of 150–250°C it is possible to carry out the dehydration of alcohols and ketones and the decarboxylation of fatty acids, as a result of which a mixture of various hydrocarbons is obtained [32, 35]. With experimental data on the conversion of organic compounds over aluminosilicates as a guide, A. V. Frost proposed various variants for the petroleum genesis schemes based on bacterial and alkaline hydrolysis of cellulose to fatty acids, ketones, and alcohols, as well as the conversion of these in the presence of clays into the corresponding hydrocarbons [33, 34].

The idea about the catalytic action of rocks in processes of transformation of organic matter into petroleum received its fullest development in the Soviet Union as a consequence of research by A. F. Dobryanskii and abroad by B. Brooks. In the *Geochemistry of Petroleum* written by A. F. Dobryanskii during the war years and published in 1948, he consistently builds up the concept of change in the organic matter and petroleum in the deposit by virtue of thermocatalytic reactions with the participation of clay-type minerals [15].

In a series of articles published by B. Brooks [38–41] on the question of origin of petroleum, catalytic processes are stated to be of paramount importance and the diversity of hydrocarbons in crude oils is said to be due to reactions which have taken place over aluminosilicates.

Further investigations in the sphere of catalytic processes for the conversion of organic compounds over aluminosilicates are associated largely with the development of catalytic cracking of petroleum. In this connection, the forties and fifties of the current century are notable through the appearance of a large number of studies on the conversion of individual hydrocarbons and various petroleum fractions, intended to elucidate the mechanism of catalytic reactions over silica-alumina catalysts. A considerable number of these studies were limited to strictly practical purposes, such as efficient selection of initial material and maximum yield of certain specific commercial products. Merely listing all of these studies would fill a good size catalog, and compiling abstracts of them would yield a monograph describing the reactions over silica-alumina catalysts. Yet the region of low temperatures for the conversion of organic compounds, specifically petroleum hydrocarbons, over silica-alumina catalysts has not adequately been investigated. The temperature range of 150–250 °C is of little interest from the practical viewpoint because the reaction velocities are insignificant under these conditions and because the technological process involved is hardly economical. Yet the region of relatively low temperatures is the only one of real interest for the problem of petroleum genesis because these conditions are suitable, with the participation of clay-type minerals, for catalytic reactions involving transformation of organic remnants into petroleum and the transformation of the petroleum itself. Besides, in the high temperature region secondary reactions take place which, largely overlapping one another, tend to disguise and distort the true course of the process. From this point of view, the catalytic reactions occurring in the temperature range up to 250 °C allow us to trace with greater clarity the peculiar process of the redistribution of hydrogen and radicals in the hydrocarbon molecules, which usually precedes their final decomposition. Consequently, the low temperature reactions involving conversion of organic compounds over clays have been given special attention recently by A. F. Dobryanskii and his collaborators. Research on this subject is carried out within the scope of the petroleum genesis problem and is a logical development of the hypothesis pertaining to the transformation of petroleum, as described in its original version in the *Geochemistry of Petroleum* by A. F. Dobryanskii.

In its original version, the "transformation of petroleum" hypothesis was insufficiently backed up by experimental data and observations in natural environments. Only recently, as a result of numerous investigations, the different features of this many-sided process have been discovered.

In a series of papers [6, 11, 16–19] it has been indicated that the thermocatalytic conversion of various hydrocarbons and petroleum fractions over activated clays is feasible in the range of 150–200 °C and substantially lower temperatures. As a result of chemical conversions of high molecular-weight petroleum hydrocarbons over clays, low molecular-weight products are formed consisting of straight-chain and branched saturated aliphatic hydrocarbons as well as naphthenic and aromatic hydrocarbons, depending on the composition of the feed stock and the severity of the process conditions. The aliphatic hydrocarbons are relatively more stable in conversion reactions, while high molecular-weight cycloparaffins and mixed naphthenic-aromatic hydrocarbons have a lower stability.†

In addition to his experimental investigations on the conversion of hydrocarbons, P. F. Andreev has been engaged in developing the

† A generalized discussion of literature on thermocatalytic conversion of individual hydrocarbons as well as different petroleum fractions over clays in the range of low temperatures will be presented in the subsequent chapters.

energy aspects in petroleum conversion processes [1, 2]. He systematically proves the proposition that transformation of organic matter into petroleum is a spontaneously developing process of the breakdown of this substance at the expense of energy gained by virtue of photosynthesis reactions in living organisms.

Under the heading of petroleum genesis, besides the above-mentioned papers, belong also miscellaneous studies dealing with the catalytic conversion of various non-hydrocarbon compounds over activated clay. In this series of papers must be included the studies on conversion of cholesterol by I.S.Sattar-Zade [28] who demonstrated that transition from levo-rotatory to dextro-rotatory compounds is feasible, and also the studies by A.N.Chistyakov on the decomposition of low molecular-weight fatty acids and polyhydric alcohols at different temperatures [36]. He presented convincing proof that in the low temperature range of 200–250 °C the conversion of low molecular-weight fatty acids over clays is directed toward their decarboxylation and that a rise in temperature is necessary to cause their decomposition into carbon monoxide, water, and olefins. Polyhydric alcohols can break down in various ways, with ethers being formed in the initial stage. A similar paper by I.N.Kamenskaya deals with the conversion of ketones over natural and activated clays in the temperature range of 200–250 °C [22]. I.N.Kamenskaya proposed a scheme for the conversion of aliphatic ketones, based on dehydration and dehydrocondensation reactions to form various unsaturated ketones and hydrocarbons.

A.I.Bogomolov and K.I.Panina [5] investigated the conversion of various high molecular fatty acids over activated clay in the temperature range of 150–250 °C. They demonstrated for the first time the formation of naphthenic hydrocarbons, both the low as well as the high molecular-weight varieties, from saturated fatty acids. It should be noted here that the high molecular-weight aromatic hydrocarbons formed thereby are similar in composition and structure to aromatic hydrocarbons separated from natural crude oil.

Current opinion on catalytic processes involved in the transformation of organic matter is based largely upon theoretical notions about the action of aluminosilicate catalysts and on data obtained in laboratory experiments on the conversion of organic compounds and petroleum fractions. This phenomenon cannot as yet be demonstrated with sufficient clarity in application to natural material. Yet we believe that the most convincing argument in favor of the catalytic effect is the composition of the natural crude oil itself and the relationships inherent in the distribution of component groups in it, as a consequence of thermocatalytic reactions on aluminosilicates. Moreover, the effect of catalysis by rocks under natural conditions can be traced in the rate of decrease of non-hydrocarbon components and particularly of the content of carboxylic acids in the bituminous portion of the rocks, from present-day organogenic slimes through Quaternary sediments to more ancient deposits [9]. This process is reflected also in the way the organic matter has been reduced and in the various phases of lithogenesis. Investigations have shown that Quaternary sediments contain an adequately large amount of alkali-soluble humic substances, reaching as much as 60% of the total organic matter. However, fossil sediments of Tertiary age in Northern Caucasus contain such substances on the average in amount of only about 40% [3], and humic substances are entirely absent in the organic matter in Devonian formations in the Volga–Ural region [27].

Finally, the effect of the metamorphic factor specific to thermo-catalytic reactions on clays is confirmed by the presence of saturated paraffinic, highly transformed crudes at great depths. The latter are exemplified by the high-paraffin, naphthene-free practically saturated aliphatic crude from the Minusinsk valley and the light paraffinic crude encountered at great depths in the Lower Cretaceous at Ozek-Suat in the Northern Caucasus, and many others.

B. CURRENT CONCEPTS ABOUT THE CATALYTIC ACTIVITY OF ALUMINOSILICATES

The study of the catalytic action of aluminosilicates has been the subject of a considerable number of papers by Soviet authors and others [4, 7, 10, 25, 26, 31]. Most of the researchers believe that silica-alumina catalysts, both natural as well as synthetic, correspond in composition and structure to the mineral montmorillonite. In the ideal case, montmorillonite has the formula $Al_2O_3 \cdot 4SiO_2 \cdot nH_2O$.

The most widely accepted structure for montmorillonite at this time is the one proposed by Endell and Wilm [48, 49].

The montmorillonite lattice as visualized by them (Fig. 43) consists of layers of two different types: a layer of $Si(O-OH)_4$ tetrahedrons and a layer of hydrargillite which consists of a layer of aluminum surrounded by O or OH groups forming an octahedron. The lamellar packs are formed in a manner such that each layer of aluminum octahedrons is linked to a layer of silicon tetrahedrons situated above and below it. The capacity of montmorillonite to swelling is associated with penetration of water into the "free space" between the packs and is due to the weak bond between them. Besides water, the montmorillonite is capable of absorbing, in the interstices between the packs also organic liquids, glycerin, ethylene glycol, and others, to form an organo-mineral complex therewith.

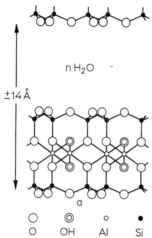

FIG. 43. Diagram of montmorillonite structure (according to Hoffmann, Endell and Wilm).

A characteristic feature of montmorillonite is its sharply defined capacity to absorb cations. The cations present in montmorillonites may be stoichiometrically replaced by other cations. This process of cation exchange is frequently termed base exchange. Base exchange is thus regarded as the capacity of aluminosilicates to exchange the cations present therein for the cations of a salt from its solution, with which they are in contact. The exchangeable cations in natural montmorillonites are usually $Ca^{..}$, $Mg^{..}$, $Na^.$ and to a lesser extent $K^.$. In certain montmorillonites the exchangeable ion is the hydrogen ion or aluminum ion. In such cases the montmorillonite possesses an exchangeable acidity [25].

At the present time a direct relationship has been established between the catalytic activity of aluminosilicates and their exchange capacity. Montmorillonite clays, being the most active catalytically, usually contain from 60 to 100 milliequivalents of exchangeable cations per 100 g substance, while kaolinite clays and hydromicas of the illite type have an appreciably lower exchange capacity. The reason why aluminosilicates exhibit this exchange capacity has been variously explained by different authors, but all of them use as a starting point the ideas formulated by A.I. Vernadskii about the aluminosilicates being alumosilicic acids whose sharply defined acid properties are responsible for their exchange capacity.

X-Ray studies of natural clays led Hoffmann, Endell and Wilm [48, 49] to conclude that the exchange capacity of aluminosilicates is due to the presence of ruptured Si–O–Si bonds between oxygen and silicon.

R. Mitra and Rajagopalan [51] think that the exchange capacity of aluminosilicates is manifested not only as a consequence of the rupture of Si—O—Si bonds but also of Al—O and Al—OH bonds. They base this conclusion on the increased capacity of finely pulverized kaolin to extract cations from solutions of electrolytes, which in their opinion is explainable by the increase in number of broken aluminum bonds.

A.P. Ballod and K.V. Topchieva [4] consider the tetrahedral bond of aluminum with oxygen atoms as the source of exchange capacity of aluminosilicates. The acid properties for aluminosilicates arise, according to these authors, when silicon in the silicon-oxygen tetrahedrons is replaced by aluminum. Under such conditions the coordination number of aluminum is equal to 4 while the valence is 3. Each aluminum atom thus satisfies only $\frac{3}{4}$ of the valence of oxygen. The oxygen, being linked in such cases to one silicon and one aluminum tetrahedron, is thus saturated to the extent of $1 + \frac{3}{4} = 1\frac{3}{4}$ of its valence instead of 2.

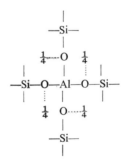

In other words, each tetrahedral ion of aluminum linked through oxygen with four silicon ions forms a negatively charged complex $[AlO_4]^-$. This complex may be linked with one ion of an alkali or one-half ion of an alkaline earth metal. It may be linked also to a hydrogen ion, endowing it with acid properties.

The exchange capacity of aluminosilicates and their catalytic activity associated therewith are explained by K. G. Miesserov [25] through the appearance of the Si—O—Al bond. According to him, the aluminum in this case is not strongly enough bound to oxygen and hence still possesses residual affinity forces. These residual affinity forces are utilized by aluminum for linking up with the hydroxyl group of the water, which in turn weakens the hydroxyl-to-hydrogen bond. Generally, a complex having the following structure is formed, which is responsible for the exchange capacity of the aluminosilicate (Fig. 44).

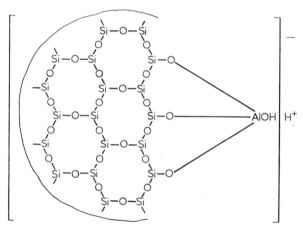

FIG. 44. Proposed structure of the complex of interchangeable aluminum with water (according to K. G. Miesserov).

Having acquired mobility, hydrogen becomes capable of participating in cation exchange reactions and in catalytic reactions involving the conversion of organic compounds with aluminosilicates. K. G. Miesserov's scheme gives a satisfactory explanation for the effect of water on the catalytic activity of aluminosilicates. In an aqueous medium, for instance, such a complex cannot exist because the aluminum ion will be hydrated and the residual affinity forces are uniformly distributed between all of the oxygen atoms in the water molecules. As the aluminosilicate is progressively dehydrated, the water bound with the exchangeable aluminum ion will be removed and the mobility of hydrogen ions will increase. The last molecule of water will be most strongly bound in the complex with the exchangeable aluminum atom because all of the residual affinity forces of this aluminum will be directed toward a single atom of the hydroxyl oxygen. In this manner a broad span of aluminosilicate activity may be obtained, ranging from zero to a maximum possible one as a function of its moisture content.

The last-mentioned conclusion is of special geochemical significance because it grants the possibility that the clays may retain their activity in natural environments, since clays always contain a certain amount of moisture. Consequently, water may be capable of reducing the catalytic properties of rocks but not completely depriving them of such properties, as follows from the theoretical considerations set forth above.

The decrease in catalytic activity of rocks takes place also because the clays most frequently contain instead of the hydrogen cation, the cations of sodium, calcium and magnesium and more seldom the cations of other metals. However, as shown by Yu. A. Bitepazh [7], the various cations are not equivalent to one another in regard to activity. The least active or entirely inactive are the cations of monovalent metals. Divalent cations have some activity which increases with decreasing radius of the cation (from $Ba^{\cdot\cdot}$ to $Mg^{\cdot\cdot}$). Trivalent aluminum $Al^{\cdot\cdot\cdot}$ and tetravalent thorium $Th^{\cdot\cdot\cdot\cdot}$ are as active as hydrogen. Consequently, the natural clays, having as exchange bases the divalent metals of Group II and higher valency metals, will always possess a certain amount of catalytic activity even if they lack mobile hydrogen.

Silica-alumina catalysts, as is known, significantly accelerate polymerization, alkylation, isomerization, depolymerization, dealkylation and cracking reactions and hydrogen disproportionation reactions. Currently a "donor–acceptor" mechanism for interpreting the catalytic activity of acid catalysts has been proposed by the American group of chemists under the leadership of F. Whitmore [56–58]. According to this mechanism the acid is regarded as a source ("donor") of protons and the compound capable of linking up with the proton is termed the proton "acceptor". An acid HA may be considered to consist of the proton H^+ and the conjugate base A^-. The catalyst-acid gives the proton to the reacting molecule Ra, converting it into a complex ion. In the complex ion RaH state, the molecule undergoes conversion and thereafter the proton returns to the acceptor to regenerate the initial acid-catalyst and set free the reaction product which is the molecule Rb. Thus the conversion in accordance to the donor–acceptor mechanism over a catalyst-acid may be represented as follows:

$$Ra + H^+A^- \rightarrow RaH^+ + A \rightarrow RbH^+ + A^- \rightarrow Rb + H^+A^-.$$

Upon proton addition to the hydrocarbon molecule a carbonium ion is formed, being a hypothetical intermediate compound in reactions of hydrocarbons over acid aluminosilicates. The carbonium ion is characterized by the presence of a trivalent carbon atom, i.e. one which lacks a pair of electrons to make a full octet. Therefore the carbonium ion is unstable and cannot exist independently, but must undergo a molecular rearrangement or react with other molecules.

Whitmore and collaborators regarded the carbonium ions as free ions having a very short lifetime because of their unstable electronic configuration. Yet their formation appears hardly probable owing to the large amount of energy necessary for separating them from anions in the system [31]. It is preferable to consider ion pairs or polar complexes as in the case of aluminum chloride and water.

C. COMPOSITION OF NATURAL CLAYS AND THE CHARACTERISTICS OF CLAYS HAVING CATALYTIC PROPERTIES

Research has shown that fine fractions of clays, siltstones, and sandstones have a complex multimineral character. Minerals of the montmorillonite and related groups hardly ever occur in nature in the pure state, but are quite broadly distributed in the form of mixtures. Thus as a first approximation it may be stated that the natural clay will be active only in so far as it contains active minerals.

The rock-forming mixtures, termed clays, contain the following minerals comprising the clay group: (1) the kaolinite group; (2) the illite group or hydromicas; (3) the montmorillonite group; (4) the group of allophanoids.

Clays of the first three types comprise the most general case. To this must be added the zeolite minerals which are widely distributed in nature and which form part of the composition of clay.

These brief remarks give an explanation why clays vary so much in regard to catalytic activity. At the same time it becomes clear why all natural clays, with the exception of some pure modifications of kaolin, possess a greater or lesser degree of catalytic activity. This is an important point in principle because the presence of true montmorillonite clays in nature, and particularly at the contact zone with petroliferous horizons, appears to be a rare exception and more commonly clays having a variable or limited activity are encountered. Yet the different geochemical trains of thought must be based upon widely occurring phenomena rather than on exceptions. It is necessary to show experimentally that even low-activity clays, in terms of geological cycles of time on one hand and with allowance for very high clay/organic matter ratios on the other hand, may ultimately give substantial results in regard to conversion of organic matter and specifically petroleum.

Clay occurs as a mixture in sandstones, marls, and limestones and if such a mixture has active properties, the results of conversion should be attributed to the presence of this mixture. It is by no means necessary that petroleum be in contact strictly with pure, activated and dry clay because the degree of conversion, which ultimately depends on catalysis and various energy relationships in the molecule, may vary within a wide range. The statistical direction of petroleum transformation is the same in all of the cases, but the paths along which the conversion proceeds and its stages and severity factor offer an infinite diversity that is algebraically expressed by the type of crude.

Various methods can be proposed for determining the activity of clays in terms of some nominal units. There were suggestions for determining the polymerizing capacity of clays. Granted that the polymerizing capacity, being based on their adsorptive capacity, also has some significance in regard to catalytic conversion, but since it is not the only factor in the conversion, we may hardly expect to obtain in such ways an objective evaluation of clays as catalytically active in terms of their "transformative" capacity. It may be possible to utilize alcohol dehydration reactions or some other reactions to provide a routine method for determining, in a rapid and reproducible manner, the results of conversion. Hydrogen disproportionation reactions in hydrocarbons appear to be an attractive method for evaluating the catalytic properties of clays because this method, naturally, reproduces most closely the conjectured reactions with hydrocarbons.

The dehydration of alcohols is rather easily accomplished in the presence of various dehydration agents, including natural and synthetic silica-alumina catalysts. The use of clays as dehydrating catalysts was investigated by A. V. Frost in the conversion of normal octyl alcohol to octylene [35].

Subsequently, a number of other researchers utilized natural clays both in the activated and unactivated state for the dehydration of various alcohols.

The dehydration capabilities of Saratov clays were studied by F. A. Slisarenko and N. G. Chen [29] in the dehydration of ethyl and isobutyl alcohol within a wide temperature range.

The investigations of these authors were interesting because of the fact that they used clays originating from the Sokolova Gora district which is the locality of a well-known oil field in the Lower Volga region. The clays used as catalysts were pretreated in various ways.

The catalyst to be tested was in every case in the form of a powder and the dehydration of alcohols over it was investigated in the temperature range of 200–450 °C. Ethyl and isobutyl alcohol were used in the dehydration. In every instance the gaseous product obtained when feeding ethyl alcohol vapors consisted of ethylene only, and when feeding isobutyl alcohol vapors, consisted only of isobutylene. No other gases were detected.

The results of experiments in the dehydration of alcohols over variously prepared clay are shown in Table 20.

From a comparison of data from the above experiments it is noted that, regardless of the method of their treatment, the clays display a substantial activity in the dehydration reactions of alcohols. Unactivated clay performs equally well as does the clay that has been acid-treated. Activation of clay with hydrochloric or sulfuric acid does not appreciably raise the degree of catalytic dehydration and in some cases, on the contrary, causes it to decrease sharply, which may be attributed to extraction of a certain portion of the dehydrating aluminosilicate from the clay during acid treatment. It is likewise worthy of note that the alkali-treated clay does not lose its dehydrating properties and therefore that not only the

TABLE 20. *Dehydration of Alcohols over Saratov Clay*
(According to F.A.Slisarenko and N.G.Chen [29])

Method of clay activation	Yield of gas in vol. % of the theoretical yield, at a temperature (°C)					
	200	250	300	350	400	450
For ethyl alcohol:						
Drying at 200°C	7.9	26.7	41.1	60.1	64.6	78.4
Calcining at 600°C	12.7	33.0	48.0	65.3	66.9	85.6
Treatment with hydrochloric acid	12.9	25.0	50.0	60.8	66.0	69.7
Treatment with sulfuric acid	7.9	23.7	47.1	57.6	65.8	68.3
Treatment with caustic alkali	13.2	14.8	15.9	28.0	37.4	60.1
For isobutyl alcohol:						
Drying at 200°C	5.6	43.0	55.8	59.9	62.2	75.2
Calcining at 600°C	20.9	43.1	59.5	63.1	72.1	79.1
Treatment with hydrochloric acid	23.7	35.1	56.0	64.9	65.5	75.7
Treatment with sulfuric acid	13.1	25.9	52.1	58.4	63.8	70.3
Treatment with caustic alkali	11.0	16.3	44.1	50.6	66.1	72.2

acidic but also the alkaline clays may fulfil their catalytic functions in the dehydration of organic compounds having an alcohol group.

The dehydrating properties of North Caucasian clays have been investigated by A.I.Bogomolov and O.A.Smirnova in 1956 in the dehydration of trimethyl carbinol to isobutylene. This alcohol splits off water with exceptional ease, a circumstance which permits evaluating the activity of weak dehydrating catalysts and rocks.

Dehydration of trimethyl carbinol was performed at a temperature of 120°C with an alcohol feed rate of 0.05 l. per l. of catalyst per hour. Through practically every rock sample of 40 ml volume there was passed 10 ml trimethylcarbinol at the rate of 2 ml alcohol per hour. In every case the gas liberated in the reaction consisted of isobutylene only, the amount of which served as a measure of the conversion of alcohol and simultaneously (conditionally) as a measure of the catalytic activity of rocks.

This method was used in testing various rock samples of Tertiary age with an organic carbon content of up to 2%, which had been recovered in the form of cores from exploratory wells drilled in the Terek-Daghestan oil region.

The results obtained for trimethyl carbinol dehydration over different rocks without their preliminary drying and activation are cited in Table 21.

The table shows the content of the clay fraction in the rock and the quantity of dehydrated alcohol under specified temperature conditions by each sample.

From the table it is apparent that every one of the sedimentary rock samples from the Terek-Daghestan oil region displays a well-defined catalytic activity in regard to dehydration of tri-methyl carbinol. The dehydration reaction is the more drastic, the greater the quantity of gas produced in the experiment and the higher the content of clay fractions in the particular sample tested.

Hence, the carrier of catalytic properties in the dehydration of alcohols, as in the polymerization of isobutylene, are likewise clay minerals. The trimethyl carbinol dehydration reaction takes place at temperatures as low as 120 °C over sedimentary rocks which have not been activated beforehand with acid or other agent. Clays, siltstones, and carbonate rocks functioned as catalysts without preliminary drying. Taking into account the formation of water in the process of decomposition of the alcohol itself, it becomes evi-dent that the doubts expressed by some geologists about the cata-lytic properties of moist natural clays have no justification at all.

TABLE 21. *Catalytic Activity of Northeast Caucasian Rocks in Regard to Dehydration of Trimethyl Carbinol (According to Data by A.I.Bogomolov and O.A.Smirnova, 1956)*

Rock	Residue insoluble in hydrochloric acid (%)	Content of clay fractions in rock (%)	Quantity of dehydrated trimethyl carbinol (%)
Calcareous clay	92.6	90.3	47.4
Silty clay	90.8	71.9	31.0
Gray siltstone	97.2	42.0	24.0
Marl	20.8	19.9	1.6
Glass (blank test)	—	—	0.1

The presence of more or less moisture certainly causes a sharp re-duction of the catalytic and adsorptive properties of rocks, but does not deprive them completely of such properties. These facts con-siderably extend the effective range of the action of clay formations

10 TP

as natural silica-alumina catalysts upon organic matter during the various phases of lithogenesis.

The reaction of the polymerization of unsaturated hydrocarbons by aluminosilicates was utilized by Brooks [38, 39] for evaluating the catalytic properties of various sedimentary rocks of the continent of America. Based on the capacity of decolorizing clays to polymerize olefins, Brooks utilized the polymerization of certain terpenes for evaluating the catalytic activity of sedimentary rocks of different lithological composition. The rock samples were first dried at a temperature of 300°C and then treated in the cold with two volumes of turpentine. Under these conditions the terpene

TABLE 22. *Polymerizing Action of Sedimentary Rocks and Some Other Minerals on Turpentine (According to Data by Brooks [38])*

Rock	Amount of polymer (%)
Fuller's earth (Georgia)	75
Sylvan shale	76
Red-bed clay	65
Tertiary clays	68
Glauconitic sand (New Jersey)	72
Glauconitic sand (Texas)	70
Serpentine (Easton)	60
Gray sandstone (Iran)	56
Stanley shale	57
Regan sandstone	50
Calvin sandstone	46
Simpson sandstone	34
Permian sandstone	30
Bentonite	34
Bauxite	58
Silica gel	23
Kaolin	12
Glaucosil (acid-leached glauconitic sand)	45
Prehnite (zeolite)	0
Stilbite (zeolite)	0
Talc	0
Infusorial earth	0
Powdered pumice	0
Ferric oxide, pure	0
Aluminum oxide, pure	0

hydrocarbons underwent condensation to high molecular polymers, the quantity of which was used as a measure of catalytic activity of rocks, other conditions being equal (Table 22).

From the data in Table 22 it is clear that all of the sedimentary rocks tested by Brooks proved to have an appreciable activity in the polymerization of unsaturated hydrocarbons and quite a number of them turned out to be as active as Fuller's earth, which is a clay of the montmorillonite group. It is notable also that two samples of the clays (red-bed clay and the clay of Tertiary age) showed an activity quite close to that of Fuller's earth, which was used as a standard of comparison. Six typical sandstones showed an activity on the average equal to more than one-half of the catalytic activity of Fuller's earth. Even bauxite manifested appreciable activity, presumably because of some contamination by clay minerals, whereas pure aluminum oxide proved to be entirely inactive under these conditions.

Nevertheless, it should be noted that polymerization of turpentine by means of clays, utilized by Brooks for evaluating the catalytic activity of sedimentary rocks, is quite a complex process. The reaction is accompanied by the formation of several products instead of a single one, since the initial turpentine is itself a mixture of different compounds rather than a single compound. Hence, there could hardly be an expectation in this case to get an objective indication of activity based on primary products.

In view of the latter fact, A. I. Bogomolov and O. A. Smirnova (in 1955) decided to evaluate the catalytic activity of rocks by the isobutylene polymerization reaction which had been thoroughly studied before by S. V. Levedev [24] and which is commercially important at the present time for the production of high octane gasoline. Isobutylene is polymerized over Floridin with extreme ease even at room temperature. Polymerization of isobutylene yields predominantly the dimer, but the possibility of also obtaining other higher molecular products is by no means excluded,

$$
\begin{array}{ccc}
CH_3 & CH_3 & CH_3 \quad CH_3 \\
| & | & | \quad\quad | \\
C{=}CH_2 + CH_2{=}C \rightarrow CH_3{-}C{-}CH{=}C{-}CH_3. \\
| & | & | \\
CH_3 & CH_3 & CH_3
\end{array}
$$

The isobutylene polymerization is convenient because the catalytic activity of rocks can be expressed quantitatively and compared through isobutylene consumption in the reaction. It is merely necessary to determine the isobutylene content in the gas before and after the reaction, which can be determined with sufficient accuracy. Unlike procedures used in other similar investigations, the catalytic activity of rocks in this case was tested without any preliminary activation with acid or other reagents. The researchers contemplated testing the activity of rocks at as low a temperature as possible and with a maximum of their natural moisture conserved in them. Therefore the isobutylene polymerization experiments were conducted at a temperature of 140°C and with humid clays without previously drying them. The moisture content of clays at the start of the experiment was found to be 14% and at the end of the experiment it was 4–6%. The clay to be tested was packed in the form of tablets into a glass tube, through which isobutylene was then passed at a constant temperature (140°C) and constant rate (45 l. gas per 1 liter rock per hour).†

The activity of each sample of rock was determined in terms of percentage of polymerized isobutylene. In accordance with this method, the tests were carried out on various samples of clay and other sedimentary rocks of Tertiary age having an organic carbon content of up to 2%. The rock samples consisted of core material recovered from exploratory wells drilled in North Caucasus. Two series of samples were tested. The first one included rocks from the vicinity of Sleptsovskaya village in Grozny province. The second series consisted of rocks from the North Osetian district of Argudan.

The latter are more metamorphized in comparison with rocks from the Grozny province, which are specific to the zone of forward mountain ranges of the Caucasus massif. According to L. P. Gmid [13] the Maikop clay rocks of the Argudan district are of fine particle size, almost completely free from sandy and silty material, and low in carbonates. In regard to mineral composition the clays are largely of the hydromicaceous, illite type. Among authigenous minerals in Maikop clay rocks of the Argudan district, finely dispersed pyrite is always present and siderite very rarely so.

The Chokrak and Karagan clays of Grozny province (vicinity of Sleptsovskaya village, Terek range) are represented by silts, siltstones and, rather infrequently, by more finely pulverized varieties.

† As a matter of fact, 3 l. isobutylene was passed through 40 ml samples of each rock for a period of $3\frac{1}{2}$ hr.

In silty clays the content of silt-sized material ranges from 2.2 to 25% and in clayey siltstones it does not exceed 39.3%. In fine particle size varieties of clays the silty material is present in negligible amounts, e.g. not over 1–5%.

As far as mineralogical composition of the colloidal fraction (0.001 mm) of clay from this district is concerned, the clays may be classified as hydromicaceous of the illite or, more rarely, of the monothermite type, in spots with an admixture of beidellite or kaolinite. In L. M. Gmid's opinion, the beidellite and kaolinite have perhaps been formed from hydromica on the bottom of the Chokrak-Karagan sea.

The composition of rocks and their catalytic activity in regard to polymerization of isobutylene are cited in Table 23.

The table indicates that clays, siltstones, and carbonate rocks of Tertiary age in Northeast Caucasus have a well-defined catalytic activity in regard to polymerization of isobutylene at a temperature of 140 °C.

The activity of clays is several times higher than that of carbonate rocks.

The catalytic activity of rocks, other conditions being equal, depends on the content of the clay fraction in the rock. This serves as a basis for the statement that the active factor in the rocks is indeed the clay minerals capable of exerting a catalytic action on various reactions of organic matter not only under laboratory conditions, but also in natural surroundings.

From Table 23 it follows also that the metamorphic processes in rocks cause an appreciable reduction in their catalytic activity. Relatively less metamorphic rocks of the Grozny province (Terek range) exhibit an appreciably higher activity as compared with the metamorphic rocks of the Argudan district in North Osetiya, which belong to the mountain zone of Chernye Gory.

It has been noted that the presence of a substantial amount of organic matter likewise appreciably decreases the catalytic properties of rocks through forming an organo-mineral complex therewith. High molecular-weight organic substances tend to block the active sites in clay minerals, thereby inactivating them.

The reaction of disproportionation of hydrogen and radicals is remarkable also in that it does not need any foreign source of hydrogen and utilizes only the hydrogen available in the system in which the particular process takes place.

Being natural silica-alumina catalysts, the clays are capable of stimulating polymerization and dehydration processes mentioned above as well as hydrogen disproportionation reactions in the molecules of organic matter.

TABLE 23. *Catalytic Activity of Rocks in Regard to Polymerization of Isobutylene (According to Data by A.I.Bogomolov and O.A.Smirnova, 1955)*

Lithological composition	Organic carbon content in the rock, %	Hydrochloric-acid-insoluble residue, %	Content of clay fractions in the insoluble residue, %	Content of clay fractions in the rock, %	Quantity of polymerized isobutylene, %
Rocks in the Groznyi province (vicinity of Sleptsovskaya village)					
Calcareous clay	1.6	91.2	94.7	86.5	47.5
Calcareous clay	1.7	91.6	88.2	81.0	45.0
Silty calcareous clay	1.0	97.6	68.8	67.2	37.3
Silty calcareous clay	1.1	97.8	60.7	59.6	36.6
Gray siltstone	0.3	97.2	43.2	42.0	24.0
Marl	1.4	20.8	95.7	19.9	9.9
Glass (blank test)	—	—	—	—	0.0
Rocks from North Osetiya (Argudan district)					
Calcareous clay	1.2	95.0	96.3	91.4	40.0
Calcareous clay	1.8	94.4	96.8	91.3	37.0
Finely divided calcareous clay	1.4	95.4	96.3	91.8	36.4
Calcareous clay	1.0	94.4	96.8	91.4	34.2
Lime-clay	1.4	93.6	90.7	85.0	26.2
Silty calcareous clay	1.3	96.4	78.5	75.7	12.4
Lime-clay	1.4	76.0	91.1	69.2	9.2

This role of clays was pointed out by A.V.Frost [33] in a series of investigations on the conversion of various organic substances over silica-alumina catalysts. These investigations led to a number of conclusions about the different degree of activity of clays and other sedimentary rocks, which are summarized as follows.

In a study of hydrogen disproportionation in hydrocarbons, the most active of all the preparations proved to be: (1) synthetic silica gels which had adsorbed aluminum salts from solution; (2) precipitates from solutions containing silicon and aluminum; (3) montmorillonite clays (Floridin, Gumbrin, Kil, Nalchikine, and others†); (4) solid gel-like products resulting from the hydrolysis of nephelines and related rocks; (5) Japanese acid clays; (6) tripoli from the Zikeev beds in Smolensk province; (7) Khalilov nickel-bearing clays; (8) bauxites from Tula province; and (9) Chovdar kaolinite from the Azerbaijan S.S.R.

Considerably less active, but capable of being activated to a varying degree by acids, were: (1) Zmiev and Muslyumkin bleaching clays (Tataria); (2) Tavtiman kaolinite clay from Bashkiria; (3) clays from the Old Groznyi oil fields; (4) Maikop clay; and (5) the fine fraction (less than 0.01 mm) from Azerbaijan oil sands.

Slightly active or inactive were: (1) Chasov Yar clay, monothermitic; (2) Glukhov clay; (3) Chelyabinsk bauxite; (4) Tikhvin bauxite; (5) Akhaltsykh kieselguhr; (6) Zhuravlin bauxite; (7) Prosyanov kaolin; (8) Popov kaolin; and (9) Volynian kaolin.

In contrast to the research discussed above, our study of the catalytic activity of rocks was conducted without preliminary activation with acid and drying [5]. The testing of clays and other sedimentary rocks was effected at a temperature of 250–280°C, specifically in the catalytic conversion of diphenylethane to benzene and the corresponding polymer:

$$2C_6H_5{-}CH_2{-}CH_2{-}C_6H_5 \rightarrow$$

$$\rightarrow C_6H_6 + C_6H_5{-}CH_2{-}CH_2{-}C_6H_4{-}CH_2{-}CH_2{-}C_6H_5 .$$

The relative catalytic activity of rocks was evaluated in this case by the degree of diphenylethane decomposition as indicated by the amount of benzene liberated in the reaction. The object of our investigation were the clays and clayey siltstones from North Caucasian oil fields. Data on the catalytic activity of rocks in the disproportionation of hydrogen and radicals in the diphenylethane molecule are presented in Table 24.

† These are varieties of clay mixtures whose names are derived from age or place of occurrence, composition, etc. For example, "Gumbrin" is a Cenomanian bleaching clay from Georgia; "Kil" is a bleaching clay composed mainly of montmorillonite and beidellite (see also footnote on p. 80). [Transl. Ed.]

TABLE 24. *Catalytic Activity of Rocks in the Disproportionation of Diphenylethane (According to Data by A.I.Bogomolov, N.V.Strigaleva and O.A.Smirnova [5])*

Catalyst	Yield of benzene, calculated on initial diphenylethane, %
Without catalyst	0.0
Synthetic silica-alumina	25.7
Acid-activated Askanite	21.8
Unactivated Askanite (montmorillonite)	13.1
Kaolinite clay (Upper Maikop, North Daghestan)	7.2
Illite clay (Lower Chokrak, North Daghestan)	4.4
Illite clay (Lower Maikop, North Daghestan)	3.7
Cambrian blue clay (Leningrad province)	2.6
Illite clay (Upper Chokrak, North Daghestan)	0.8
Monothermitic clay (Lower Chokrak, North Daghestan)	0.5
Quartz sand	0.0
Carbonate rock	0.0

The data in Table 24 indicate that, if the activity of activated Askanite be taken as a standard, the unactivated Upper Maikop clay from North Daghestan is one-third as active and the Cambrian blue clay is only one-ninth as active.

From the data in the table it follows that the activity of clays depends on their composition. Clays of the montmorillonite group contain a lesser amount of alkaline elements and have well-defined catalytic properties. On the other hand clays of the illite group have a higher content of alkalies and a considerably lower activity. The quantity of alkali metals in illite clays is 3–6%. Clay minerals from Chokrak and Karagan formations in Northeastern Caucasus are relatively inactive, being hydromicas of the illite group with a substantial content of alkali in them. According to geological surveys [13], accumulation of sediments in Chokrak time in the eastern part of North Caucasus took place in a weakly alkaline environment. The conditions in the sediment accumulation medium and the composition of salts in the basin must undoubtedly have an effect on the catalytic and other properties of clay minerals towards increasing or decreasing their activity. Yet the catalytic properties of clays, of course, may change as the deposits pass into a different physical environment. The catalytically active clays may prove to be only slightly active or entirely inactive, while on the other hand clays which had a low activity may become activated to a greater or lesser degree.

Based on general theoretical precepts about the activity of silica-alumina catalysts, the deactivation of clays may be readily accomplished by replacing the hydrogen cation with the cation of an alkali metal through changing the acid or neutral medium to a weakly alkaline one. The present authors have carried out in the laboratories of VNIGRI† some experiments relating to activation of low-activity clays by agents which, in principle, might occur under natural conditions. Such activating agents may be organic acids, particularly their low molecular-weight representatives.

Fifty to sixty per cent of the oil fraction of bitumen from contemporary deposits are acids. The content of organic acids in the oil fractions of the bitumen from fossil deposits can be traced down to Devonian age.

The processes of the transformation of organic matter, especially in the early stages, are accompanied to a considerable extent by the formation of the simplest organic acids, such as butyric and acetic acids. Acetic acid may be formed also in later stages of the transformation of organic matter, since it has been discovered in coal, peat, and lignite. Hence organic acids may be regarded as potentially responsible for activation of clays under natural conditions. With this reasoning in mind, activation of inactive and slightly active clays was carried out with acetic acid of very low concentration. Two samples of inactive clays from Northeastern Caucasus on treatment with a weak solution of acetic acid showed an activity equal to 31% and 10%, respectively, of that of unactivated Askanite (montmorillonite). The catalytic activity of clays depends upon, among other factors, the qualitative composition of the organic substance present in the rock. Together, the organic substance and the rock form an intricate and fairly stable organo-mineral complex. The high molecular-weight organic compounds of kerogen and asphaltic-resinous substances may block the active sites in clays and thus to a substantial extent reduce their catalytic and adsorptive properties. This presumably is the reason for the low catalytic activity of natural clays, which always contain a greater or smaller amount of organic material.

† All-Union Petroleum Scientific Research Institute for Geological Exploration. [Transl. Ed.]

To establish the significance of this factor, a study was made in which the organic material was removed from rocks by oxidation with hydrogen peroxide without appreciably disturbing the mineral portion of the rock. A clay sample containing 0.7 % of organic carbon had after treatment with hydrogen peroxide only 0.2 % of organic matter in its composition. Another sample with 13.8 % of organic carbon had after treatment a total of 0.3 % organic matter. Clays that had been freed from organic matter by the above method were tested for catalytic activity. Removal of organic matter had sharply changed their properties. The activity as compared with montmorillonite rose from practically zero to 26 % in the first case and from 3 to 43.5 % in the second case.

BIBLIOGRAPHY

1. ANDREEV, P. F. *Geol. Sbornik VNIGRI*, No. 2, nov. ser., issue 95 (1965).
2. ANDREEV, P. F. *Geokhim. Sbornik VNIGRI*, No. 4, issue 105, 1957.
3. ANDREEV, P. F., MASAGUTOVA, D. A., POLYAKOVA, N. N. and CHERNYSHOVA, A. S. *Geol. Sbornik VNIGRI*, No. 1, nov. ser., issue 83 (1955).
4. BALLOD, A. P. and TOPCHIEVA, K. V. *Usp. Khimii*, **20**, No. 2 (1951).
5. BOGOMOLOV, A. I., GORSKAYA, A. I. and MESSINEVA, M. A. *Sbornik "Origin of Petroleum"*, Gostoptekhizdat, 1955.
6. BOGOMOLOV, A. I. and SMIRNOVA, O. A. *Zh. prikl. Khimii*, **27**, No. 6 (1954).
7. BITEPAZH, YU. A. *Zh. Obshchei Khimii*, **17**, 199 (1947).
8. VERNADSKII, V. I. *Geochemical Essays*, ONTI, 1934.
9. VEBER, V. V., *et al. Accumulation and Transformation of Organic Matter in Contemporary Marine Sediments*, Gostoptekhizdat, 1956.
10. HANSFORD, R. *Sbornik "Catalysis, Catalysts in Organic Reactions"*, Translated from English. IL. M., 1955.
11. GALINSKAYA-RIVLIN, G. YA. Studies in the sphere of catalytic conversion of petroleum. Author's abstract of his own candidate thesis. Publ. by LGU, 1952.
12. GUSTAVSON, G. G. *Zh. Russk. Khim. Obshch.* **16**, 244 (1884).
13. GMID, L. P. *Geol. Sbornik VNIGRI*, No. 1, nov. ser., issue 83 (1955).
14. GURVICH, L. G. *Zh. Russ. Khim. Obshch.* **44** (1912).
15. DOBRYANSKII, A. F. *Geochemistry of Petroleum*, Gostoptekhizdat, 1948.
16. DOBRYANSKII, A. F. *Vestn. LGU*, No. 1 (1950).
17. DOBRYANSKII, A. F. and BOGOMOLOV, A. I. *Geokhim. Sbornik VNIGRI*, No. 1, nov. ser., issue 28 (1949).
18. DOBRYANSKII, A. F., BOGOMOLOV, A. I. and SHKLYAR, I. V. *Zh. prikl. Khimii*, **22**, No. 10 (1949).
19. DOBRYANSKII, A. F. and GAVRILOV, B. G. *Byull. LGU*, No. 23 (1949).
20. ZELINSKII, N. D. *Selected Works*, vol. 1, Izd. Akad. Nauk SSSR, 1941, pp. 627–60.
21. IPAT'EV, V. N. *Catalytic Reactions at High Temperatures and Pressures*, Moscow, 1936.

22. KAMENSKAYA, I.N. Chemistry and technology of products of shale processing, *Trudy VNIIPS*, No. 2, 1954.
23. LEBEDEV, S.V. The Problem of Polymerization of Ethylenic Compounds. Paper, 3rd Mendeleev Conference, 1922.
24. LEBEDEV, S.V. and BORGMAN, A. *Zh. Obshchei Khimii*, **5**, 1545 (1935).
25. MIESSEROV, K.G. *Usp. Khimii*, **22**, No. 3 (1953).
26. NENITESCU, K.D. *Usp. Khimii*, **26**, No. 4 (1957).
27. PETROVA, YU.N., KARPOVA, I.P. and KASATKINA, N.F. *Sbornik VNIGRI "On Conditions of Petroleum Genesis"*, 1955.
28. SATTAR-ZADE, I.S. and FROST, A.V. *Trudy Azerb. Gos. Univ., Seriya Khim.*, No. 1 (1951).
29. SLISARENKO, F.A. and CHEN, N.G. *Zh. prikl. Khimii*, **23**, No. 8 (1950).
30. TISHCHENKO, V.E. *Zh. Russk. Fiz.-Khim. Obshch.* **33**, 173 (1901).
31. FARKAS, A. *Physical Chemistry of Hydrocarbons*. Transl. from English, Gastoptekhizdat, 1957.
32. FROST, A.V. *Usp. Khimii*, **14**, No. 6 (1945).
33. FROST, A.V. *Uch. Zap. MGU*, issue 86, kn. 1 (1946).
34. FROST, A.V. and OSNITSKAYA, L.K. *Sbornik "In Memoriam of Acad. I.M. Gubkin"*, Publ. by Akad. Nauk SSSR, 1951.
35. FROST, A.V. *Dokl. Akad. Nauk SSSR*, **37**, Nos. 7–8, 255 (1942).
36. CHISTYAKOV, A.N. Thermocatalytic conversions of some oxygenated compounds over silica-alumina catalyst. Author's abstract of his own candidate thesis, Leningrad Technol. Inst., 1954.
37. CHUKHROV, F.V.*Colloids in the Earth's Crust*,Publ. byAkad. Nauk SSSR,1955.
38. BROOKS, B. *Bull. Am. Ass. Petr. Geol.* **15**, 611 (1931).
39. BROOKS, B. *Bull. Am. Ass. Petr. Geol.* **32**, No. 12 (1948).
40. BROOKS, B. *Bull. Am. Ass. Petr. Geol.* **33** (1949).
41. BROOKS, B. *Ind. Eng. Chem.* **40**, No. 11 (1952).
42. ENGLER, C. *Berichte d. Deutsch. Chem. Ges.* **21**, 2816 (1888).
43. ENGLER, C. and SEVERIN, E. *Zeitschr. f. Angew. Chem.* **153** (1912).
44. ENGLER, C. *Das Erdöl*, vol II.
45. GRAEFE, E. *Petroleum*, No. 2, 69–79 (1910).
46. HEUSLER, *Zeitschr. f. Angew. Chem.* No. 10, 288·(1896).
47. HVIID, N. *Petroleum*, No. 8, 459 (1911).
48. HOFFMANN, U., ENDELL, K. and WILM, D. *Kristallstruktur und Quellung von Montmorillonit, Zs. Krist.* **86** (1933).
49. HOFFMANN, U., ENDELL, K. and WILM, D. *Zeitschr. f. Angew. Chem.* **30**, 539 (1934).
50. KÜNKLER, *Zentralblatt*, 2031 (1910).
51. MITRA, R. and RAJAGOPALAN, K. *J. Phys.* **22**, 129 (1948).
52. SABATIER and SENDERENS, J. *Comptes Rend.* **149**, 213–15 (1909).
53. SABATIER, B. and MAILHE, A. *Comptes Rend.* **156**, 1731 (1913).
54. OCHSENIUS, *Natur.* No. 29 (1882).
55. OCHSENIUS, *Zeitschr. f. Angew. Chem.* **33** (1881).
56. WHITMORE, F. *Ind. Eng. Chem., Ind. Ed.* **26**, 94 (1934).
57. WHITMORE, F. *Chem. Eng. News*, **26**, No. 10, 668 (1948).
58. WHITMORE, F. and WILSON, C. *J. Am. Chem. Soc.* **63**, 2035.
59. UBBELOHDE and WORONIN, S. *Petroleum*, No. 7, 333 (1912).
60. ZALOZIECKI and KLARFELD, *Chemische Zeitung*, No. 49, 1170 (1907).

CHAPTER VII

THERMOCATALYTIC TRANSFORMATIONS OF HETEROGENEOUS ORGANIC COMPOUNDS

Two fundamental points of view exist about the genesis of hydrocarbons from originally deposited organic matter.

According to one viewpoint the hydrocarbons are inherent compounds of the initial organic material. From this viewpoint, all of the subsequent transformations consist of the separation of this hydrocarbon fraction as a result of various supposed but unproved processes or through disappearance of the non-hydrocarbon mass, resulting in the relative accumulation of hydrocarbons. As a certain concession, the supporters of such hypotheses admit, to some extent, the biological formation of hydrocarbons during the stage of organogenic ooze. From this viewpoint the further destiny of hydrocarbons does not involve the conversion of some types of hydrocarbons into other types, but in the disappearance of a certain portion of them as a result of oxidation or through assimilation by bacteria at some later stages of geochemical development. If this viewpoint is accepted, then, of course, there is no longer any inherent interest in discussing the way hydrocarbons have originated, because this process is then shifted into the sphere of action of living organisms.

The other point of view likewise accepts the existence of native hydrocarbons, but the role of such hydrocarbons is absolutely negligible. The main source of hydrocarbons is considered to be the organic matter that undergoes various successive transformations involving the loss of hetero atoms. The very complexity of such transformation processes excludes the possibility that the structure of the original substance is retained. Thus the hydrocarbons are a secondary product as compared with the components of organisms. Nevertheless, according to this point of view, inevitably it must be assumed that various intermediate products exist as links between the original organic matter and petroleum hydrocarbons. The necessity for such an assumption arises because under conditions of low temperatures no direct transition is possible from the complex structures of organic matter to the relatively simple structures of hydrocarbons.

The problem facing the researcher involves the study of processes capable of transforming non-hydrocarbon compounds into hydrocarbons. To begin with, the composition of buried organic matter is practically unknown. There may, of course, be present varying amounts of humic substances, acids, waxes, and other heterogeneous compounds, but along with these compounds the buried organic matter contains also a preponderant amount of substances of unknown functional type in the form of insoluble residue. It is well known that this material contains oxygen, sulfur and nitrogen in varying quantities. However, little is known of the varieties of functional groups that contain these atoms. They are difficult to determine because of the exceptionally complex structure of the material itself. Investigations have shown that this material is formed in part during the initial stages in the transformation of organic matter as a consequence of biogenic and abiogenic processes, the chemical mechanisms of which are entirely unknown at present.

Though the composition of the predominant portion of the organic matter is not known, yet it may be stated with complete assurance that the functional nature of hetero atoms is no secret. Oxygen may be present in the form of hydroxyl, carbonyl, carboxyl or ether groups. Thus the compound containing an oxygen atom may be regarded as being of the alcohol, ketone, acid or ether type. Likewise in the case of nitrogen or sulfur it is quite reasonable to expect the presence of groups that are typical for the different heterogeneous compounds. The functional character of hetero atoms in the organic substance of sedimentary rocks cannot be determined in every case because the insoluble nature of the organic substance present in rocks does not permit separation of the compounds of given functional type nor determination of their quantitative content. Abiogenic, including also catalytic, processes of transformation of buried organic matter involve elimination of hetero atoms, and a study of this process may yield valuable information for comprehending the genesis of compounds containing successively smaller numbers of hetero atoms and finally of the hydrocarbons themselves. This applies also to natural petroleum because any crude contains oxygen, sulfur and nitrogen compounds in greater or lesser amounts. Consequently, the transformations of such compounds, e.g. various acids, alcohols, ketones, and sulfur compounds, may furnish some indication of the transformations of organic matter in rocks and of heterogeneous compounds in petroleum. Hence there arises the need to study the behavior of different types of organic compounds, particularly under mild temperature conditions and in the presence of catalytic agents. Quite evidently, the transformation rates of heterogeneous compounds of different types will be different. It is understood that some of them will be converted with relative difficulty while for others these processes may take place with greater ease. Thus it is not possible to draw a boundary between the transformations of various non-hydrocarbon compounds comprising a complex mixture. Yet certain relationships derived for representative individual compounds may be extended to a substance of unknown composition but having known functions. Unfortunately, only a scant amount of pertinent data is available in the literature, especially in regard to conversions of organic compounds at temperatures up to 250–300 °C. The information given below represents merely a first attempt at systematic arrangement of literature references and the experimental data on the conversion of organic compounds of different types. This information, of course, does not solve the problem of the fate and of chemical transformations of buried organic matter and heterogeneous compounds of petroleum, yet it tends to provide markers defining the course of further studies in this sphere.

A. CONVERSION OF OXYGEN COMPOUNDS OVER ALUMINOSILICATES

1. Conversion of acids

(a) Reaction mechanisms

The conversion of organic acids in the presence of aluminosilicate catalysts may take place according to different mechanisms. In one of them the formation of the saturated hydrocarbon takes place without rearrangement of the carbon framework of the molecule, merely by splitting-off of carbon dioxide. Processes of this sort are known as decarboxylation reactions of acids and may be expressed for monobasic saturated aliphatic acids by the mechanism

$$C_nH_{2n+1}-COOH \rightarrow C_nH_{2n+2} + CO_2. \tag{1}$$

In the second case the reaction may proceed likewise without disturbance of the framework of the molecule, but with formation of an olefinic hydrocarbon, carbon monoxide, and water.

$$C_nH_{2n+1}-COOH \rightarrow C_nH_{2n} + CO + H_2O. \tag{2}$$

According to a third variant, a ketone may be obtained as the principal reaction product. The latter reaction is likewise well known in organic chemistry as ketonization of acids. Ketones are formed from acids not only on contact with aluminosilicates, but also in the thermal decomposition of salts and in a number of other processes.

The ketone, being in a certain sense an intermediate reaction product, may in turn be converted to hydrocarbons via different mechanisms to give different hydrocarbons.

$$2C_nH_{2n+1}-COOH \rightarrow C_nH_{2n+1}-CO-C_nH_{2n+1} + H_2O + CO_2. \tag{3}$$

Finally, the conversion of acids may proceed with destruction to the final reaction products which are methane, carbon, carbon dioxide, and water.

$$C_nH_{2n+1}-COOH \rightarrow CO_2 + qCH_4 + mC. \tag{4}$$

Of course, the above-mentioned variants are not the only possible mechanisms. In the last of the foregoing cases (4), the decomposition of the acid may not occur all at once to methane and carbon, since this would require a high energy potential, but may take place sequentially via a series of hydrocarbon-like compounds having varying degrees of hydrogen saturation and thus belonging to different types. This applies especially to the higher homologs of fatty acids, which explains the diverse composition of the products of their conversion at different temperatures.

In evaluating the relative probability of reactions for the conversion of oxygenated compounds, i.e. acids, ketones, and alcohols, it is necessary to consider from the energy point of view the fact that the values of free energy for carbon dioxide and water are very substantial and have a negative sign. It is known that the free energy of formation ($\Delta F°$) of carbon dioxide from the elements under standard conditions is $-94,260$ cal/mol. For water it is $-54,640$ cal/mol. The formation of carbon dioxide and water as final reaction products in the irreversible process should incur a substantial reduction in the free energy level of the entire system. Therefore the reactions occurring with the formation of carbon dioxide and water are "profitable" from the energy viewpoint and that is the reason why organic acids and alcohols are prone to all kinds of decarboxylation and dehydration reactions, even at relatively moderate temperatures. This is true also to some extent for reactions occurring with the formation of methane and elemental carbon. For methane, $\Delta F° = -12,140$ cal/mol, and for elementary carbon (graphite), its value is zero. For example, the conversion of butyric acid according to the first mechanism to form propane and carbon dioxide†

$$C_3H_7-COOH \text{ (liq.)} \rightarrow C_3H_8 + CO_2$$

$$-90,750 \qquad\qquad -5610 \quad -94,260$$

$$\Delta F_s° = -9120$$

is accompanied by a reduction of -9120 cal/mol in the free energy of the system. Consequently, the decarboxylation of butyric acid under these conditions is thermodynamically opportune. Calculations of this sort were carried out by us [6] on the basis of data available in the literature [9, 17, 19, 27] also for other acids, not only according to the first reaction mechanism of decarboxylation but also according to other reaction mechanisms.

The change in the amount of free energy $\Delta F°$ in reactions relating to conversion of acids has been calculated for the temperatures of 298, 400, 500, and 800°K, which correspond to 25, 127, 227, and 527°C, respectively.

The results of such calculations are presented in Tables 25–28 and plotted in Figs. 45–48

† In this example the computations have been made for a standard temperature of 298.16°K or 25°C. The compounds were assumed to be present in the following state: the acid as a liquid, and the propane and carbon dioxide as gases.

TABLE 25. *Change in Free Energy (ΔF^0) in cal/mol in the Decarboxylation of Acids at Different Temperatures, According to Mechanism 1*

Acid	298.16°K	400°K	500°K	800°K
Formic (liq.)	−11,560	− 16,884	− 21,978	−37,412
Acetic (liq.)	−12,600	−20,541	−26,916	−45,738
n-Butyric (liq.)	−9120	−15,385	−21,532	−39,969
Palmitic (solid)	+4210	−7442	−18,688	−52,423
Benzoic (solid)	−4710	−12,200	−19,680	−42,094

TABLE 26. *Change in Free Energy (ΔF°) in cal/mol in the Conversion of Acids to Olefins and Carbon Dioxide at Different Temperatures, According to Mechanism 2*

Acid	298.16°K	400°K	500°K	800°K
Formic (liq.)	− 4744	−11,054	− 17,215	−35,697
Acetic (liq.)	+14,503	+6242	− 1800	−25,947
n-Butyric (liq.)	+18,296	+7903	−2309	− 32,945
Palmitic (solid)	+32,056	+15,845	+487	−45,586

TABLE 27. *Change in Free Energy (ΔF°) in cal/mol in the Ketonization of Acids at Different Temperatures, According to Mechanism 3*

Acid	298.16°K	400°K	500°K	800°K
Acetic (liq.)	+1102	−3913	−8535	−22,403
n-Butyric (liq.)	+741	−4318	−9262	− 24,900
Acetic (liq.) to ketone	+25,564	+18,960	+12,550	− 6680

TABLE 28. *Change in Free Energy (ΔF°) in cal/mol in the Conversion of Acids with Breakdown of the Carbon Framework of the Molecule at Different Temperatures, According to Mechanism 4*

Acid	298.16°K	400°K	500°K	800°K
Acetic (liq.)	−12,600	−20,541	−26,916	−45,738
n-Butyric (liq.)	−27,790	−36,679	−45,410	−71,603
Polmitic (solid)	−111,380	− 142,539	−173,000	−263,400
Benzoic (solid)	− 53,770	−62,229	−70,542	−95,482

The data cited in the graphs and tables indicate that decarboxylation of acids according to mechanism 1 with the formation of carbon dioxide and the corresponding hydrocarbon is quite consistent

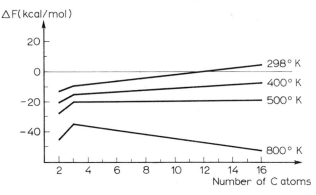

FIG. 45. Change in free energy in decarboxylation reactions of the homologous series of saturated fatty acids at different temperatures.

from the energy viewpoint (Table 25 and Fig. 45). These data likewise indicate that in the low temperature region, below $500\,°K$ ($227\,°C$), the tendency to decarboxylation decreases in the homologous series of acids with rise in molecular weight. For lower representatives of this series these reactions are relatively easy to

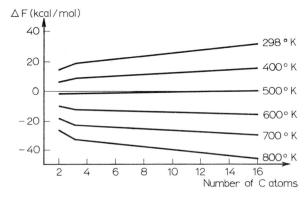

FIG. 46. Change in free energy in decomposition reactions with the formation of olefins and carbon monoxide in the homologous series of saturated fatty acids at different temperatures.

accomplish, but for the high molecular representatives they are somewhat more difficult. The formation of olefins and carbon monoxide according to mechanism 2 is thermodynamically feasible only at a temperature of 500°K (227°C) or higher, and in the region of low temperatures a reaction of this type is less likely from the energy viewpoint than the decarboxylation reaction (Table 26 and Fig. 46).

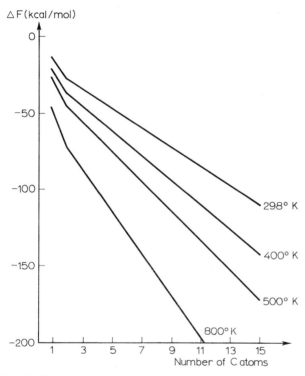

Fig. 47. Change in free energy in decomposition reactions of the homologous series of saturated fatty acids at different temperatures.

Since breakdown of acids is accompanied by the formation of compounds having high negative values of $\Delta F°$, such reactions are thermodynamically the most justified and all other conceivable reactions are merely a step in the path to their complete breakdown (Table 27 and Fig. 47). In natural reducing environments the organic acids may form a series of intermediate products, including hydrocarbons of different molecular weights and different types. Yet the final products of all these conversions on the way to complete mineralization of organic matter during geological time will be carbon dioxide, water, graphite and methane, which are in conformity with the thermodynamic outline. On comparing the change in amount of free energy for the individual acids in reactions according to the different mechanisms, it may be noted that breakdown of acids to olefins and carbon monoxide is hardly probable in the low temperature region. Conversion to ketones appears more probable.

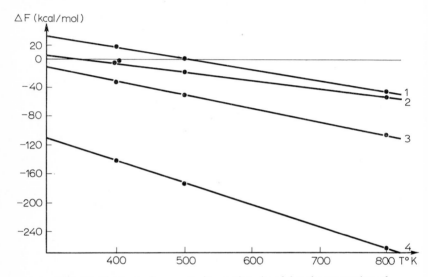

Fig. 48. Change in free energy in reactions involving the conversion of palmitic acid. *1* formation of olefin and carbon monoxide (mechanism 2); *2* decarboxylation (mechanism 1); *3* decomposition with incomplete breakdown; *4* decomposition with complete breakdown of the carbon skeleton (mechanism 3).

A similar situation obtains also in the case of other fatty acids, but with rise in molecular weight of the acid the breakdown may give decomposition products of great diversity.

For high molecular-weight acids the breakdown may vary in extent from simple decarboxylation to total decomposition into carbon, methane, and carbon dioxide.

The presence of larger size fragments of the carbon chain (incomplete breakdown) in the reaction products gives an intermediate value of ΔF. In the graph plotted for ΔF as a function of T, the straight lines corresponding to such reactions will lie between the marginal values of the variables (Fig. 48).

An example selected at random relates to the conversion of palmitic acid via the reaction

$$2C_{15}H_{31}COOH \text{ (solid)} \rightarrow C_6H_6 + 2C_6H_{12} + C_8H_{18} + 4CH_4 + 2CO_2$$

$$\begin{array}{cccccc} -80,000 & +30,850 & +7590 & +4140 & -12,140 & -94,260 \end{array}$$

$$\Delta F° = -11,380 \text{ cal/mol.}$$

In the above example the group composition of the conversion products approximately corresponds to experimental data on the conversion of high molecular acids: aliphatic hydrocarbons 42%, naphthenes 39%, and aromatics 19%.

Thus in conditions of petroleum genesis, the most significant reactions are those involving the breakdown of acids, including decarboxylation as a special case. In the process of evolution of acids together with other buried organic remnants, the breakdown reactions incur the formation of hydrocarbons and their further conversion ultimately to graphite and methane. Consequently, the hydrocarbons originating from acids in the earth's crust are merely a temporary and yet an unavoidable and, from the energy viewpoint, justifiable stage along the path to complete mineralization of acids to carbon dioxide, water, graphite, and methane.

(b) Experimental data on the conversion of acids

The literature contains a considerable amount of data on the pyrolysis of acids and on their catalytic conversion over oxide type catalysts and salts of heavy metals. However, the thermocatalytic conversions of acids over aluminosilicates have been investigated to a very limited extent as yet. The few studies relating to this subject are limited chiefly to investigations of low molecular-weight fatty acids, whereas catalytic conversions of high molecular-weight members of this series have not been studied at all.

Low molecular-weight fatty acids

The conversion of acetic acid over alumina and barium, calcium, and strontium carbonates was studied for the first time in considerable detail by V. N. Ipat'ev [14].

On the basis of experimental investigations the author came to the conclusion that among all of the forms of acid decomposition, its conversion to ketone at 500 °C is the most vigorous one.

R. D. Obolentsev and Yu. N. Usov [25] investigated the conversion of acetic acid over aluminosilicate catalyst at a temperature of 400 °C and likewise observed the formation of substantial amounts of acetone. The gas contained CO_2, H_2, C_2H_4, iso-C_4H_8, C_4H_{10} and other components. The isobutylene noted in the experiments must obviously be regarded as a secondary reaction product formed during the decomposition of acetone.

The most detailed study of the conversion of acetic, butyric and caprylic acids at a temperature of 450 °C was carried out by M. Demorest, D. Moobery and D. Damfort [60]. The catalyst used in the experiments was a synthetic silica-alumina and the components of this catalyst were pure aluminum oxide and silica gel. As demonstrated by the investigations, in the presence of this catalyst the fatty acids undergo a conversion to ketones and decompose to give an olefin, carbon monoxide, and water. For butyric acid, this is expressed by the following reactions:

$$2CH_3CH_2CH_2COOH \rightarrow C_3H_7\!-\!CO\!-\!C_3H_7 + CO_2 + H_2O;$$

$$CH_3CH_2CH_2COOH \rightarrow C_3H_6 + CO + H_2O.$$

The conversion indicated by the second equation proceeded most energetically. In the conversion of acetic acid, however, the reaction producing carbon monoxide, olefin, and water proved to be a subordinate reaction, and the major portion of the acetic acid was converted to acetone, carbon dioxide, and water. The components of the silica-alumina catalyst, being silica gel and pure aluminum oxide, accelerate the decomposition of acids principally to ketones and carbon dioxide, whereas aluminosilicates at this temperature favor their decomposition predominantly to carbon monoxide, olefin, and water.

The foregoing examples of the conversion of low molecular fatty acids refer mainly to their decomposition at cracking temperatures. Low temperature conversion of butyric acid at a temperature of 200–250 °C over activated clay was carried out for the first time by A. V. Frost and A. V. Ochkin [46]. As demonstrated by the experiments, butyric acid, when heated in the presence of activated Askan clay, undergoes mainly ketonization and decarboxylation, i.e. its breakdown occurs in accordance with mechanisms 1 and 3 (p. 303, 323).

Except for hydrogen, which was attributed to the interaction of the acid with the walls of the autoclave, the gas consisted only of propane and carbon dioxide. Propylene and carbon monoxide were entirely absent as components of the gas. This would exclude decomposition of acid to carbon monoxide, water, and olefin. From the liquid products, dipropyl ketone was recovered in good yield.

On repeating A. V. Frost's experiments in the decomposition of low molecular-weight acids, A. N. Chistyakov likewise observed decarboxylation and ketonization of acids at low temperatures [53]. Acetic, propionic, and butyric acids were studied at atmospheric pressure in a flow type apparatus in the temperature range of 200–400 °C and a volumetric rate of 0.11–0.20 volume of acid per volume of catalyst per hour. At 200 °C the conversion of acids takes place with the formation of corresponding ketones. It was noted that with rise in temperature the decomposition of acids increases and the carbon dioxide content in the gas relatively diminishes while the content of carbon monoxide and unsaturates becomes higher.

High molecular-weight fatty acids

High molecular-weight saturated acids decompose according to the same mechanisms as the low molecular-weight acids with the difference, however, being that the decomposition of the former gives a large diversity of breakdown products owing to destruction reactions. Stearic acid on heating with Group II metal salts decomposes principally with the formation of stearone.

However, along with it there is formed a certain quantity of hydrocarbons because of secondary reactions involving the disintegration of the ketone formed.

The conversion of stearic acid over aluminosilicates and other catalysts was studied originally by Severin [82]. Decomposition of the acid was conducted in the presence of clay and quartz at a temperature of 450 °C. From the conversion products oils were recovered representing a mixture of different hydrocarbons. More detailed studies of the conversion of stearic acid in the presence of activated clay were carried out by A. I. Bogomolov and K. I. Panina in 1955 [5]. In contrast to previous investigations, in this case the ratio of acid to clay was sharply changed. For each part by weight of acid, five parts of clay were used. With such proportions it was possible to shorten the length of the experiment† and increase considerably the conversion of the acid at a given temperature. These experiments were performed at temperatures ranging from 150 to 250 °C. The process of conversion of stearic and other acids yielded gaseous reaction products, liquid hydrocarbons, a highly carbonaceous residue on the clay, water of decomposition, and acidic

TABLE 29. *Group Compositions of Hydrocarbons Obtained in the Conversion of Stearic Acid over Activated Clay at 250°C [5]*

Boiling range of fractions °C	Yields of the fractions, %	Maximum aniline point		Group composition calculated from the anilin point, %					
		before sulfonation	after sulfonation	Aromatics		Naphthenes		Paraffins	
				in the fraction	in the oil	in the fraction	in the oil	in the fraction	in the oil
up to 65	10.4	—	—	—	—	—		100.0	10.4
65–95	10.5	66.8	69.2	2.7	0.3	4.3	0.4	93.0	9.8
95–122	10.7	65.3	68.2	3.5	0.4	8.9	0.9	87.6	9.4
122–150	10.9	64.2	68.0	4.8	0.5	23.8	2.6	71.4	7.8
150–200	11.0	59.8	69.6	14.8	1.6	36.2	4.0	49.0	5.4
200–250	16.8	58.8	76.6	24.0	4.0	35.7	6.0	40.3	6.8
250–300	6.3	63.8	84.6	34.7	2.2	27.7	1.7	37.6	2.3
300–400	6.5	64.2	86.2	39.8	2.6	46.0	3.0	14.2	0.9
400–500	6.7	78.4	96.4	38.2	2.6	60.1	4.0	1.8	0.1
Residue	10.3								
Total				14.2		22.6		52.9	
Composition of distillate				15.8		25.2		59.0	

resins. In the series of experiments carried out at 250 °C, the yield of liquid hydrocarbons was equal to 32 % by weight, or 48 % of the theoretical yield calculated on reacted acid.

In regard to chemical composition, the separated hydrocarbons

† The heating time in these and other experiments was 10 hr.

represented a mixture of paraffinic, naphthenic and aromatic hydrocarbons in proportions quite close to those in natural paraffin-base
petroleums (Table 29 and Fig. 49).

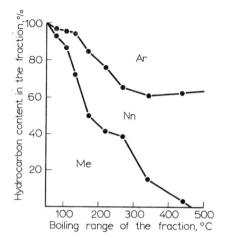

Fig. 49. Group composition of hydrocarbons in the conversion of stearic
acid over activated clay: Ar—aromatics; Nn—naphthenes; Me—paraffins.

For paraffin-naphthenic fractions the carbon-to-hydrogen ratio
was equal to about 6:1, which appears to suggest the presence
of naphthenes along with the paraffinic hydrocarbons. This was
confirmed by structural group analysis data by the *n-d-M* method
(Table 30).

TABLE 30. *Structural Group Composition of Paraffinic-naphthenic Hydrocarbons
separated from Stearic Acid Conversion Products (n-d-M method)*

Boiling range of fractions (°C)	Molecular weight	Density d_4^{20}	Refractive index n_D^{20}	Carbon content (%)		Average number of naphthene rings per molecule
				in naphthene rings C_n	in paraffin structures C_p	
225–300	220	0.8195	1.4526	38.8	61.2	1.10
300–400	246	0.8254	1.4544	39.0	61.0	1.25
400–500	327	0.8525	1.4692	36.0	64.0	1.72

The carbon content in naphthenic rings of the paraffinic-naphthenic oil fractions is 36–39 %. The number of naphthenic rings in the average molecule increases from 1.1 to 1.7 with rise in molecular weight.

The paraffin hydrocarbons consist largely of branched-chain hydrocarbons of iso structure. This is substantiated by complete absence of solid paraffins in high molecular-weight oil fractions, from which they usually can be easily precipitated with suitable solvents. Straight-chain paraffinic hydrocarbons were practically absent also in kerosene fractions, as indicated by the negative result of the qualitative reaction with urea, with which they form organic complexes. Thus it has been established for the first time that naphthenic and isoparaffinic hydrocarbons are formed from saturated aliphatic acids in thermocatalytic conversions of the latter in the presence of activated clay.

Unsaturated acids and hydroxy acids

The behavior of unsaturated acids in decomposition is similar to that of their saturated analogs with the difference, however, that in the presence of acid catalysts the breakdown reactions are usually

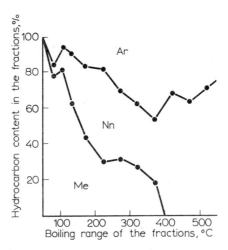

FIG. 50. Chemical group composition of hydrocarbons separated from conversion products of oleic acid: Ar—aromatics; Nn—naphthenes; Me—paraffins.

preceded by isomerization and polymerization reactions whereby cyclic structures and branched-chain compounds are formed. As a consequence, cyclic hydrocarbons and hydrocarbons of iso structure predominate among the conversion products. For instance,

TABLE 31. *Elemental Composition and Empirical Formulae of Hydrocarbons Separated from Conversion Products of Oleic Acid*

Boiling range of fraction (°C)	Elemental composition %			C/H ratio	Molec-ular weight	Empirical formula	Series
	C	H	O				
Paraffinic-naphthenic hydrocarbons							
300–350	85.7	14.0	0.3	6.1	191	$C_{13.5}H_{26.5}$	$C_nH_{2n-0.5}$
350–450*	85.6	14.1	0.4	6.1	245	$C_{17.5}H_{34.3}$	$C_nH_{2n-0.7}$
450–500	85.7	13.9	0.4	6.1	330	$C_{23.5}H_{45.5}$	$C_nH_{2n-1.5}$
Aromatic hydrocarbons							
300–350	89.2	10.0	0.8	8.9	180	$C_{13.4}H_{17.9}$	$C_nH_{2n-8.9}$
350–450*	88.8	10.2	1.0	8.7	225	$C_{16.6}H_{22.8}$	$C_nH_{2n-10.4}$
450–500	88.1	10.7	1.2	8.7	303	$C_{22.2}H_{32.2}$	$C_nH_{2n-12.2}$

* The fractions were combined.

according to investigations by N. D. Zelinskii [12] the conversion of oleic acid in the presence of aluminum chloride yields cyclic and paraffinic hydrocarbons which are chiefly isoparaffins. Even the high boiling oil fractions were virtually free from solid hydrocarbons with normal paraffinic structures, whereas the conversion products of stearic acid under similar conditions contained appreciable amounts of high melting normal paraffins. In the presence of acti-vated clay on heating to 250°C, oleic acid undergoes complex con-versions which, as in the case of stearic acid, produce hydrocarbons, water of decomposition, a highly carbonaceous residue on the clay, and acid resins (A. I. Bogomolov and K. I. Panina, in 1955).

The amount of hydrocarbons formed was 32%, calculated on the initial acid. Their composition is indicated in Fig. 50 and Table 31.

The table shows that, for most of the natural crudes, the amount of aromatic and naphthenic hydrocarbons increases and the amount of paraffins decreases with rise in boiling point of the fractions.

The group composition of hydrocarbons resulting from the conversion of stearic acid was as follows:

$$\begin{array}{ll} \text{paraffinic hydrocarbons} & 59\% \\ \text{naphthenic hydrocarbons} & 25\% \\ \text{aromatic hydrocarbons} & 16\% \end{array}$$

These proportions are characteristic for the hydrocarbon distribution in paraffin-base crudes from Grozny and Daghestan oil fields.

Polynaphthenic and aromatic hydrocarbons, upon separating them by adsorption on silica gel, were studied to determine their elemental composition and molecular weight.

The data obtained are cited in Table 32.

TABLE 32. *Elemental Composition and Empirical Formulae of Hydrocarbons Separated from Conversion Products of Stearic Acid*

Boiling range of fraction °C	Elemental composition %			C/H ratio	Molecular weight	Empirical formula	Series
	C	H	O				
Paraffinic-naphthenic hydrocarbons							
225–300	85.2	14.5	0.3	5.9	220	$C_{15.6}H_{31.6}$	$C_nH_{2n+0.4}$
300–400	85.4	14.3	0.3	6.0	246	$C_{17.5}H_{34.9}$	$C_nH_{2n-0.1}$
400–500	85.3	14.6	0.1	5.9	327	$C_{23.9}H_{48.8}$	$C_nH_{2n+1.0}$
Aromatic hydrocarbons							
225–300	89.2	10.4	0.4	8.5	190	$C_{14.1}H_{19.6}$	$C_nH_{2n-8.6}$
300–400	89.4	10.3	0.3	8.7	228	$C_{17.0}H_{23.3}$	$C_nH_{2n-10.7}$
400–500	89.1	10.8	0.1	8.3	300	$C_{22.2}H_{32.1}$	$C_nH_{2n-12.3}$

The data cited above indicate that in regard to chemical composition the hydrocarbons formed from acids consist of a mixture of paraffinic, naphthenic and aromatic hydrocarbons. The content of aromatic and naphthenic hydrocarbons increases with rise in boiling range of the fractions, and oil fractions boiling above 400°C are virtually free from paraffinic hydrocarbons. Thus, the paraffinic hydrocarbons in oil fractions appear as though they were displaced by naphthenic and aromatic hydrocarbons. The latter, as in natural crudes, consist of mixed (hybrid) forms of hydrocarbons. In molecules of this kind there are present, along with actual aromatic rings, also naphthenic rings whose linkage to the aromatic ring is not clear at present. However, their carbon-to-hydrogen ratio and empirical formulae correspond better with those of mixed types of naphthenic-aromatic hydrocarbons. For paraffinic-naphthenic fractions of hydrocarbons the carbon-to-hydrogen ratio, which is distinctive for the content of polymethylene rings, is equal to 6.1.

Hydroxystearic acid undergoes similar conversions at a temperature of 250°C in the presence of activated clay and breaks down completely with separation of a substantial amount of moisture. In the decomposition, 25% hydrocarbons, 40% acid resins, and 16% water are formed. The carbon-rich residue on the clay and unavoidable losses make up a total of 9% (A. I. Bogomolov and L. I. Khotyntseva, 1955). The chemical and fractional composition of the hydrocarbons formed was close to that of the conversion products of stearic acid. The distillate below 500°C consisted of 54.8% paraffin hydrocarbons, 26.4% naphthenes, and 18.8% aromatic hydrocarbons. Unsaturated hydrocarbons were absent.

Naphthenic acids

Naphthenic acids decompose in the presence of catalysts at elevated temperature to form hydrocarbons.

G. L. Stadnikov [34, 35], investigating the cracking of naphthenic acids, has demonstrated that their breakdown at a temperature of 450°C over iron oxide is accompanied by the formation of unsaturated hydrocarbons.

A. D. Petrov [30] studied the cracking of naphthenic acids in the presence of aluminum oxide as catalytic agent. Based on the analysis products obtained, he established that the following reactions took place:

1. Formation of naphthenic hydrocarbons through splitting off of carboxyl groups.

2. Formation of the simplest naphthenic acids through breaking away of side chains.

3. Formation of paraffinic hydrocarbons and low molecular-weight fatty acids as a result of rupture of rings, breaking away of side chains, and formation of fragments containing the carboxyl groups.

Particularly interesting appear to be the investigations of Z. G. Zul'fugarov [13] dealing with the catalytic conversion of naphthenic acids over aluminosilicate and molybdeno-silicate catalysts. At 450°C, atmospheric pressure, and a feed rate of 0.5 volume per volume of catalyst per hour in cracking naphthenic acids under the action of the foregoing catalysts, various reactions take place to produce naphthenic, aromatic, and unsaturated hydrocarbons in varying quantitative proportions. In addition, various oxygenated compounds, water, carbon dioxide and other gaseous products are formed.

A naphtha of 200°C end point, obtained from naphthenic acids, had a content of 10–14 % unsaturated and 44–63 % aromatic hydrocarbons, depending on the temperature of the process. In conformance with the cyclic nature of naphthenic acids, the content of aromatic hydrocarbons in the naphtha is higher than the amount obtained in cracking a petroleum feed stock.

The foregoing discussion of data on the conversion of different acids in the presence of aluminosilicate type catalysts serves as a basis for assuming that low molecular-weight fatty acids, in the region of low temperatures, undergo predominantly ketonization and decarboxylation, i.e. their decomposition proceeds in accordance with mechanisms 1 and 3. Their decomposition to olefins begins only at elevated temperatures, which is in accordance with data from thermodynamic computations.

High molecular-weight fatty acids decompose in accordance with the same mechanisms as the low molecular-weight acids, but their decomposition yields an extraordinary diversity of breakdown products owing to secondary disintegration reactions. In the case of unsaturated acids and hydroxy acids, the disintegration reactions are usually preceded by polymerization, isomerization, and dehydration reactions with the formation of cyclic structures and branched-chain compounds. Incomplete disintegration of high molecular-weight acids causes the formation of olefinic hydrocarbons as intermediate products which are further converted over aluminosilicate catalysts to naphthenic and aromatic hydrocarbons. In addition, paraffinic hydrocarbons are formed, but they are chiefly the branch-ed-chain variety because of the isomerizing action of clays. Regard-less of the degree of saturation of the acids and their structures, the thermal catalysis process yields all three types of hydrocarbons occurring in natural petroleum. Open-chain saturated fatty acids under moderately elevated temperature conditions and in the pres-ence of clays give both monocyclic and high molecular-weight poly-cyclic naphthenic hydrocarbons, predominantly the methylated homologs. Aromatic hydrocarbons are definitely formed in every case in thermocatalytic conversions of the acids. However, their amounts and rates of accumulation in the fractions vary with the chemical nature and structure of the initial acid. Nevertheless, as in natural crudes, the content of aromatic hydrocarbons in the fractions increases with rise in their boiling range or, in other words, their molecular weight. The chemical composition of aro-matic hydrocarbons formed under identical conditions in the ex-periments is the same for all aliphatic and unsaturated acids. The hydrocarbons have the same elemental composition and correspond-ingly close empirical formulae and series formulas (Tables 31 and 32). The aromatic hydrocarbons recovered from natural crude oils have similar elemental compositions and empirical formulas.

Investigations have shown that aromatic hydrocarbons separated from products of the low temperature catalysis of acids consist, as do the aromatic petroleum hydrocarbons, of mixed (hybrid) forms of naphthenic-aromatic compounds in which the carbon is distri-buted between purely aromatic rings, naphthenic rings, and alkyl radicals forming part of the aromatic hydrocarbon molecule. The mixed naphthenic-aromatic structure of the aromatic hydrocarbon molecules, burdened with alkyl radicals, is specific chiefly for pro-cesses of low temperature conversion of organic matter in the pres-ence of aluminosilicate catalysts, i.e. clay minerals. High tempera-tures cause a severe destruction of organic compounds and formation of products including principally aromatic compounds free from sub-stituents or free from naphthenic rings. In other words, the high temperature processes tend to give products which are substantially different from petroleum products and are not characteristic of natural crude oils. A comparison of data on the properties of aro-matic hydrocarbons separated from low temperature catalysis prod-ucts of acids with those of aromatic hydrocarbons separated from natural petroleums has convinced us that the overwhelming majority of aromatics in crudes are secondary, newly formed compounds as a result of long-time conversion processes of buried organic remnants.

Petroleum hydrocarbons, being compounds which do not owe their origin to the unaltered initial organic matter, could obviously have been formed principally only as a result of complex conversion reactions of such matter with the participation of natural catalysts of aluminosilicate type.

In the process of modification of organic matter, such reactions are favorable to formation of petroleum hydrocarbons, further transformation of which yields their complete mineralization products, namely methane and carbonaceous residue.

2. Conversion of ketones

(a) Reaction mechanisms

The conversion of ketones, as that of acids, may take place via different mechanisms and in several stages. However, as shown by studies in the temperature range of 200–250 °C over aluminosilicate catalysts, the main trend of the decomposition of ketones is via a stepwise dehydration-condensation reaction. First two and then three molecules of the ketone interact successively to form an unsaturated ketone, the dehydration-condensation of which yields an aromatic hydrocarbon. For acetone, reactions of this sort may be represented as follows:

$$2CH_3-CO-CH_3 \rightarrow H_2O + (CH_3)_2C{=}CH-CO-CH_3;$$

$$(CH_3)_2C{=}CH-CO-CH_3 + CH_3-CO-CH_3 \rightarrow$$

$$\overset{\displaystyle CH_3}{\underset{\displaystyle |}{}}$$

$$\rightarrow H_2O + (CH_3)_2C{=}CH-C{=}CH-CO-CH_3;$$

$$\overset{\displaystyle CH_3}{\underset{\displaystyle |}{}}$$

$$(CH_3)_2C{=}CH-C{=}CH-CO-CH_3 \rightarrow H_2O + CH_3- \underset{\displaystyle CH_3}{\overset{\displaystyle CH_3}{\bigcirc}}$$

However, the mesityl oxide so formed may break down to form ketene and isobutylene. Ketene, upon reacting with water, gives acetic acid.

The last-mentioned reaction mechanisms have been confirmed by data obtained by M. Ya. Kagan and R. I. Savchenko [15] on the conversion of mesityl oxide over aluminosilicate catalyst in the presence of water vapor. They demonstrated that the yield of isobutylene and acetic acid varies depending on the relative proportions of water and mesityl oxide. A similar mechanism of the breakdown of mesityl oxide to isobutylene and ketene and the subsequent conversion of ketene may be utilized to explain the formation of acetic acid and isobutylene in the experiments carried out by A. V. Frost and A. Ya. Larina [47, 48] and also by I. N. Kamenskaya [16] on converting acetone and mesityl oxide over active aluminosilicates in the above-mentioned temperature range. A similar breakdown was observed by McAllister and other researchers when using a silicate-phosphate catalyst in the conversion of mesityl oxide to isobutylene and acetic acid [57].

Still, it should be borne in mind that along with the main reactions indicated above, other reactions also take place, which, being superposed upon each other, considerably distort the normal course of the process.

(b) Experimental data

According to A. V. Frost and A. Ya. Larina [47, 48], acetone in the vapor phase, in contact with activated clay over a temperature range of 170–260 °C, is converted to acetic acid and isobutylene. The acid and isobutylene are formed virtually in equimolecular proportions. At the same time there are also formed dehydration-condensation products of acetone, namely mesitylene, mesityl oxide, and phorone.

I. N. Kamenskaya [16] in experiments under static conditions in an autoclave under pressure, in the presence of activated clay at a temperature of 220–250 °C, noted the formation of mesitylene, mesityl oxide, and isophorone. Along with these, the reaction products were found to contain acetic acid, isobutylene, and olefins more complex than isobutylene. Yet at a higher temperature [60], a profound breakdown of acetone takes place, forming largely hydrocarbons and water. Thus, for example, Midorikawa [74] and Kyoken

Fyji [66] in the catalytic decomposition of acetone in the presence of Japanese acidic at a temperature of 400–450 °C obtained principally mesitylene and isobutylene. Mesityl oxide and acetic acid are formed under these conditions only in small amounts as a by-product.

Methyl ethyl ketone in the vapor phase at a temperature of 250 °C, according to observations by A. V. Frost and A. Ya. Larina [48], is converted predominantly to acetic acid and 3-methyl-2-pentene. In experiments conducted at 400 °C, the main reaction products were propionic acid and 2-methyl-1-butene.

Consequently, for methyl ethyl ketone the proposed reaction mechanism may be as follows:

$$2C_2H_5-CO-CH_3 \rightarrow C_2H_5-\overset{\underset{\displaystyle CH_3}{|}}{C}=\overset{\underset{\displaystyle CH_3}{|}}{C}-CO-CH_3 + H_2O;$$

$$C_2H_5-\overset{\underset{\displaystyle CH_3}{|}}{C}\underline{\quad}\overset{\underset{\displaystyle CH_3}{|}}{C}-CO-CH_3 + H_2O \rightarrow C_2H_5 - \overset{\underset{\displaystyle CH_3}{|}}{C}CH-CH_3 + CH_3COOH;$$

$$2C_2H_5-CO-CH_3 \rightarrow C_2H_5-\overset{\underset{\displaystyle CH_3}{|}}{C}=CH-CO-C_2H_5 + H_2O;$$

$$C_2H_5-\overset{\underset{\displaystyle CH_3}{|}}{C}=CH-CO-C_2H_5 + H_2O \rightarrow C_2H_5-\overset{\overset{\displaystyle CH_3}{|}}{C}=CH_2 + C_2H_5COOH.$$

The dehydration-condensation products of methyl ethyl ketone under static conditions in an autoclave [16] at a temperature of 220–250 °C were: 3-methyl-3-hepten-5-one, 3,4-dimethyl-3-hexen-2-one, homophorone, and homomesophorone. 2-Methyl-1-butene, 3-methyl-2-pentene, and acetic and propionic acids were also found.

Acetophenone, when passed over the catalyst at 200 °C for 15 min, gave about 65% of conversion products and water. Since benzoic acid was recovered from the conversion products, the reaction of acetophenone decomposition may be represented by a similar equation. Upon decomposition of acetophenone in an autoclave at 220–250 °C, I. N. Kamenskaya [16] separated triphenylmethane among other products.

Benzophenone undergoes complex conversions at 300°C, in which 68% of reaction products is obtained, calculated on the basis of the original benzophenone. In the complex mixture of reaction products, benzene has been identified [48]. Under similar conditions pinacoline likewise undergoes drastic conversions in the presence of clay to give appreciable quantities of light and heavy products, the nature of which has not been identified [48]. Cyclohexanone with activated clay at a temperature of 230°C forms cyclohexane in limited amounts.

From the experimental results discussed above it follows that conversion of ketones in the temperature range of 200–250°C in the presence of aluminosilicate catalysts comprises a complex combination of dehydration-condensation, hydration, polymerization, cyclization, decarboxylation (of the acids formed), and hydrogen disproportionation reactions. The reaction products are hydrocarbons, unsaturated ketones, acids, decomposition water, and resins. The acids decompose to form hydrocarbons of different types. It is worthy of note that the sequentially occurring dehydration-condensation reactions and breakdown of unsaturated ketones formed as intermediate reaction products cause the straight-chain aliphatic ketones to be converted into the corresponding iso-olefins. As a result of subsequent reactions of hydrogen disproportionation, the latter are transformed to isoparaffins. The possible products of dehydration-condensation of ketones include aromatic hydrocarbons.

3. Conversion of alcohols

(a) Reaction mechanisms

The conversion of alcohols over aluminosilicate catalysts may occur in different ways. Depending on the surroundings and on temperature and pressure conditions, ethers, aldehydes and ketones may be obtained as well as various hydrocarbons.

One of the principal alcohol decomposition reactions is dehydration with the formation of water and the corresponding olefin. For monohydric primary alcohols this reaction proceeds according to the general equation

$$C_nH_{2n+1}OH \rightarrow C_nH_{2n} + H_2O. \tag{5}$$

Dehydration is entirely justified from the energy viewpoint because the change in free energy ΔF in the dehydration of monohydric primary alcohols at $400°K$ ($127°C$) and higher is a negative value (Table 33).

TABLE 33. *Change in the Free Energy ($\Delta F°$) in cal/mol in Dehydration of Monohydric Normal Primary Alcohols at Different Temperatures (According to Mechanism 1)*

Alcohol	298°K	400°K	600°K	800°K
Ethyl	+1355	−1639	−7719	−13,795
Propyl	−330	−3827	−10,707	−17,587
Butyl	+1010	−2627	−9767	−16,907
Amyl	+950	−3017	−11,797	−18,577
Hexyl	+1660	−2365	−10,439	−19,513
Octyl	+2600	−1967	−10,687	−19,407

Note: In the calculations, the compounds were assumed to be in the following states: alcohols–liquid, water–liquid, olefins–gaseous.

A similar behavior in the dehydration reaction may be noted also for secondary and tertiary alcohols, with the difference that in the latter case water and iso-olefins are obtained as reaction products. Iso-olefins are obtained frequently also from normal primary and secondary alcohols, but in such instances they are formed as a secondary product owing to the isomerizing action of aluminosilicates. Another possible route for dehydration of alcohols is the formation of ethers (6). In the dehydration of various alcohols, a number of authors [24, 49, 50, 69, 75, 83] have demonstrated that in the first stage of alcohol dehydration over aluminosilicate and other catalysts an ether is obtained and only later on, at a relatively higher temperature, olefins are formed

$$2C_nH_{2n+1}OH \rightarrow (C_nH_{2n-1})_2O + H_2O$$

$$(C_nH_{2n+1})_2O \rightarrow 2C_nH_{2n} + H_2O. \tag{6}$$

Another feasible course of the conversion of primary alcohols is their dehydrogenation to form an aldehyde and hydrogen.

$$R—CH_2OH \rightarrow R—CHO + H_2. \tag{7}$$

The dehydrogenation of alcohols is catalyzed by copper and brass catalysts which assist the conversion of primary alcohols to aldehydes. There is information, however, that, at a temperature of 200 °C, normal primary alcohols are converted partly to aldehydes over activated clay [67].

In processes of petroleum and gas genesis, the highest importance is attached to reactions of dehydration and disintegration of alcohols with the formation of different hydrocarbons. This applies in particular to high molecular-weight alcohols present as constituents in the liquid portion of vegetable and animal organisms.

The decomposition of alcohols under conditions prevailing in the earth's crust may occur via a series of intermediate stages taking place consecutively. Each stage would be associated with the formation of hydrocarbons having a different degree of saturation and therefore belonging to different types. The final products of all such transformations over a geological period of time in the earth's crust under conditions precluding access of air will ultimately be water, methane, and graphite (8), i.e. products of complete mineralization of alcohols under conditions of the reducing environment in the sediment.

$$C_nH_{2n+1}OH \rightarrow H_2O + qCH_4 + mC. \tag{8}$$

The conversion of secondary and tertiary alcohols will occur generally along the same mechanisms as for primary alcohols.

Considerably more complex is the decomposition of dihydric and, generally, of polyhydric alcohols and their conversion over aluminosilicate catalysts to various oxygenated compounds and hydrocarbons. Data obtained by R. D. Obolentsev and N. N. Gryazev [26] and subsequently confirmed by A. N. Chistyakov [53] indicate that the conversion of ethylene glycol over aluminosilicate catalyst at 200–300 °C proceeds via the ether formation stage.

The conversion of glycerin proceeds via a more complicated mechanism but obviously here again an ether is formed in the initial phase because of partial dehydration.

(b) Experimental data on the conversion of alcohols

The literature contains a considerable amount of data on the decomposition of alcohols, including their conversion over aluminosilicate catalysts. Some of the more representative data are cited below.

Primary normal monohydric alcohols

Methyl alcohol decomposes over an aluminosilicate catalyst at 400 °C to form H_2O, CO_2, H_2, CH_4, and C_2H_4 [28]. Dehydration of ethyl alcohol may proceed, depending on temperature conditions, to give an ether or an olefin. The conversion of alcohol into ether over Japanese acidic clay was already observed by Hori in 1939 [64]. Diethyl ether is obtained in large quantities on passing ethyl alcohol over bauxite at a temperature of 270–290 °C. Under the specified conditions of the experiment only 10% of alcohol is converted to ethylene [63].

Over Japanese acidic clay, as stated by Murai, ethyl alcohol at a temperature of 220 °C is converted predominantly to diethyl ether [75]. The ether yield is 63%. At a higher temperature (350 °C) practically all of the alcohol is converted to ethylene. Pure ethylene, free from any admixtures, is obtained by dehydration of ethyl alcohol over activated bleaching clay at a temperature of 280 °C or higher. According to Joshi [65], ethyl alcohol is converted over Indian bauxites at 360 °C to a gas which has an ethylene content of up to 95%. High yields of ethylene are also obtained by passing alcohol over Voronezh and Saratov clays without their preliminary activation by chemical agents or acid. According to N. Z. Kotelkov [18], under the influence of these clays, at 250 °C, 84% of the ethyl alcohol is converted to ethylene. At 350 °C the dehydration of alcohol to ethylene was quantitatively close to 100%.

Propyl alcohol, according to Kh. I. Areshidze [1] is converted in the presence of Askanite (a bentonite clay from Askan village in Georgia) at 450 °C to yield 40% propylene. Under these conditions 1.2 l. of gas were obtained per 10 ml of the alcohol used.

Butyl alcohol has been the subject of repeated investigations dealing with its conversion reactions over various catalysts. Early in 1929, Kashima [67] observed the conversion of butyl alcohol in the presence of Japanese acidic clay at a temperature of 200 °C to butylene and other products. The gas was found to contain, in addition to butylene, CO and CO_2. In the liquid condensate, small amounts of aldehyde and an ester were identified, but the latter was no longer present when conducting the experiment at a higher temperature. Noriyuki Sakinawa [77], conducting his experiments in 1951 with clay as catalyst in an autoclave under a pressure of 100–200 atm and a temperature of 300–400 °C, obtained 17% aromatic hydrocarbons and butylene from butyl alcohol. In the presence of activated clay and otherwise the same conditions, up to 70% aromatic hydrocarbons and 30% olefins are formed. The clay, like other catalysts, dehydrates higher alcohols to olefins and then isomerizes them. Butyl alcohol, on being heated to 450°C, is converted to a mixture of butylenes, in which 1-butene predominates. In the dehydration of butyl alcohol over Gumbrin at a temperature of 450°C, a mixture of all three isomers of butene is obtained. Under these conditions the primary 1-butene becomes isomerized to 2-butene and isobutene [2].

Amyl alcohol on heating over Japanese acidic clay to 260–270°C breaks down into amylene and water. At the same time a small amount of diamyl ether $(C_5H_{11})_2O$ and traces of CO are formed. The amylene yield is equal to 32% based on the alcohol used [67].

Hexyl and normal heptyl alcohol undergo similar conversions on being heated over aluminum oxide as dehydrating agent. From hexyl alcohol at a temperature of 350°C, 1-hexane was obtained [68] and heptyl alcohol gave 1-heptene [70]. No isomerization of the hydrocarbons was noted when using aluminum oxide as catalyst, whereas in the dehydration of normal alcohols over aluminosilicate type catalysts branched-chain olefins are formed.

Octyl alcohol, according to A. V. Frost [50], in the presence of activated clay at a temperature of 140–180°C, is practically entirely dehydrated to form a complex mixture of unsaturated and saturated hydrocarbons. The yield of octylenes was 33% and other olefins 17%. Octane and other saturated hydrocarbons resulting from reactions of hydrogen disproportionation over aluminosilicate catalyst reached a total of 10%. However, as demonstrated by V. V. Shchekin in his investigations [55], the reaction of alcohol dehydration precedes other possible reactions over aluminosilicates. With rapid removal of products from the reaction zone, water and the corresponding olefin are obtained exclusively. On heating primary octyl alcohol with activated clay at a temperature of 197–207°C, the author obtained a mixture of normal octylenes free from saturated hydrocarbons and branched-chain hydrocarbons.

Decyl alcohol on heating with aluminum oxide at 325–350°C splits off water to give decylene. Under these conditions, dehydration of the alcohol takes place, exclusively without any other reactions.

Primary branched-chain monohydric alcohols

Isobutyl alcohol over aluminum oxide at a temperature of 340 °C is broken down into water and isobutylene [23]. According to A. I. Bogomolov and O. A. Smirnova in 1955, isobutylene is obtained in a yield of up to 80% by dehydration of isobutyl alcohol over activated Gumbrin at a temperature of 350 °C. Dehydration of the alcohol starts virtually at a temperature of 200 °C, but the isobutylene yield is low in such a case.

Isoamyl alcohol (2-methyl-1-butanol), as reported by N. A. Butovich [8], is dehydrated over Gumbrin at a temperature of 380–400 °C to form a mixture of olefins including isopropylethylene (3-methyl-1-butene) as principal constituent. He thinks that the dehydrating properties of Gumbrin are associated with the presence of alumina which is the carrier of catalytic properties.

Secondary alcohols

Isopropyl alcohol on being heated at a temperature of 160 °C over activated clay is converted largely to di-isopropyl ether. According to A. S. Nekrasova and B. A. Krentsel' [24], decomposition of isopropyl alcohol begins at a temperature of 95 °C and the maximum yield of ether, which is 54.6%, corresponds to a temperature of 160–170 °C. No decomposition of isopropyl alcohol to propylene was noted at temperatures below 160 °C. At a temperature of 160–170 °C the propylene yield was 4.8%, based on isopropyl alcohol fed through the catalyst. At higher temperatures (240–250 °C), isopropyl alcohol is practically entirely dehydrated to propylene, the yield of which reaches 90% of the initial alcohol. This fact justifies the assumption that dehydration of isopropyl alcohol occurs in a stepwise manner. In the first stage the ether is formed, which thereafter loses water to form an olefin. According to A. V. Frost and S. S. Khain [49], the ether is formed also in the conversion of isopropyl alcohol over activated Gumbrin, Saratov, and Glukhov clays. In one of the experiments with Glukhov clay, the yield of diisopropyl ether at 130 °C was equal to 64 mole per cent of the reacted alcohol.

Tertiary alcohols

Tertiary butyl alcohol readily splits off one molecule of water under the action of various dehydrating agents and at a relatively low temperature. According to research by A. I. Bogomolov and O. A. Smirnova (1956), tertiary butyl alcohol decomposes at an appreciable rate on being passed, at a temperature of 120°C, over unactivated and undried clay from the Maikop series in Northeastern Caucasus. In one of the experiments the isobutylene yield was equal to 47% of the initial alcohol. At higher temperatures the dehydration rate increases and the isobutylene yield rises.

Tertiary amyl alcohol (2-methyl-2-butanol) decomposes over Floridin and alumina on heating, to form a mixture of amylenes in which 1-pentene and 2-methyl-2-butene were identified [76].

Monohydric cyclic alcohols

Cyclopentanol on being heated together with phthalic anhydride splits off a molecule of water and is converted almost quantitatively to cyclopentene [84]. In the presence of aluminosilicate type catalysts, cyclohexanol decomposes quite readily at 300°C or much lower temperatures. According to Kh. I. Areshidze and E. K. Tavartkiladze [3], Gumbrin not only causes its dehydration to cyclohexene but also its isomerization into methylcyclopentene.

Cholesterol is a substance widely distributed in animate nature and its conversion over clays is of special importance for the problem of genesis of petroleum.

According to I. S. Sattar-Zade and A. V. Frost [51], cholesterol undergoes complex conversions on being heated at a temperature of 150–300°C with activated clay. Liberation of water takes place at 160–170°C, which is the dehydration temperature of cholesterol. Raising the temperature to 250–300°C stimulates the destructive reactions of hydrogen disproportionation. Specifically, under these conditions a 63.2% yield of a product was obtained comprising a mixture of hydrocarbons, the properties of which are cited below (Table 34).

The above data lead to the conclusion that the decomposition of cholesterol includes first a dehydration reaction followed by more complex conversions of the hydrocarbons formed.

It must be pointed out in particular that the hydrocarbons re-

11a TP

TABLE 34. *Fractional Composition and Optical Activity of Products of the Catalytic Conversion of Cholesterol [31]*

Boiling range of fractions (°C)	Yield of fractions, in % of the product	Refractive index n_D^{20}	Angle of rotation $[a]_D$
50–100	12.4	1.3929	+0.14
100–150	16.5	1.4175	+0.28
150–200	3.3	1.4389	+0.34
200–320	2.8	1.5119	+0.36
320–370	22.3	1.5393	+0.65
370–380	7.6	1.5515	+0.52
Residue	35.0	—	+8.69

sulting from the decomposition of cholesterol are dextrorotatory compounds while the initial cholesterol itself rotates the plane of polarized light towards the left. As for natural crudes, the amount of optical rotation increases with rise in boiling point of the fractions or, in other words, with rise in their molecular weight.

Dihydric and polyhydric alcohols

Ethylene glycol undergoes complex conversions over alumino-silicate catalysts in the temperature range of 200–300°C, to form in the first stage a partial and then a complete ether. Thereafter the complete ether of ethylene glycol (dioxane) breaks down on the one hand into acetaldehyde and on the other hand into acetic acid and ethylene as follows:

$$2 \begin{array}{c} CH_2{-}OH \\ | \\ CH_2{-}OH \end{array} \xrightarrow{-2H_2O} O\left\langle \begin{array}{c} CH_2{-}CH_2 \\ CH_2{-}CH_2 \end{array} \right\rangle O \rightarrow$$

$$\rightarrow CH_3{-}CH \left\langle \begin{array}{c} O{-}CH_2 \\ | \\ O{-}CH_2 \end{array} \right\rangle \begin{array}{l} CH_3COOH + CH_2{=}CH_2 \\ 2CH_3CHO \end{array}$$

According to R. D. Obolentsev and N. N. Gryazev [26] who studied this reaction, ethylene glycol was passed over aluminosilicate catalyst at a volumetric rate of 1 volume per volume of catalyst per hour and at a temperature of 300 °C to give 97.1 % of conversion product, 1.7% gas and 1.2% of a high-carbon residue (coke).

Trimethylene glycol is decomposed over aluminum oxide at 250–350 °C, according to Yu. K. Yur'ev and I. S. Levi [56], into acrolein, propionaldehyde, allyl alcohol, α-methylacrolein, di-trimethylene glycol, and gaseous products. On the basis of experimental data, the authors proposed a mechanism for the decomposition of trimethylene glycol via allyl alcohol and trimethylene oxide which is unstable under these conditions and suffers isomerization into propionaldehyde. The conversion of other glycols proceeds in a somewhat different way. According to Bourns and Nicholls [58], 1,4-butanediol is converted almost completely at 250–300 °C over activated bentonite into tetrahydrofuran, without evolution of gaseous products. However, at higher temperatures (400–500 °C) the decomposition of the glycol occurs with formation of gaseous products including ethylene and other unsaturated hydrocarbons. The liquid products consisted of highly polymeric compounds, in which formaldehyde and tetrahydrofuran were also found.

Glycerin does not undergo appreciable change on being heated for a period of 8 hr at a temperature of 200 °C. Yet in the presence of activated clay and otherwise the same conditions, A. N. Chistyakov [53] obtained 5.3% of a distillate having the sharp odor of acrolein. At a temperature of 250 °C, 13.6 % of liquid products, based on the glycerin charge, was collected in the receiver. In addition, a substantial quantity of gas was recovered, which contained 44 % carbon monoxide and 53% carbon dioxide. From the liquid conversion products of glycerin, the authors separated and identified acrolein, glycidol and diglycerol.

Based on the foregoing discussion of experimental results relating to conversion of different alcohols over aluminosilicate catalysts, it may be concluded that all of them undergo changes to a greater or lesser extent, whereas in the absence of catalysts and under the same temperature conditions they persist as relatively stable compounds. A common feature for all alcohols is dehydration reactions.

At relatively low temperatures the dehydration takes place to form ethers, which subsequently decompose to form unsaturated hydrocarbons. Nevertheless, in the decomposition of alcohols over aluminosilicate catalysts virtually always a complex mixture of products is formed, in which, along with olefins, varying amounts of other hydrocarbons are present. In such cases the dehydration of alcohols is accompanied by isomerization, polymerization, and hydrogen disproportionation reactions with the formation of a carbonaceous residue. The subsequent stage of conversion of the products formed are the breakdown reactions which give rise to hydrocarbons of different types. The entire complex of such reactions serves to explain that hydrocarbons can be formed from the lipid portion of organic matter, which contains high molecular alcohols in their free state or in the form of esters.

B. THERMAL STABILITY
AND CONVERSION OF SULFUR COMPOUNDS OVER
ALUMINOSILICATES

Sulfur compounds are present in all petroleums, but their content varies within a wide range. A study of crude oils with respect to their geographic distribution will often show that some oil provinces stand out quite sharply among others by virtue of higher sulfur content of the oils. In such cases the term geochemical areas of sulfur-bearing crudes might be justified.

It has been noted that petroleums associated to a greater or lesser extent with carbonate or cemented terrigenous sedimentary rocks are high in sulfur and resins. Examples of these are the crudes from the Volga-Ural oil-bearing region and crudes from the Middle and Near East, e.g. Iran, Irak, Saudi Arabia, and many others.

It has been established that the sulfur in petroleums is in the form of hydrogen sulfide and organic compounds of divalent sulfur: mercaptans, sulfides and polysulfides, thiophanes, thiophenes, and sulfur compounds of the type of thionaphthene homologs. A study of vacuum distillates has shown the presence of substantial amounts of sulfide sulfur in most of them [33]. The sulfide form of sulfur predominates in all oil fractions over any other forms of sulfur and this statement evidently applies also to asphaltic and resinous substances in addition to the components of the oil fraction. The significance of elemental sulfur in crudes has been unduly emphasized by some authors [33] because, according to investigations by A. K. Kotina [20], elemental sulfur is practically absent even in such high-sulfur crudes as those from Second Baku.

The determination of thermal stability of sulfur compounds is undoubtedly of scientific and practical interest. Yet this problem has not been sufficiently clarified in the literature and the individual sulfur compounds used in the tests were as a rule limited, with a few exceptions, to compounds of the aliphatic series.

At the end of the last century, Otto and Rossing [78] found that ethyl, n-propyl, and n-butyl disulfides virtually do not decompose on heating. Amyl disulfide gradually decomposes during distillation, to form sulfur and sulfides.

Faragher, Morrell and Comay [61] investigated the decomposition of mercaptans, sulfides, disulfides, and thiophene at a temperature of 500°C. They demonstrated that mercaptans are most readily decomposed and thiophenes with considerably more difficulty. The breakdown products of mercaptans were hydrogen sulfide, sulfur, gas, and resinous substances. Decomposition of sulfides resulted in hydrogen sulfide, mercaptans, and thiophene derivatives. The liberated gas contained unsaturated hydrocarbons. Disulfides were decomposed with the formation of hydrogen sulfide, sulfur, mercaptans, and sulfides. The sulfides, in turn, suffered further decomposition as indicated above. Thiophene does not decompose even at high temperatures.

Malisoff and Marks [71] studied the conversion of aliphatic mercaptans at temperatures of 300, 425, and 475°. They established that aliphatic mercaptans decompose at a temperature of 425°C and that their decomposition gives hydrogen sulfide and olefins. The easiest to decompose are the high boiling branched-chain mercaptans. The same authors also demonstrated [72] that sulfides are more difficult to break down than mercaptans. Thus, for example, butyl sulfide is not appreciably decomposed below a temperature of 500°C.

An investigation of the thermal stability of certain sulfur compounds in the pure state and in solution in a narrow-cut kerosene fraction was conducted by M. G. Rudenko and V. N. Gromova [32]. They studied various mercaptans, sulfides, and thiophenes. The results obtained serve as a support for the conclusions drawn formerly by Malisoff and Marks in regard to unequal thermal stability of mercaptans, sulfides, and thiophenes. Mercaptans have the lowest thermal resistance, sulfides are considerably more stable, and thiophenes have a high thermal stability.

On the basis of their research the authors come to the conclusion that the presence of a mobile hydrogen ion bonded to sulfur in an organic compound tends to render the molecule less resistant. Upon replacement of hydrogen in the —SH group with a radical, i.e. on transition from mercaptans to sulfides, the thermal stability of the compound is many times higher. All sulfur compounds containing sulfur in the ring are characterized by high thermal resistance. The thermal stability of sulfur compounds present in some crudes from Second Baku was investigated by E. I. Skripnik, V. I. Isagulyants and I. K. Shtof [33]. The thermal resistance of sulfur compounds in petroleums from the Devonian and Carboniferous sediments in Kuibyshev province was determined on ten samples. As shown by the investigations, a characteristic feature for all samples of the crudes (even for Radaev crude with 3.4% sulfur content) is the relatively high thermal stability of sulfur compounds in the temperature range up to 150°C. For oils from the Devonian beds (Zol'nyi Ovrag, Mukkanovo), which are relatively low in sulfur content (0.6–0.7%) and occur at relatively great depths (down to 2800 m), the characteristic feature is the high thermal stability of sulfur compounds in the temperature range up to 350°C. However, a further rise in temperature intensifies the destruction of sulfur compounds and causes an abundant formation of hydrogen sulfide in amounts more than several times greater than the initial yields.

Petroleums from Carboniferous beds in the same oil fields (Zol'nyi Ovrag and Mukhanovo), with a sulfur content of 1.3–1.4%, which occur at shallower depths than the Devonian oils, are characterized by substantial liberation of hydrogen sulfide at temperatures as low as 190–210°C. This means that the older, low-sulfur crudes of Devonian age in Kuibyshev province contain sulfur compounds having a relatively high thermal stability while the sulfur compounds of Carboniferous crudes, which have a higher sulfur content and are in a different geochemical environment, are generally less stable. In this case the transformation of petroleums is accompanied by a decrease in their content of sulfur compounds.

A considerable amount of data is available in the literature on the conversion of sulfur compounds in contact with various metallic, oxide, and sulfide type catalysts. Yet up to a recent date virtually no research was done on the catalytic conversions of sulfur compounds over aluminosilicate catalysts. This gap has been filled in by I. N. Tits-Skvortsova and her collaborators in their research on conversion of sulfur compounds of various types over alumino-silicate catalyst, to provide considerable information relative to the mechanism of the process.

1. Conversion of sulfur compounds of the aliphatic series

The circumstances relating to conversion of mercaptans of the aliphatic series were investigated by I. N. Tits-Skvortsova in the decomposition of decyl mercaptan as an example [36, 37]. The product obtained on passing this substance over an aluminosilicate catalyst at 250°C contained 1-decene (30.3% by weight of the product), initial decyl mercaptan (20.5%) and white crystals of didecyl sulfide (23.8%). The conversion products of decyl mercaptan at 300°C were separated to recover 1-decene (18.6% by weight of the product) and initial decyl mercaptan (27.4%). Didecyl sulfide was isolated in negligibly small amounts. In both experiments an abundant liberation of hydrogen sulfide was noted.

The catalytic decomposition of decyl mercaptan, as determined, takes place in two directions

$$2C_{10}H_{21}SH \xrightarrow{250\,°C} C_{10}H_{21}{-}S{-}C_{10}H_{21} + H_2S;$$

$$C_{10}H_{21}SH \xrightarrow{300\,°C} C_{10}H_{20} + H_2S.$$

Depending on temperature, the mercaptan breaks down into an olefin or a sulfide: at lower temperature two molecules of mercaptan give the sulfide and hydrogen sulfide, whereas at higher temperature the olefin and hydrogen sulfide are formed. Similar results were obtained by P. Sabatier and C. Mailhe [80] in studying the conversion of ethyl and isoamyl mercaptans over cadmium sulfide. They, too, have established that mercaptans at lower temperatures (of the order of 300–360°) are converted to the corresponding sulfides and at higher temperatures (360–400°C) to olefins.

Dinonyl sulfide on being passed over aluminosilicate catalyst at 300°C gave a product, from which 1-nonene and primary nonyl mercaptan were separated by I. N. Tits-Skvortsova and colla-borators [36, 37]. To determine the decomposition mechanism of aliphatic sulfides, 1-decene was heated under the same conditions over aluminosilicate catalyst in a stream of hydrogen sulfide. No addition of hydrogen sulfide to the olefin was noted under these conditions. The authors [36, 37] believe that, among the various possible ways for decomposition of aliphatic sulfides, the most probable is as follows:

$$C_9H_{19}\text{---}S\text{---}C_9H_{19} \xrightarrow{300\,°C} C_9H_{18} + C_9H_{19}SH.$$

The sulfide molecule breakdown is accompanied by hydrogen disproportionation to form an olefin and mercaptan. The mercaptan formed is, in turn, partially converted to olefin with the liberation of a hydrogen sulfide molecule. The same applies also with respect to conversion of disulfides.

Decomposition of dinonyl sulfide at 300°C takes place with formation of primary nonyl mercaptan in 27% yield and 1-nonene in 4% yield [36, 37]. Hence, the conversion of aliphatic disulfides may be described by the following general formula:

$$R\text{---}S\text{---}S\text{---}R \xrightarrow{+H_2} 2RSH \xrightarrow{-2H_2S} 2R_{-1} \text{ (olefin)}.$$

Through destructive hydrogenation, the disulfide is reduced to form two molecules of mercaptan, and the resulting mercaptan is partially converted to olefin. The rate of hydrogenation exceeds the rate of further decomposition of mercaptan, so that nonyl mercaptan is the main product of dinonyl sulfide decomposition. The hydrogen necessary for the reduction is formed as a result of cracking reactions occurring over the aluminosilicate catalyst, even at 300°C. Analysis of the product gas revealed the presence of hydrogen in the amount of 20%.

Thus a number of diverse processes take place in sulfur compounds of the aliphatic series in contact with aluminosilicate catalysts. They include reactions occurring with liberation of hydrogen sulfide, hydrogen disproportionation reactions, and destructive hydrogenation. Sulfur compounds of different types behave in different ways under identical conditions, but all of the processes run irreversibly towards the formation of olefins, i.e. compounds which no longer contain any sulfur.

The mechanisms discussed above envisage, in principle, the possibility of complete decomposition of aliphatic mercaptans, sulfides, and disulfides present in crudes upon their coming in contact with clay minerals. The aliphatic mercaptans, sulfides, and disulfides from this viewpoint are merely a temporary step on the way to their complete desulfurization and transition first into olefins and then into hydrocarbons of other types.

2. Conversion of sulfur compounds of the naphthenic series

Cyclopentanethiol is converted, according to I. N. Tits-Skvortsova and collaborators, over aluminosilicate catalyst at 300 °C into cyclopentane in 33 % yield [38, 39]. In this reaction, 69.1 % of sulfur originally present in the cyclopenthanethiol was liberated in the form of hydrogen sulfide. Consequently, cyclopentanethiol behaves like the thiols of the aliphatic series: at 300 °C it splits off a molecule of hydrogen sulfide and is converted to cyclopentene

$$C_5H_9SH \rightarrow C_5H_8 + H_2S.$$

The reactions are more complex in the decomposition of cyclohexanethiol under the same conditions [39]. From the reaction product, methylcyclopentane was recovered in good yield (43 %) along with the initial cyclohexanethiol (9.4 %)

$$C_6H_{11}SH \xrightarrow{-H_2S} C_6H_{10} \rightarrow C_5H_7CH_3 \xrightarrow{+H_2} C_5H_9CH_3.$$

The cyclohexanethiol, on splitting off a molecule of hydrogen sulfide, is converted to cyclohexene which is a cyclic olefin. The latter is isomerized to methylcyclopentane and then, owing to hydrogen disproportionation at the expense of higher condensation products, is hydrogenated to methylcyclopentane.

The simplest sulfide of the cyclopentane series, namely dicyclopentyl sulfide, was studied over aluminosilicate catalyst at 300 °C [38, 39]. The reaction product contained only 60.9 % by weight of cyclopentene and traces of cyclopentanethiol. Besides, 75 % of the sulfur originally present in dicyclopentyl sulfide was liberated in the form of hydrogen sulfide. The decomposition of dicyclopentyl sulfide may be expressed as follows:

$$C_5H_9-S-C_5H_9 \leftarrow 2C_5H_8 + H_2S.$$

Dicyclopentyl disulfide, a disulfide of the naphthenic series, is converted according to I. N. Tits-Skvortsova [38, 39] over aluminosilicate catalyst at 300°C into cyclopentanethiol (26.7%) and cyclopentene (21.4%). Formation of these compounds appears to take place as follows:

$$C_5H_9\text{—}S\text{—}S\text{—}C_5H_9 \xrightarrow{+H_2} 2C_5H_9SH \rightarrow 2C_5H_8 + 2H_2S.$$

As a result of destructive hydrogenation, dicyclopentyl disulfide is reduced to cyclopentanethiol. The latter, on splitting off a molecule of hydrogen sulfide, is partially converted to cyclopentene. In this case, along with rupture of the S—S bond in the disulfide, a far-reaching destruction of its molecule and condensation of the resulting fragments are noted. As a result of these processes, the high boiling fractions of the product are formed and the hydrogen necessary for the reaction is liberated. The complete analogy between the conversion of dicyclopentyl disulfide and that of disulfides of the aliphatic series under similar conditions is quite remarkable.

Conversion of cyclopentylcyclohexyl sulfide over aluminosilicate catalyst at 300°C [39] is accompanied by abundant liberation of hydrogen sulfide in amounts equal to 87.7% of the sulfur present in the original sulfide. This points to drastic destructive processes occurring in its molecule. Cyclopentene, 1-methyl-1-cyclopentene, and methylcyclopentane were recovered from the product.

$$C_5H_9\text{—}S\text{—}C_6H_{11} \rightarrow C_5H_8 + C_6H_{10} + H_2S;$$

$$C_6H_{10} \rightarrow C_5H_7CH_3 \xrightarrow{+H_2} C_5H_9CH_3.$$

These breakdown products indicate a complex course of the process. The normally formed cyclohexane is isomerized to methylcyclopentene and then dehydrogenated to methylcyclopentane. The higher boiling fractions were found to contain also dicyclohexyl and 3,3'-dimethylcyclopentyl, which are condensation products of radicals.

Thus the conversion of sulfur compounds of the naphthenic series over aluminosilicate catalysts depends on various reactions which proceed with liberation of hydrogen sulfide, and hydrogen disproportionation and destructive hydrogenation reactions. Additional reactions are the isomerization of the cyclohexene ring which is unstable under these conditions and its subsequent conversion to cyclopentane derivatives. All of the processes, which are likewise irreversible, lead to the formation of hydrocarbons.

3. Conversion of sulfur compounds of the aromatic series

Thiophenol was selected as a representative of the aromatic series for study by I. N. Tits-Skovortsova [36]. The experiments were conducted at 200, 300, 400 and 500 °C. Liberation of hydrogen sulfide took place in every case. Benzene and thianthrene were recovered from the product. Thiophenol apparently undergoes conversion in two different ways, which may be represented as follows:

$$2C_6H_5SH \rightarrow C_6H_4 \underset{S}{\overset{S}{<}} \!\!\! > C_6H_4 + 2H_2;$$

$$2C_6H_5SH + 2H_2 \rightarrow 2C_6H_6 + 2H_2S.$$

As a consequence of the dehydrogenation reaction, from two molecules of thiophenol the complex thianthrene molecule is formed. The hydrogen liberated thereby reduces the other molecule of thiophenol to benzene. These conversions are associated with hydrogen disproportionation reactions, which usually take place in the presence of aluminosilicate catalysts.

Thianthrene may be regarded as the sulfur analog of anthracene. Yet at the same time it is a sulfide, because its sulfur atoms are linked by two of their valencies to carbon. Hence thiophenol, like an aliphatic mercaptan, decomposes in contact with aluminosilicate catalysts into hydrocarbon and sulfide. The latter has a more complicated structure than a sulfide of the aliphatic series and is more stable. In order to test the thermal resistance of thianthrene, it was passed over aluminosilicate catalyst at 400 °C. It was found that thianthrene may be decomposed under these conditions with liberation of hydrogen sulfide, though the decomposition is incomplete.

p-Thiocresol, being the closest homolog of thiophenol, was investigated at 300, 400 and 500 °C [40, 41]. From the product obtained at the aforementioned temperatures, toluene and the initial p-thiocresol were recovered. With rise in temperature, the amount of toluene increases and the amount of thiocresol diminishes. 2,6-Dimethylthianthrene was not found in any of the tests.

$$CH_3C_6H_4SH + H_2 \rightarrow CH_3C_6H_5 + H_2S.$$

Dithioresorcinol [41], having two sulfhydryl groups in the molecule, decomposes at 300°C into benzene (23.8% by weight of the product), thiophenol (11.9%) and thianthrene (25.3%).

Diphenyl sulfide is the simplest representative of sulfides of the aromatic series. Its conversion at 300 and 400°C gave a product, from which benzene, thianthrene and traces of thiophenol were separated. According to these data, diphenylsulfide as a consequence of the destructive hydrogenation reaction is decomposed first into benzene and thiophenol. Then thiophenol undergoes changes, being converted into benzene and thianthrene. The latter, in turn, is converted to benzene. All of the processes occur irreversibly towards the formation of an aromatic hydrocarbon. Diphenyl disulfide was subjected to thermocatalytic conversions at 400°C [36, 40]. The product resulting from the experiments contained 6% thiophenol and 9% thianthrene. On the basis of these data, the conversion of diphenyl disulfide under such conditions may be described as follows: initially as a result of destructive hydrogenation the disulfide breaks down to give two molecules of thiophenol. Thereafter thiophenol in accordance with the mechanisms established above is converted to benzene and thianthrene and ultimately into benzene alone.

The closest homolog of diphenyl disulfide, which is p,p'-ditolyl disulfide, behaves in a similar manner in thermocatalytic conversions [40]. α-Thionaphthol, being a thiol of the naphthalene series undergoes conversions which are somewhat different from the conversions of thiophenol. From conversion products of α-thionaphthol, only naphthalene was separated in a yield of 51.6% [42]. No compound similar to thianthrene, having sulfur in the ring, was found among the thermal catalysis products. Consequently, in the case of α-thionaphthol the reaction in the presence of aluminosilicate catalyst proceeds in accordance with the equation

$$C_{10}H_7SH + H_2 \rightarrow C_{10}H_8 + H_2S.$$

Only the destructive hydrogenation reaction with liberation of hydrogen sulfide takes place. In the case of ar-β-thiotetralol, the carbon structure of which is a condensed system of benzene and cyclohexane, a new process is brought into play, namely the dehydrogenation of the cyclohexane ring [42, 43]. The contacting of ar-β-thiotetralol with aluminosilicate gave a product containing tetralin

(34 % by weight of the product), naphthalene (28 %), and initial ar-β-thiotetralol (7 %). Twenty-one percent of the sulfur present in the initial thiol was recovered in the form of hydrogen sulfide. The reaction product contained a certain amount of elemental sulfur.

Primary process
$$C_{10}H_{11}SH + H_2 \rightarrow C_{10}H_{12} + H_2S.$$

Secondary process
$$C_{10}H_{12} - 2H_2 \rightarrow C_{10}H_8.$$

As a result of destructive hydrogenation, ar-β-thiotetralol is converted to tetralin and hydrogen sulfide, just as it occurs with thiophenol [37]. Thereafter naphthalene is formed because of dehydrogenation of tetralin.

It seemed more probable that under these conditions an isomerization of the hexamethylene ring of tetralin into a pentamethylene ring would take place to form a mixture of 1- and 2-methylhydrindenes. Yet the reaction product contained no such compounds. Research specially conducted by I. N. Tits-Skvortsova [43] on dehydrogenation and isomerization of tetralin under the same conditions as in contacting sulfur compounds with aluminosilicate catalyst likewise failed to show the formation of methylhydrindenes and naphthalene. The product contained only 1.4 % naphthalene, the remainder being initial tetralin, compared with 28 % naphthalene produced in the catalysis of ar-β-thiotetralol. Such a difference in the amount of naphthalene may be explained only by assuming that dehydrogenation of tetralin is caused not by the action of aluminosilicate alone, but because the elemental sulfur formed in the experiment acts likewise as a dehydrogenating agent. Dehydrogenation of tetralin under the action of sulfur has been repeatedly described in the literature and demonstrated not to be a catalytic process. The feasibility of tetralin dehydrogenation by elemental sulfur is corroborated also by the fact that no hydrogen was found in the gas mixture, whereas in the event of dehydrogenation under the action of aluminosilicate catalyst it should have been liberated in the free state.

The breakdown of ar-α-thiotetralol [44] takes place in the same way as that of ar-β-thiotetralol.

As a summary of research on the conversion of sulfur compounds of the aromatic series over aluminosilicate catalysts, a certain resemblance between the mechanisms of these conversions should be pointed out. The fundamental reaction here appears to be destructive hydrogenation and the elimination of sulfur in the form of hydrogen sulfide. Thiols of the aromatic series are converted to the corresponding hydrocarbons, except for thiophenol which is partially converted to thianthrene; sulfides and disulfides are converted to hydrocarbons and thiols, with the latter subsequently converted likewise to hydrocarbons. Thus all processes irreversibly lead to compounds which are entirely free from sulfur, in other words to hydrocarbons.

Conversion of mixed sulfides and other sulfur compounds over aluminosilicate catalyst. The decomposition of hexyldecyl sulfide, according to I. N. Tits-Skvortsova [36] takes place with the formation of 48% decyl mercaptan and 16% methylcyclopentane. No cyclohexanethiol is formed.

Primary process

$$C_6H_{11}—S—C_{10}H_{21} \rightarrow C_6H_{10} + C_{10}H_{21}SH;$$

Secondary process

$$C_6H_{10} \rightarrow C_5H_7CH_3 \xrightarrow{+H_2} C_5H_9CH_3.$$

The primary products in these reactions consist of decyl mercaptan and cyclohexane. Only as a result of secondary reactions, the latter is converted to methylcyclopentane. The break in the molecule occurs between sulfur and the naphthene ring. Conversion of cyclopentyldecyl sulfide, which has a similar structure, occurs in accordance with the same mechanism [42].

Exactly as in the previous case, the rupture of the bond occurs only at one point in the molecule, namely between the cyclopentane ring and sulfur. The reaction is accompanied by hydrogen disproportionation, to form cyclopentane and decyl mercaptan.

Entirely different is the behavior of aliphatic-aromatic sulfides in such cases.

Phenyldecyl sulfide, decomposing at 300°C, forms 1-decene (11% by weight of the product) and thiophenol amounting to 20% [36]. Not even traces of benzene and decyl mercaptan have been found in the reaction product. These results give quite a clear picture of the course of the decomposition of aliphatic-aromatic sulfides. The phenyldecyl sulfide molecule splits into thiol and olefin, the rupture taking place solely at the bond between sulfur and the aliphatic radical

$$C_6H_5-S-C_{10}H_{21} \rightarrow C_6H_5SH + C_{10}H_{20}.$$

At the same time one portion of the molecule is reduced by hydrogen originating from the other portion. The breakdown of the molecule of a mixed aliphatic-aromatic sulfide takes place with hydrogen disproportionation.

A similar picture is noted in the case of phenylcyclopentyl sulfide [36] which is a mixed sulfide consisting of an aromatic and a cyclopentane ring. The product obtained on passing this sulfide over aluminosilicate catalyst at 300°C contained 39% thiophenol and 5% cyclopentane

$$C_6H_5-S-C_5H_9 \rightarrow C_6H_5SH + C_5H_8.$$

As in the case of phenyldecyl sulfide, the break occurs only at a single point of the molecule, namely between sulfur and the cyclopentane ring. The rupture is accompanied by hydrogen disproportionation and formation of cyclopentane which remains stable under these conditions and thiophenol which may undergo further conversions in accordance with the mechanisms discussed above. Similar but more complex conversions occur with phenylcyclohexyl sulfide, a mixed sulfide whose components are aromatic and cyclohexane rings. From the conversion products obtained on passing this sulfide over aluminosilicate catalyst at 300°C, thiophenol in amount of 52% and methylcyclopentane in amount of 19% by weight of the product were separated.

The conversion of the aforementioned mixed aliphatic-aromatic sulfides may be expressed by the general scheme

$$C_6H_5-S-C_nH_{2n+1} \leftarrow C_6H_5SH + C_nH_{2n}.$$

The rupture in the sulfide molecule of this type occurs always at a single point, namely between sulfur and the radical, and there has never been a case where the rupture takes place between sulfur and the aromatic nucleus.

Significantly, dibenzyl sulfide cannot undergo conversions of this sort owing to absence of hydrogen in β-position to sulfur. Its conversion under similar conditions at 300°C proceeds according to an

entirely different mechanism [45]. From the product obtained, 27%
toluene and 24.3% dibenzyl (symmetrical diphenylethane) were
recovered. 90% of the sulfur present in the original sulfide was
trapped as PbS. Consequently, almost all of the sulfur was separated
from the sulfide in the form of hydrogen sulfide. Based on the results of catalysis, the breakdown of the dibenzyl sulfide molecule
may be represented as follows:

$$C_6H_5-CH_2-S-CH_2-C_6H_5 + H_2 \rightarrow H_2S + C_6H_5-CH_2-CH_2-C_6H_5$$

$$C_6H_5-CH_2-CH_2-C_6H_5 + H_2 \rightarrow 2C_6H_5CH_3.$$

An unexpected result was obtained in the study of α-naphthyl-
decyl sulfide [42]. Since the structure of this sulfide consists of a
naphthalene radical and an aliphatic radical, it could be expected
that the breakdown would occur by rupture of the bond between
sulfur and the aliphatic radical in the molecule to form α-thio-
naphthol and 1-decene. However, examination of the product showed that it contains naphthalene (31.6% by weight of the product),
decyl mercaptan (13.1%), and 1-decene (7.8%). No thionaphthol
was found in the product. These data indicate that decomposition of
α-naphthyldecyl sulfide takes place as follows:

$$C_{10}H_7-S-C_{10}H_{21} + H_2 \rightarrow C_{10}H_8 + C_{10}H_{21}SH.$$

Destructive hydrogenation occurring with rupture of the bond
between the naphthalene ring and sulfur, results in the formation
of naphthalene and decyl mercaptan. The latter undergoes further
conversions as indicated above.

Thus the bond between the naphthalene ring in α-position and
sulfur is less resistant than the bond between sulfur and the alkyl
group, and in this particular case the naphthalene ring, as far as
stability of the bond with sulfur is concerned, displays closer resemblance to naphthene rings than to the aromatic nucleus. This
fact may be explained only by the greater reactivity of the naphthalene ring at the α-position.

To summarize some of the results of research on the conversion
of mixed sulfides over aluminosilicate catalyst, it should be first
of all pointed out that the preponderant process in these conversions
is the hydrogen disproportionation reaction and rupture of the

weakest bond between sulfur and the corresponding radical. In the case of aliphatic-naphthenic sulfides the weak link is the bond between the naphthenic ring and sulfur, and the split in the molecule occurs at this point. The primary products always consist of the corresponding unsaturated cyclic hydrocarbon and an aliphatic mercaptan.

In aliphatic-aromatic and naphthenic-aromatic sulfides, which contain phenyl, the break in the molecule likewise occurs at one point, namely between sulfur and the naphthenic or aliphatic radical, and there is no record of this break ever having occurred between sulfur and the aromatic nucleus. Consequently, the bond between sulfur and the aromatic (benzene) ring is more stable than the bond between sulfur and the aliphatic radical or between sulfur and a naphthenic ring. In every instance, the primary breakdown products of these sulfides consist of thiophenol and an unsaturated hydrocarbon.

In α-naphthyl sulfides the bond between the naphthalene ring in the α-position and sulfur is less stable than the bond between sulfur and the alkyl radical. In this case the naphthalene ring is comparable to the naphthenic ring with respect to strength of its bond with sulfur. This is explicable through lack of equivalance between the individual bonds in the aromatic ring of naphthalene and the substantial reactivity of sulfur in the α-position of the naphthalene ring.

In mixed sulfides having tetralyl as part of the molecule, the bond between sulfur and the aromatic nucleus is weakened to an appreciable extent by the influence of the condensed hexamethylene ring. Therefore the rupture of the bond in tetralylalkyl sulfides occurs to an equal degree for both valencies of sulfur, including the bond with the aliphatic radical as well as the bond with the aromatic nucleus.

As a result of irreversible processes, the breakdown of mixed sulfides ultimately causes elimination of sulfur in the form of hydrogen sulfide and formation of hydrocarbons. Still, this does not preclude the development of intermediate, more resistant forms of sulfur compounds such as thiophenols, thianthrenes, and other ring structures, which do not provide complete desulfurization under laboratory conditions.

4. Conversion of sulfur-bearing petroleum compounds

At present the catalytic desulfurization of petroleum is utilized on a broad scale in the industry. This process is accomplished by the use of catalysts including, along with metal oxides, bauxites, natural clays, and synthetic aluminosilicates [54]. For instance, Bottomley [59] reports the highly effective use of clays in the vapor phase refining of gasolines as practiced in the U.S.A.

According to M. G. Mamedli [21], certain samples of Apsheron clays without previous activation may be used as very effective catalysts for breaking down sulfur compounds in the desulfurization of some crudes.

Experiments have shown that the desulfurization of gasoline fractions takes place very effectively at a temperature as low as 200°C. The extent of purification for some of the gasolines approaches 70%.

With increase in temperature the process of breaking down the sulfur compounds goes further. For example, the sulfur content in Karachukhur gasoline at 400°C is lowered by almost 85%. It should be noted that the extent of gasoline desulfurization with thermally activated clays is almost the same as with natural clays that had not been thermally treated.

The desulfurization process under identical conditions, i.e. with the same clay, proceeds differently for gasolines of different origin. Whereas the sulfur content in Karachukhur gasoline on treatment at 200°C was reduced by 70%, in Balakhany gasoline the decrease amounted to only 7%.

A similar effect may be noted in treating various gasolines with bauxites. As reported by Schulze and Alden [81] and by Foster [62], treatment with bauxite may be used for complete removal of the mercaptans, sulfides, and disulfides present in gasoline, breaking them down to hydrogen sulfide. Cyclic sulfur compounds are more difficult to destroy but their content in straight-run gasolines is negligibly small. This fact contributed to the widespread use of bauxite treatment for desulfurizing straight-run gasolines on an industrial scale in the U.S.A. The application of bauxite treatment for desulfurizing Soviet crudes has been tested by Ya. A. Botnikov, L. D. Nersesov and K. Kh. Fishman [7]. Experiments have shown that on passing Ishimbaevo gasoline over bauxites at 400°C and at a velocity of 1–2 l. liquid gasoline per liter bauxite per hour, the sulfur content is reduced from 0.47% to 0.02%. The degree of desulfurization thereby reaches 96%. In Krasnokamsk gasoline under similar conditions the sulfur content is reduced from 0.11% to 0.03%, corresponding to an efficiency of 73%.

Similar results in treating various gasolines were obtained by L. I. Berents and A. V. Frost [4].

These data are cited in Table 35.

TABLE 35. *Desulfurization over Bauxites, as Reported by Berents and Frost (Atmospheric pressure, at flow rate of 0.45 l. liquid product per 1 liter bauxite per hour, temperature 400° C)*

Feed stock	Sulfur content		Extent of desulfurization (%)
	in initial gasoline	in treated gasoline	
Ishimbaevo straight-run gasoline	0.52	0.08	85
Ishimbaevo straight-run ligroin	0.47	0.06	87
Cracked gasoline	0.35	0.12	66
Shale gasoline	0.40	0.20	50

From the table it follows that, other conditions being equal, the efficiency of removing sulfur from Ishimbaevo straight-run gasoline amounts to 85%, compared to 66% for cracked gasoline and only 50% for shale gasoline.

It is quite evident that the desulfurizing efficiency depends on the chemical nature of sulfur compounds, i.e. on their stability. In the thermal treatment (cracking) of petroleum the most stable compounds resist destruction, therefore the efficiency of treating cracked gasoline with bauxites is considerably lower than that of straight-run products which contain relatively unstable sulfur compounds. The most stable sulfur compounds proved to be those present in shale gasoline, which were formed under pyrolysis conditions. The sulfur compounds present in gasolines from high-sulfur crudes are less resistant to catalytic conversions than sulfur compounds of similar molecular weight and boiling point but originating from crudes of low sulfur content. It seems as if the high-sulfur crudes with their relatively unstable sulfur compounds, owing to special geological conditions, had not been subjected to thermocatalytic treatment in the natural environment and the sulfur compounds contained in these crudes have survived up to the present time. In low-sulfur crudes, only the highly stable forms of sulfur compounds remained, and even these will, as a result of irreversible processes, likewise be converted sooner or later to compounds which are free from sulfur, and the crudes will be classified as sulfur-free crudes. In support of this contention are the available data indicating a positive correlation of high-sulfur crudes with carbonate rocks. In carbonate reservoirs the thermocatalytic processes, which have been shown to be enhanced by presence of aluminosilicates, are inhibited or weak; in contrast low-sulfur crudes appear to be associated with clay facies, where such processes would tend to be favored. The destruction of sulfur compounds in the presence of aluminosilicates evidently took place both in the source rock where the petroleum originated and in the reservoir, since clay fractions are present in varying amounts even in well-sorted sandstones.

C. BEHAVIOR OF NITROGEN COMPOUNDS IN PRESENCE OF ALUMINOSILICATE-TYPE CATALYSTS

The nitrogen content in crudes is usually of the order of several tenths and sometimes hundredths of one percent. If it is assumed that 1% nitrogen corresponds to about 10% of nitrogen compounds, the content of the latter in crude oils should not exceed 2–3% of the total, even in heavy resinous crudes.

A definite relationship exists between the type of crude, its degree of transformation, and its content of nitrogen compounds. The higher the specific gravity of the crude, the lower its degree of transformation and the higher the concentration of nitrogen compounds. There is likewise a parallel relationship between the content of resinous substances in the crude and its nitrogen content. With few exceptions, a linear relationship is maintained, and this alone establishes the association of nitrogen compounds with the resinous portion of the crudes.

The previously established opinion about the nitrogen compounds in petroleum being organic bases continues to be held until the present time, although it has been definitely established for a number of crudes that the overwhelming portion of nitrogen is present in the form of non-basic compounds. Research by F. Richter *et al.*

[79] has shown that only 25–34% of the total nitrogen present in petroleum is in the form of nitrogen bases, and the remaining 64–75% exist as neutral forms of nitrogen compounds, the chemical structures of which are obscure. For fourteen samples of Texas, Californian, Mid-Continent, South American, and Middle Eastern crudes covered in the study, the ratio of basic nitrogen to total nitrogen is a constant value regardless of the type of crude and varies within the narrow range from 0.25 to 0.34. Almost at the same time similar results were obtained by V. Getseu [10] in a study of Daghestan crudes, for which this ratio on the average is equal to 0.28. The bases separated from crude oils comprise alkylated pyridines and quinolines, whereas the bases separated from petroleum distillates contain also compounds of more complex structure represented by condensed systems including a pyridine nucleus with five-membered naphthenic rings (one or two) and designated as naphthenic or pyridazine bases. The latter compounds are not present in the free state in petroleums and are presumably formed from more complicated non-basic nitrogen compounds during the distillation of the petroleum.

The distribution of nitrogen compounds among the individual petroleum fractions is unequal. According to V. Getseu [10], the asphaltic-resinous portion of crudes accounts for about 70% of the total nitrogen present in crudes, whereas the oil fraction contains the remaining 30%. Investigations have shown that the nitrogen compounds in asphaltenes do not display the properties of organic bases and are non-basic in character. In silica gel resins, the overwhelming portion of them (85%) is represented by neutral nitrogen compounds, but practically all of the nitrogen in the oil fraction has basic properties.

The data discussed above give a picture of the content and distribution of nitrogen compounds in petroleum fractions. They also indicate that the presence of nitrogen bases is limited chiefly to the oil fractions of petroleum and that their content amounts to less than 0.5%, based on the whole crude. Organic bases, like the ions of alkali and alkaline earth metals, act as poisons toward aluminosilicate catalysts according to reports by various researchers. Their negative effect on the catalytic properties of aluminosilicates appears to consist in their irreversible chemisorption by the catalyst and their high chemical stability, which makes the active catalyst surface inaccessible for molecules of the reactants. The existence of a strong bond between nitrogen bases and catalyst, according to research by A. V. Frost [52], has been proved by direct study of the adsorption of pyridine on active aluminosilicates, which showed that a substantial amount of pyridine adsorbed at ordinary temperatures cannot be removed by prolonged heating in high vacuum even at a temperature of 300 °C.

In a study of the poisoning of aluminosilicate catalyst with pyridine, Mills, Bodeker and Oblad, [73] have established that the active portion of aluminosilicate is acid and that the poisoning action of organic bases and alkali metal ions merely involves neutralization of this acid. As visualized by K. G. Miesserov [22], the exchange acidity of aluminosilicate is due to the presence of exchange ions of aluminum on their surface, which constitute the active sites of aluminosilicate catalysts. Pyridine is capable of forming a stable complex with the exchange aluminum and thus deprives the aluminosilicate of its catalytic properties. For this reason the conversion of organic bases over aluminosilicate catalysts involves as an initial phase the poisoning of the catalyst, followed by their thermal decomposition at a given temperature.

The literature contains only a few references relating to conversions of nitrogen bases in the presence of aluminosilicate type catalysts. According to A. V. Frost [52], pyridine remains virtually stable on heating over an aluminosilicate catalyst to a temperature of 450 °C, showing no evidence of decomposition at this temperature. More frequently, nitrogen compounds were tested as additives to the material to be cracked, in order to determine their effect on the rate of cracking with aluminosilicates. Such investigations have been carried out by D. Orochko, A. V. Frost, and I. V. Schchekin [52] in cracking a standard feed stock (cycloparaffinic kerosene) over a synthetic aluminosilicate catalyst at a temperature of 450 °C.†
The nitrogen additives included: (1) pyridine bases formed as by-products in the coke industry, (2) a mixture of crude pyridine bases recovered from tar in the semi-coking of coal, and (3) technical quinoline.

The relative deactivating effect of organic bases in the catalytic cracking, under standard conditions, of a standard feed stock with the addition of 2% by weight of various bases is cited in Table 36.

The data in Table 36 indicate that the presence of pyridine bases

† The volumetric feed rate of the stock was equal to 0.6, and the time for each cycle (t) was 30 min.

and quinoline in the feed stock has a substantial effect on the results of cracking. The greatest inhibiting effect is caused by quinoline. The latter is thus a highly powerful poison for aluminosilicates with respect to their catalytic properties.

TABLE 36. *Relative Deactivating Effect of Organic Bases [52]*

Type of base	Relative decrease in reactivity of the standard feed with the addition of 2% of a base $\frac{1}{R_{rel}}$ *	Relative deactivating effect of the bases	
		with the effect of quinoline as unity	with the effect of mixture no. 1 as unity
Mixture no. 1. Pyridine bases from tar in the coking of coal		0.12	1.00
Mixture no. 2. Crude pyridine bases from tar in the semi-coking of coal	3.9 1.5	0.05	0.44
Quinoline (technical)	31.0	1.00	8.30

* The relative reactivity of the stock R_{rel} is defined as the ratio of the reaction velocity constants of the feed mixture (a_{fm}) being tested and of the standard feed stock (a_{st}), both obtained under standardized conditions.

Pyridine bases obtained from the tar in the coking of coal have an appreciably greater effect compared with pyridine bases recovered from semi-coking products of coal. Thus the closer the nitrogen bases are related to primary products, the less is their poisoning effect toward the aluminosilicate. This is obviously because nitrogen bases present in natural sources have a more complex structure than the bases formed under drastic conditions during the pyrolysis of petroleum or the coking of coal. A great majority of them are polyakyl-substituted derivatives of quinoline and pyridine, as well as pyridazine compounds that have appreciably weaker basic properties. Therefore the nitrogen bases, despite their being potential poisons for clay minerals as alumonosilicate catalysts, cannot have any decisive importance because their quantity is infinitesimal as compared with the rock mass serving as reservoir for petroleum and organic matter.

BIBLIOGRAPHY

1. ARESHIDZE, KH.I. *Zh. prikl. Khimii*, **18**, Nos. 4–5 (1945).
2. ARESHIDZE, KH.I. *Izv. Akad. Nauk SSSR, Otdel. Khim. Nauk*, 178–84 (1950).
3. ARESHIDZE, KH.I., TAVARTKILADZE, E.K. *Zh. prikl. Khimii*, **22**, No. 2 (1949).
4. BERENTS, L.I. and FROST, A.V. *Dokl. Akad. Nauk SSSR*, **29**, 197 (1940).
5. BOGOMOLOV, A.I., GORSKAYA, A.I. and MESSINEVA, M.A. *Sbornik "Origin of Petroleum"*, Gostoptekhizdat, 1955, p. 288.
6. BOGOMOLOV, A.I. and SHIMANSKII, V.K. *Geokhim. Sbornik VNIGRI*, No.4 (1957).
7. BOTNIKOV, YA.A., NERSESOV, L.D. and FISHMAN, K.KH. *Vostochnaya Neft'* **2**, No. 9, 34 (1940).
8. BUTOVICH, N.A. *Zh. prikl. Khimii*, **23**, No. 2, 221–4 (1950).
9. VENNER, R. *Termokhimicheskie Raschety IL*, 1950.
10. GETSEU, V.V. Study of Daghestan Crudes. Author's own abstract of his candidate thesis, Makhachkala, 1954.
11. DOBRYANSKII, A.F. *Geochemistry of Petroleum*, Gostoptekhizdat, 1948.
12. ZELINSKII, N.D. *Selected Works*, vol. 1, publ. Akad. Nauk SSSR, 1941.
13. ZUL'FUGAROV, Z.G. *Izv. Akad. Nauk Azerbaijan SSR*, No. 5 (1953).
14. IPAT'EV, V.N. *Catalytic Reactions at High Temperatures and Pressures*, Publ. Akad. Nauk SSSR, 1936.
15. KAGAN, M.YA., SAVCHENKO, R.I. *Dokl. Akad. Nauk SSSR*, **19**, No. 6 (1949).
16. KAMENSKAYA, I.N. Chemistry and technology of shale processing, *Trudy VNIIPS*, No. II (1954).
17. KARAPET'YANTS, M.KH. *Chemical Thermodynamics*, Goskhimtekhizdat, 1953.
18. KOTELKOV, N.Z. *Zh. prikl. Khimii*, **24**, No. 6, 576–82 (1951).
19. KOROBOV, V. and FROST, A. *Free Energies of Organic Compounds*, 1950.
20. KOTINA, A.K. *Geokhim. Sbornik VNIGRI*, No. 4 (1957).
21. MAMEDLI, M.G. *Zh. prikl. Khimii*, **18**, Nos. 1–2, 61–8 (1946).
22. MIESSEROV, K.G. *Dokl. Akad. Nauk SSSR*, **91**, No. 3, 553–6 (1953).
23. MUSAEV, M.R. and ZIZIN, V.G. *Zh. prikl. Khimii*, **29**, No. 5 (1956).
24. NEKRASOVA, A.S. and KRENTSEL', B.A. *Zh. Obshchei Khimii*, **19**, No. 5, 941–50 (1949).
25. OBOLENTSEV, R.D. and USOV, YU.N. *Dokl. Akad. Nauk SSSR*, **71**, No. 3 (1950).
26. OBOLENTSEV, R.D. and GRYAZEV, N.N. *Dokl. Akad. Nauk SSSR*, **73**, No.2, 319–22 (1950).
27. PARKS, G. and HUFFMAN, G. *Free Energies of Organic Compounds*, ONTI, 1936.
28. German patent 801329, 4 January, 1951.
29. Japanese patent 157864, 21 July, 1943.
30. PETROV, A.D. *Zh. Russk. Khim. Obshch.* **61**, 1849–50 (1929).
31. PETROV, A.A. and SHCHEKIN, V.V. *Dokl. Akad. Nauk SSSR*, **78**, No. 5, 913 (1951).

32. RUDENKO, M.G. and GROMOVA, V.N. *Dokl. Akad. Nauk SSSR*, **81**, No. 2 (1951).
33. SKRIPNIK, E.I., ISAGULYANTS, V.I. and SHTOF, I.K. *Khimiya i Tekhnologiya Topliva*, No. 5 (1956).
34. STADNIKOV, G.L. and IVANOVSKII, E.Z. *Neftyanoe i Slantsevoe Khozyaistvo*, No. 3, 470–6 (1925).
35. STADNIKOV, G.L. *Origin of Coal and Petroleum*, Publ. Akad. Nauk SSSR, 1937.
36. TITS-SKVORTSOVA, I.N., LEVINA, S.YA., LEONOVA, A.I. and KARASEVA,E.A. Uchenye Zapiski MGU, issue 132, kn. 7 (1950).
37. TITS-SKVORTSOVA, I.N., LEVINA, S.YA., LEONOVA, A.I. and KARASEVA,E.A. *Zh. Obshchei Khimii*, **21**, No. 2, 242–50 (1951).
38. TITS-SKVORTSOVA, I.N., LEONOVA, A.I. and LEVINA, S.YA. *Dokl. Akad. Nauk SSSR*, **94**, No. 4, 741–3 (1952).
39. TITS-SKVERTSOVA, I.N., LEONOVA, A.I. and LEVINA, S.YA. *Sbornik Statei po Obshchei Khimii*, vol. 2, publ. Akad. Nauk SSSR, 1953.
40. TITS-SKVORTSOVA, I.N., LEONOVA, A.I., LEVINA, S.YA. and KARASEVA,E.A. *Sbornik Statei po Obschei Khimii*, vol. 1, publ. Akad. Nauk SSSR, 1953.
41. TITS-SKVORTSOVA, I.N., LEONOVA, A.I. and LEVINA, S.YA. *Dokl. Akad. Nauk SSSR*, **80**, No. 3 (1951).
42. TITS-SKVORTSOVA, I.N., LEVINA, S.YA., LEONOVA, A.I. and DANILOVA,T.A. *Uchenye Zapiski MGU*, issue 151, kn. 8 (1951).
43. TITS-SKVORTSOVA, I.N. and DANILOVA, T.A. *Zh. Obshchei Khimii*,**23**,No.8, 1384–92 (1953).
44. TITS-SKVORTSOVA, I.N. and Danilova, T.A. *Vestnik MGU, Seriya fiz.-mat. Nauk*, issue 1, No. 2 (1956).
45. TITS-SKVORTSOVA, I.N., LEONOVA, A.I. and LEVINA, S.YA. *Dokl. Akad. Nauk SSSR*, **88**, No. 6 (1953).
46. FROST, A.V. and OCHKIN, A.V. *Vestnik MGU*, issue 5, 73 (1947).
47. FROST, A.V. and LARINA, A.YA. *Dokl. Akad. Nauk SSSR*,**54**, No. 5 (1946).
48. FROST, A.V. and LARINA, A.YA. *Dokl. Akad. Nauk SSSR*,**59**, No. 7 (1948).
49. FROST, A.V. and KHAIN, S.S. *Zh. prikl. Khimii*, **18**, No. 6, 301–8 (1946).
50. FROST, A.V. *Dokl. Akad. Nauk SSSR*, **37**, Nos. 7–8, 255–7 (1942).
51. FROST, A.V. and SATTER-ZADE, I.S. *Trudy Azerbaijan. Gos. Univ., Seriya Khim.*, issue 1 (1951).
52. FROST, A.V. *Research on Kinetics and Catalysis*, Publ. Akad. Nauk SSSR, 1956, pp. 480–6.
53. CHISTYAKOV, A.N. Thermocatalytic Conversions of Some Oxygenated Compounds over Aluminosilicate Catalyst. Author's own abstract of candidate thesis, Leningrad Technol. Inst., 1954.
54. CHERNOZHUKOV, N.I. *Technology of Petroleum*, Part III, Gostoptekhizdat, 1940, pp. 110–11.
55. SHCHEKIN, V.V. *Trudy Inst. Nefti Akad. Nauk SSSR*, **2** (1952).
56. YUR'EV, YU.K. and LEVI, I.S. *Dokl. Akad. Nauk SSSR*, **78**, 725 (1951).
57. MCALLISTER, S.H. BAILEY, WM.A. and BOUTON, C.M. *J. Am. Chem. Soc.* **62**, No. 11, 3210–15 (1940).
58. BOURNS, A.N. and NICHOLLS, R.V. *Can. J. Res.* **26**, 81–88 (1948).
59. BOTTOMLEY, N. *Nat. Petr. News*, **33**, No. 42, 330 (1941).

60. DEMOREST, M., MOOBERY, D. and DAMFORT, D. *Ind. Eng. Chem.* **43**, No.11, 2569–72 (1951).
61. FARAGHER, W., MORRELL and COMAY, S. *Ind. Eng. Chem.* **20**, 527 (1928).
62. FOSTER, A. *Oil and Gas Journal*, **38**, No. 19, 67, 528 (1939).
63. HEINEMANN, H., WERT, R. and McCARTER, *Ind. Eng. Chem.* **41**, No. 12, 2928–37 (1949).
64. HORI, M., OIKE, K.Y. and HUKUSIMA. *J. Agr. Soc. Japan*, **15**, 483–95 (1939).
65. JOSHI, H.K. and PAI, M.U. *J. Scient. and Industr. Res.* **13**, No. 9, 619–25 (1954).
66. KYOKEN FYJI, *J. Chem. Soc. Japan*, **65**, 181–4 (1944).
67. KASHIMA, K. *Bull. Chem. Soc. Japan*, **4**, No. 8, 179–90 (1929).
68. KOMAREWSKY, V.I., UHLICK, S.C. and MURRAY, M.J. *J. Am. Chem. Soc.* **67**, 557–8 (1945).
69. KOMAREWSKY, V.I., RIESZ, C.H. and THODOS, G. *J. Am. Chem. Soc.* **61**, No. 9, 2525–8 (1939).
70. KAPRANOS, S.W., APPLEBY, N.G. and DOBRATZ, C.J. *J. Am. Chem. Soc.* **66**, No. 11, 1398–9 (1944).
71. MALISOFF, W. and MARKS, E. *Ind. Eng. Chem.* **25**, 780 (1928).
72. MALISOFF, W. and MARKS, E. *Ind. Eng. Chem.* **28**, 114 (1931).
73. MILLS, G.A., BODEKER, E.K. and OBLAD, A.G. *J. Am. Chem. Soc.* **72**, 1554 (1950).
74. MIDORIKAWA, ITO. *Reports Scient. Research Inst.* **25**, No. 1, 25–32 (1949).
75. MURAI, J. and JOKOYAMA, WASEDA. *Applied Chem. Soc. Bull.* **18**, No. 2, 16–22 (1941).
76. MATUSZAK, A.H. *J. Am. Chem. Soc.* **66**, No. 10, 1649–52 (1944).
77. NORIYUKI SAKINAWA, *J. Chem. Soc. Japan, Pure Chem. Sect.* **72**, 227–230 (1951).
78. OTTO, R. and ROSSING, A. *Ber.* **19**, 3134 (1886).
79. RICHTER, F.P., CAESAR, P.O., MEISEL, S.L. and OFFENHAUER, R.D. *Ind. Eng. Chem.* **44**, No. 11, 2601 (1952).
80. SABATIER, P. and MAILHE, C. *Comptes Rend.* **150**, 1570 (1910).
81. SCHULZE, W. and ALDEN, R. *Refiner*, **18**, No. 11, 96 (1939).
82. SEVERIN, E. and ENGLER, C. *Zeitschr. f. Angew. Chemie*, **25**, No. 4, 153–8 (1912).
83. SUCHIRO, *J. Chem. Soc. Japan, Ind. Chem. Sec.* **52**, 17–19.
84. WALDMANN and FRANTISEK PETRU. *Ber.* **83**, No. 3, 287–91 (1950).

CHAPTER VIII

THERMOCATALYTIC CONVERSIONS
OF HYDROCARBONS

EXPERIMENTAL verification of the hypothesis concerning the transformation of petroleum aims at reproducing in the laboratory the natural processes to which petroleum is subjected in the depths of the earth.

The conversion of hydrocarbons, in accordance with thermodynamic considerations, may take place spontaneously in the course of redistribution of the energy of molecules. The presence of catalytic substances may result in a considerable reduction in temperature requirements of the process, without altering the course of the reaction. This provides a means for observing, within brief periods of time in the laboratory, processes which in nature require geological periods of time. Making allowances for the temperature factor of the reaction, it may be calculated that a reaction which at 200 °C is completed within one year will require at 300°C only 9 hr and at 450 °C just 1 sec. Calculations of this sort are, generally speaking, incorrect because they fail to allow for the activation of molecules, which requires different temperatures for different hydrocarbons, so that direct extrapolation into the region of low temperatures may produce erroneous results. It may be assumed, however, that extrapolation over temperature intervals which are not too large would provide a possibility, for example, of reproducing at 150 and 250 °C a natural process occurring at lower temperatures such as 100 and 200 °C, respectively.

Experiments with various hydrocarbons and their mixtures were carried out at the lowest temperatures at which the changes susceptible to analysis could still be reliably noted.

The literature contains a large number of references relating to thermocatalytic conversion of hydrocarbons of different series, as well as petroleum fractions. The latter constitute the feed stocks for catalytic cracking on a commercial scale. The well-known researches by A. V. Frost, R. D. Obolentsev, K. P. Lavrovskii, B. L. Moldavskii and many others were carried out in the overwhelming number of cases in the liquid phase at temperatures of the order of 400–450°C and a negligibly short residence time of the product under such temperature conditions. Such conditions are quite drastic and the authors, experimenting with aromatic hydrocarbons, always noted that radicals were split off in the form of olefins.

High temperatures such as 450°C would hardly permit extrapolating the results into the region of very much lower temperatures, and consequently all of this research has little significance for the geochemistry of petroleum. Still, A. V. Frost conducted an experiment on the conversion of fuel oil to gasoline at 250°C, i.e. in the liquid phase, and this experiment is of substantial significance for the geochemistry of petroleum transformations. It is known that A. V. Frost was the first to express the idea that thermocatalytic reactions with non-hydrocarbon substances may be of value for explaining the origin of oil.

The experimental investigations carried out by one of the authors of the present book were intended to serve a more modest purpose: rather than studying the mechanism of petroleum formation, they dealt with its transformations in an attempt at interpreting the origin of the different types of petroleums in nature as individual stages of a single and strictly directional process.

A study of the conversion of petroleum as a whole faces tremendous procedural difficulties, so that in this case it is justified to proceed from the individual to the whole. It was contemplated to study first the behavior of individual hydrocarbons of the same series in order to establish potential relationships in the process and extend them to the entire series as a whole, followed by a systematic study of the various series of hydrocarbons and other organic compounds of interpreting the behavior of the hydrocarbon mixture, i.e. petroleum.

It was found that, at low temperatures and long periods of thermal and catalytic action, hydrocarbon reactions occur according to a somewhat different mechanism than those at high temperatures and short-term thermocatalytic conditions. Thus, for example, virtually no gas formation takes place at 200–300°C with any hydrocarbon series, although sufficiently large changes in hydrocarbon composition can always be noted. Because of the longer contact time, there is also no formation of olefins. It has been noted also that for certain hydrocarbons of particular structure the conversion takes place easily at a temperature of 100 °C. All of this seems to indicate that at low temperatures a rearrangement of hydrocarbons rather than their cleavage occurs, and specifically in the case of homologs of benzene and naphthalene a redistribution of radicals takes place. The actual observations of conversion at low temperatures are certainly of much greater significance for the geochemistry of petroleum than are high temperature reactions, and a thermodynamic interpretation of the results obtained opens new paths for research.

On the basis of the data obtained, the composition of petroleum need not necessarily depend on the nature of initial material, thereby broadening the range of natural sources for the genesis of petroleum. Furthermore, a number of relationships established for the conversion of hydrocarbons provides an insight into relationships pertaining to the composition and properties of oil, though such relationships had been previously stated merely as facts or were given a wrong interpretation.

The catalyst used in most cases consisted of activated Gumbrin or Askanite. Upon activation with acid and washing with water to remove sulfates, the remainder of Gumbrin was molded in the form of tablets of 4–6 mm diameter and dried at 300 °C for 3 hr. Losses sustained in the activation of Gumbrin comprise about 15%, chiefly in the form of alum.

The dried catalyst was mixed in proportions of 1:1 by weight with the hydrocarbon to be tested. In some cases a catalyst-to-reactant ratio of 3:4 was used. Thereafter the mixture was heated in glass flasks or metallic vessels or, at times, in autoclaves. Pressure is of no consequence in the conversion process, except that it permits the retention of volatile reaction products in the reaction zone. Experiments in the autoclaves were carried out whenever a charge material boiling below the predetermined reaction temperature was used (for example, toluene or xylene) or whenever it was intended to keep the volatile reaction products in the reaction zone (for example, in the conversion of kerosene and oils).

Many high-boiling hydrocarbons can be converted so easily that difficulties arise in maintaining the desired temperature because it is lowered through the formation of low boiling products (for example, in the case of isopropylbenzene, cyclohexylbenzene, mineral oils, etc.). In cases of this sort the low boiling products formed were withdrawn via a condenser.

With individual hydrocarbons it has been frequently noted that an equilibrium is reached after a more or less protracted heating time (for instance, with toluene and cyclohexane). With mineral oils the principal conversions proceed more rapidly. Thus, for instance, mineral oils and paraffin wax give the major part of low boiling fractions already within the initial hour or two at 250 or 300 °C, and further heating produces no appreciable changes in the distribution of the fractions obtained. The reason is that the catalyst, being present in insufficient amount, is soon fouled by resinous products of the reaction. By increasing the ratio of catalyst to reactant in such cases it is possible to obtain very much higher yields of low boiling products; i.e. the conversion reaction proceeds much further. For individual substances it is quite evident that the results of conversion depend on molecular weight and structure of hydrocarbons.

At the end of the experiment the volatile products were driven off from the reaction mixture at temperatures not higher than the temperature of the experiment, after which the residue was allowed to cool and then extracted with petroleum ether or acetone. Upon removal of solvent, the sum total of residue and previously recovered distillate was calculated. Owing to formation of resinous substances not extractible by the solvent, the product balance sheet usually showed a deficit of 3–10%.

The products obtained were subjected to both chemical and physical analysis. Individual hydrocarbons of the aromatic series gave upon oxidation the corresponding benzenecarboxylic acids which were also examined by the titration method, by investigating the resulting methyl or ethyl esters, and by other methods. Mixtures of components obtained from petroleum fractions were investigated by the conventional methods used for determining the group composition of standard fractions.

One of the important factors in experiments relating to conversion of hydrocarbons by the action of aluminosilicate type catalysts is the quantity of catalyst used per unit weight of the substance to be converted. In the thermocatalysis experiments described below, the amount of catalyst used was in the ratio of 1:1 to the substance to be converted. With this ratio a considerable amount of the substance remains unadsorbed by the catalyst, a factor presenting certain conveniences as far as procedure is concerned. However, theoretically this amount of catalyst may prove to be insufficient whenever the resinous substances formed in the reaction tend to settle onto the catalyst surface and block its active sites. Of course, it is reasonable to expect that when the resinous substances have been distributed over a larger surface, the catalyst will show a better performance or at least remain active over a longer period of time.

Such considerations carry much weight in discussing the feasibility of catalytic processes in natural conditions when the ratio of catalyst to the substance to be converted is much higher than $1:1$. At typical saturations of mineral rocks with oil, the amount of the latter is not more than $\frac{1}{20} - \frac{1}{30}$ of the amount of rock. Taking into account that in the organogenic ooze stage the proportion of mineral matter may be still higher, it is clear that the initial conversions of buried organic matter may take place at greatly increased intensity.

The importance of the amount of aluminosilicate used was repeatedly noted: for instance, in polymerizing a diesel fuel fraction from shale oil, the optimum amount of catalyst required for obtaining the highest yield of lubricating oils is approximately equal to $1:1$ by weight of the fraction. However, the amount of active aluminosilicate may be reduced to one-half of the weight of the diesel fraction, without decrease in the yield of lubricating oils, by adding to the active catalyst an equal amount of absolutely inactive blue Cambrian clay, which is capable of adsorbing resinous substances but does not induce any catalytic processes.

A. I. Bogomolov has demonstrated that stearic acid at 250°C undergoes only a slight change in properties at an acid-to-catalyst ratio of $1:1$. Yet under the same conditions, but with an amount of catalyst 5 times greater than the amount of acid, the conversion factor reaches very high values. Finally, it may be pointed out also that with the amount of catalyst raised to 5 times as much as the weight of isopropylbenzene, the conversion of the latter at 100°C already proceeds to an appreciable degree after a few hours, though at a ratio of $1:1$ it is necessary to continue the heating for dozens of hours in order to obtain appreciable conversion.

Systematic tests to determine the effect of the amount of catalyst were conducted with S-110 oil and with paraffin wax.

The properties of S-110 oil are as follows: 0.8854 density at 20°C, 1.4860 refractive index at 20°C, molecular weight 496. Elemental composition: C = 86.0, H = 13.80%. The carbon content in cyclic structures is 38.77% and in aliphatic chains it is 61.63%, as determined by the *n-d-M* method. The number of rings in the molecule is 2.92. The oil is commercially produced by the adsorption method and is completely free from any traces of aromatic hydrocarbons.

The S-110 oil was heated in iron vessels in a bath of low-melting metal for 10 hr at 250°C. The light fractions thus produced were distilled off via the condenser mounted atop the vessel. After heating for 10 hr, the contents of the vessel were flushed with carbon dioxide gas and the distillate was collected in a common container. Upon cooling, the oil remaining in the catalyst was extracted with ether. The catalyst was used in proportions of 1, 2, and 4 parts per one part of oil.

The results of the experiments are cited in Table 37.

TABLE 37. *Thermocatalytic Conversion of S-110 Oil over Different Proportions of Catalyst*

Fractions	Oil-to-catalyst ratio					
	1:1		1:2		1:4	
	yield	density	yield	density	yield	density
Below 150°C	10.0	0.7203	10.1	0.7369	16.3	0.7263
150–200	3.0	0.7799	4.5	0.7881	12.1	0.7860
200–250	4.8	0.8119	6.4	0.8290	11.2	0.8262
250–300	4.2	0.8452	8.3	0.8505	9.9	0.8452
Above 300	74.2	0.8662	62.9	0.8686	36.5	0.8659
Residue	3.8		7.8		14.0	

	Group composition of fractions								
	1:1			1:2			1:4		
	P	N	A	P	N	A	P	N	A
Below 150°C	74.2	23.4	2.4	74.2	23.6	2.3	73.5	24.2	2.3
150–200	35.6	58.1	6.3	37.4	56.3	6.3	38.2	55.0	6.8
200–250	22.1	67.9	10.0	27.5	59.9	12.6	37.1	48.1	14.8
250–300	30.0	57.0	13.0	40.3	45.4	14.3	43.0	38.3	18.7
Above 300			10.0			12.5			17.2

P = paraffins; N = naphthenes; A = aromatics.

It is notable that, with increase in conversion, the amount of fully saturated gasoline fractions continuously grows to a certain limit and, strictly speaking, defines the yield of distillates in the conversion. The group composition of the gasoline fraction remains practically the same in all of the experiments and is close to the group composition of certain paraffinized crudes. A highly important feature is that despite complete absence of aromatic hydrocarbons in the initial oil they appear in amounts of 4.7% in fractions boiling up to 300 °C and their distribution displays a complete analogy with that in crudes where the aromatic hydrocarbon content likewise rises with the boiling range of fractions (Table 38).

TABLE 38. *Group Composition of Fractions, Calculated as per cent of Initial Oil. Ratio of Oil to Catalyst*

Fractions	1:1			1:2			1:4		
	P	N	A	P	N	A	P	N	A
Below 150°C	7.42	2.34	0.24	8.16	2.60	0.25	12.00	3.95	0.38
150–200	1.07	1.74	0.19	2.03	3.06	0.34	4.63	6.66	0.82
200–250	1.08	3.33	0.49	2.19	4.78	1.01	4.17	5.40	1.67
250–300	1.26	2.39	0.54	2.10	2.36	0.74	4.26	3.79	1.85
Total	10.83	9.80	1.46	14.48	12.80	2.34	25.06	19.71	4.72

P = paraffins; N = naphthenes; A = aromatics.

Even if the residue above 300 °C is regarded as undecomposed oil, Table 37 indicates that with change in the ratio from 1:1 to 1:4 the amount of residue above 300 °C has been cut in half, the yield of gasoline up to 200 °C was doubled, and the amount of naphtha-insoluble residue deposited on the catalyst was 3.7 times larger. Thus, at 1:4 ratio of oil to catalyst, more than 50% of the oil was converted into saturated hydrocarbon fractions boiling up to 300 °C.

Still more significant results were obtained with paraffin wax. The procedure had been changed in that the weight loss of paraffin wax, uniformly distributed throughout the body of catalyst, was determined after heating for 6 hr at 250–260 °C. The catalyst was dried to constant weight at 300 °C. At a paraffin wax-to-catalyst ratio of 1:1 the weight loss was equal to only 0.89%, compared with 9.68% at 1:3 ratio and 24.48% at 1:5 ratio, the latter showing an almost thirty fold increase over the original 1:1 condition. The amount of distillate obtained at 1:3 ratio in an experiment conducted on a large scale was 45.7%. Examination of the 39–223 °C fraction showed 10.4% aromatic and 89.6% paraffinic hydrocarbons, complete absence of naphthenic hydrocarbons, and mere traces of unsaturated hydrocarbons.†

The study of the effect of the quantity of catalyst on the course of the hydrocarbon conversion process has shown that the relative concentration of organic matter in the inorganic mineral environment (i.e. in the catalyst) is of tremendous importance. At low concentrations of organic matter the catalyst appears to be capable of complete conversion into low boiling fractions and an insoluble residue including resinous or carbonaceous substances at temperatures as low as 250°C, at which temperature oils or paraffin wax will not undergo appreciable decomposition even over long periods of time.

Thus it seems very probable that the experiments, described below, dealing with conversion of different hydrocarbons classes, would have resulted, at a higher catalyst-to-reactant ratio, in entirely different degrees of conversion. It is possible also that at a high catalyst-to-hydrocarbon ratio any appreciable changes would have taken place at very much lower temperatures than those at which the experiments described below had actually been carried out.

A. AROMATIC HYDROCARBONS

In view of the stability of the aromatic ring and the number of chemical properties specific to aromatic hydrocarbons, which facilitate determination of the properties of compounds resulting from the catalytic conversion, the hydrocarbons of this series are a convenient object for investigation. A fairly large number of papers relating to conversion of aromatic hydrocarbons are available.

B. L. Moldavskii and L. S. Bezdel' [1] subjected a number of benzene homologs to conversion at 450°C over aluminosilicates

† The paraffin wax conversion experiments were carried out by G. V. Markina.

and demonstrated that no appreciable changes occur in ethyl-, normal propyl-, para-methylisopropyl-, and normal butylbenzene, whereas isobutyl- and sec.-butylbenzene yield about 3% benzene and up to 20% isopropylbenzene. In the last-mentioned cases the conversion involved merely the removal of an alkyl group in the form of an olefin, i.e. stripping of the ring. Similarly, 1,3-methyl-isopropyl-benzene gave 45% toluene, and the 1,2 isomer gave as much as 67% benzene. Tertiary butylbenzene gave 67% benzene, and 1,4-tert.-butyl-toluene was 100% converted to toluene. These experiments were purposely conducted with a low-activity catalyst; furthermore the reactants were in the vapor phase and therefore were subject to catalytic action for a limited duration. R. D. Obolentsev and N. N. Gryaznov [2] observed the conversion of isopropylbenzene likewise at 450°C and noted the formation of propylene and a certain amount of diisopropylbenzene. K. P. Lavrovskii[3] studied the conversion of normal butylbenzene and isopropyl-benzene and got similar results. Hiven and Hammick [4] found that the more complex the alkyl group, the easier it can be stripped off at 450°C. That is the reason why in the case of toluene a transfer of the methyl group occurs, to form xylene, while only a small amount of benzene is obtained. For ethylbenzene and propylbenzene the predominant reaction is decomposition. Sachanen, Hansford and Mayers [5] verified the data of the preceding authors in the study of xylene, pseudocumene, methylnaphthalene, and diethylbenzene. Thomas, Hextra and Pinkston [6] have likewise found that the aromatic hydrocarbons which are most readily dealkylated are those in which the alkyl groups contain three or more carbon atoms. Greensfelder [7] showed that the structure of the alkyl group is also significant. Toluene was decomposed to the extent of merely 1%, compared to 11% for ethylbenzene and 43% for propylbenzene under identical conditions. G. A. Natanson and M. Ya. Kogan [8], in experimenting with ethylbenzene, found benzene and ethylene (at 400°C) and noted also that diethylbenzene was present.

In summarizing the results obtained by various authors in investigations at 400–450°C, it may be stated that the splitting-off of an alkyl group is the predominant reaction. For purposes of the geochemical study of petroleum conversion, however, all of these investigations are of little value because temperatures of the order of 450°C are entirely improbable under conditions obtaining in petroleum-bearing horizons both at present as well as, no doubt, in the past. The experimental investigations described below have been conducted at very much lower temperatures and it was established that the predominant, or perhaps exclusive, reaction is a transfer of radicals (alkyl groups) in the course of disproportionation. No splitting-off of radicals is noted. At the same time it appears that radicals having more than three carbon atoms have a higher mobility, but in conditions of low temperatures such mobility is expressed in terms of transfer, rather than splitting-off, of alkyl groups. Isomerization of the alkyl group appears to be also of very substantial importance.

Benzene. On heating with aluminosilicates at temperatures of about 350°C for 10 hr, benzene does not undergo any changes.

Toluene. Because of the strength of the bond between the alkyl group and the nucleus in toluene, no great ease of conversion had been anticipated. Indeed, the experiments showed that toluene undergoes a relatively insignificant degree of conversion even when heated at 300°C over a period of 20 hr in an autoclave. The product obtained on distillation was as follows:

Fraction (°C)	Yield (%)	Density at 20°C	Refractive index at 20°C
80–95	1.1	0.8782	1.5009
108–112	87.3	0.8664	1.4968
130–145	1.0	0.8634	1.4966
Residue	4.2		

Only the 130–145°C fraction was studied more closely. It proved to consist exclusively of meta-xylene. In the residue, 1,3,5-trimethylbenzene was determined qualitatively [10].

Xylene—$C_6H_4(CH_3)_2$. Among the xylenes, the least reactive with respect to conversion is the meta-isomer. The ortho- and para-isomers can be isomerized at 650°C without any catalysts, to give the meta-isomer [11]. Aluminum chloride also causes an enrichment of meta-xylene in the mixture of isomers, and it was anticipated that aluminosilicate catalysts would act in a similar way.

The conversion of xylene was conducted at 300°C for 15 and 45 hr in an autoclave with activated Gumbrin. The results were as follows:

Fraction (°C)	Yield (%)	Fraction (°C)	Yield (%)	Fraction (°C)	Yield (%)
90–108	0.8	135–145	60.2	175–180	1.1
108–115	11.2	145–160	5.3	180–200	1.4
115–135	6.4	160–175	9.7	200–210	3.7

The main fractions proved to be toluene and trimethylbenzene, the latter in the form of 1,3,5-trimethylbenzene. An attempt to determine the structure of the tetramethylbenzene failed, and from the fraction corresponding to this hydrocarbon merely a tetrabasic acid was obtained.

According to research by V. V. Rybkina [12], ortho-xylene yielded after heating for 20 hr in the vapor phase at 225°C about 15% meta-xylene. At 175°C only 2.4% meta-xylene was obtained.

Ethylbenzene—$C_6H_5C_2H_5$. Theoretically, the conversion of ethylbenzene should occur much more easily than that of toluene and xylenes. High temperature conversion of ethylbenzene had been studied previously, but only in a single instance could the formation of diethylbenzene be reported [10]. The experiment with ethylbenzene was conducted at 300°C for 3 hr, with the pressure of ethylbenzene vapors rising in the autoclave to 28 atm. Examination of the products obtained gave the following product yields:

benzene	24.4%
toluene	22.1%
ethylbenzene	40.1%
triethylbenzene	2.5%
residue	9.6%
losses	1.3%

The molar ratio of benzene to ethylbenzene was 2.3:1.8, presumably because of partial conversion of diethylbenzene to triethylbenzene. The diethylbenzene consisted mainly of the meta-isomer.

V. V. Rybkina [12] reported that conversion of ethylbenzene in the vapor phase at 250°C in one of the experiments gave the following distribution of isomers:

ortho	11.0
para	50.3
meta	37.3

Isopropylbenzene—$C_6H_5CH(CH_3)_2$. With isopropylbenzene several experiments were carried out at different temperatures in the autoclave. The primary experiment was conducted at 300°C for a period of 30 hr with a hydrocarbon-to-catalyst ratio of 2:1 since drastic conversion could be expected even under these conditions. As a result, about 3.4 l. of a saturated gas was obtained from 300 g isopropylbenzene. The liquid reaction products consisted of:

below 75°C	0.95%
75–85	27.17%
85–115	0.91%
115–130	0.6%
130–148	11.42%
148–155	27.16%
155–198	9.74%
198–205	8.80%
205–215	3.60%
residue	6.88%
losses	2.77%

The main products proved to be benzene (about 28%) and diisopropylbenzene (about 7.5%). Besides, the presence of triisopropylbenzene was qualitatively determined.

In another experiment, on simply boiling the isopropylbenzene together with catalyst in a flask with reflux condenser, the boiling point of the mixture dropped from 140 to 132°C after only 1 hr of heating owing to formation of benzene, and after 25 hr heating time the temperature became stabilized at 127°C. Upon distillation the following products were identified:

benzene	8.8%
diisopropylbenzene	13.7%
triisopropylbenzene	0.4%
remainder	isopropylbenzene

Another experiment involved heating the isopropylbenzene and catalyst on a water bath for 50 hr, whereby about 2.5% benzene and about 5% diisopropylbenzene were obtained.

Methylisopropylbenzene—$CH_3C_6H_4CH(CH_3)_2$. The hydrocarbon used for the experiments had a density (d_4^{20}) of 0.8581, a refractive index at 20°C of 1.4917, and a boiling point of 173–174°C. The conversion was effected by simply boiling it with the catalyst for 23 hr, with the temperature being held at 153°C toward termination of the heating. The yield was 78% of liquid products and 7.7% resinous substances. The increase in the weight of catalyst and the losses were 14%. Fractional distillation gave, calculated on the basis of the sum total of conversion products as 100%:

toluene	35.8%
xylene	2.8%
diisopropylbenzene	61.3%

In addition, a small amount of diisopropyltoluene was found. V. V. Tishchenko and S. G. Chepurina explain the presence of toluene through splitting-off of the isopropyl radical, which alkylated a portion of methylisopropylbenzene to diisopropyltoluene. On the other hand, the toluene formed was partly converted to benzene which removed the methyl group from methylisopropylbenzene to form toluene and diisopropropylbenzene. A specially conducted experiment for the thermocatalysis of a mixture of benzene and methylisopropylbenzene actually gave toluene and diisopropylbenzene, though in limited yields.

Sec.-butylbenzene—$C_6H_5CH(CH_2)(CH_2H_5)$. The synthesized hydrocarbon had the following properties: density (d_4^{20}) of 0.8631, refractive index = 1.4907, and boiling point = 172–174°C. The experiment was conducted in an autoclave at 300°C for 15 hr with the hydrocarbon-to-catalyst ratio equal to 1:0.6. The yield of liquid products was 88.7%, and losses through catalyst deposits were 11.3%. Upon distillation, the yield, calculated on converted material, was:

1,3-dibutylbenzene	52.1%
1,3,5-tributylbenzene	7.9%
benzene	40.0%

The exact structure of the tributylbenzene has not been determined [14].

Tert.-butylbenzene—$C_6H_5C(CH_3)_3$. The conversion of this hydrocarbon, in which the radical is linked to the nucleus through quaternary carbon, appeared of special interest because of its anticipated great ease of conversion. The synthesized hydrocarbon had the following properties: density (d_4^{20}) = 0.8649, refractive index at 20°C = 1.4919, and boiling point = 169–170°C. The conversion experiment with the catalyst (1:1) was carried out in a small iron vessel. The initial boiling temperature proved to be only 130°C and after 2 hr it remained at 120.5°C, after which the heating was continued for another 2 hr. As a result of the test, 86.3% of liquid products was recovered. The remainder consisted of losses and the residue deposited on the catalyst, which was not soluble in benzene. Distillation showed the following result:

benzene	12.5%
para-di-*tert.*-butylbenzene	24.2%

The latter hydrocarbon was obtained in the form of crystals having a melting point of 76.5–77.5°C (according to literature data it should be 76°C). Unreacted *tert.*-butylbenzene was recovered in amounts of about 40%. Formation of the para-substituted instead of the meta-substituted hydrocarbon may be explained by steric hindrances [15].

Ethyltoluene—$CH_3C_6H_4C_2H_5$. Ethyltoluene was subjected to conversion by boiling with a reflux condenser in the presence of activated Gumbrin (1:1). The initial boiling point of the mixture had been about 155°C but after 20 hr it fell to 147°C. Examination of the products showed that reacted toluene was converted to

dimethylethylbenzene	34.0%
methyldiethylbenzene	45.7%
toluene	11.3%
ethylbenzene	10.0%

Thus the conversion proceeded in two different ways. On the one hand, two molecules of the initial ethyltoluene were converted into a molecule of ethylbenzene and a molecule of dimethylethylbenzene. On the other hand, two initial molecules gave a molecule of toluene and a molecule of methyldiethylbenzene. The second trend predominates owing to greater mobility of the ethyl compared with that of the methyl group [12].

Butyltoluene—$CH_3C_6H_4C_4H_9$. The experiment with butyltoluene was conducted in a manner to that with ethyltoluene. The initial temperature was 187°C and at the termination of heating, after 42 hr, it fell to 171°C. Investigation of the resulting mixture showed that conversion was about 27% and the products, in percentage of reacted charge material, were

toluene	14.7%
butylbenzene	10.0%
dimethylbutylbenzene	26.2%
methyldibutylbenzene	49.1%

As in the preceding case, here again is a sharp predominance of the reaction involving displacement of the butyl radical, i.e. the formation of methyldibutylbenzene and toluene, while conversion to butylbenzene and dimethylbutylbenzene is only about one-half as much [12].

Tert.-*amylbenzene*—$C_6H_5C_5H_{11}$. According to investigations by B. G. Gavrilov and R. A. Ten, tertiary amylbenzene is a compound as unstable in thermocatalysis as is tertiary butylbenzene. A series of experiments on catalysts was conducted at atmospheric pressure and in an autoclave (200 °C, 13 hr, with a catalyst-to-hydrocarbon ratio of 1:1). The experiment in the autoclave showed that the 27–29 °C fractions contain isopentane (refractive index at 20 °C = 1.3551). In addition, about 12 % benzene was present, and the 255–260 °C fraction of 0.880 density and 1.5013 refractive index contained diamylbenzene, the isomeric constitution of which was not ascertained. The conversion factor in the autoclave experiments reached 50 %.

Hexylbenzene—$C_6H_5C_6H_{13}$. It may be of interest to compare the thermocatalytic conversion of hexylbenzene with the conversion of cyclohexylbenzene. The study was carried out by B. G. Garilov and R. A. Ten. A mixture of hexylbenzenes had been synthesized, but the structure of the radical was not determined. The conversion experiment was carried out in an autoclave over a period of 17 hr at a temperature of 250 °C. Examination of the mixture showed that it contains about 10 % of a 60–64 °C fraction and about 5 % of a 64–68 °C fraction. Of these fractions, the 60–64 °C fraction was separated. It appears to consist of 2-methylpentane and 3-methylpentane. The higher boiling products were not further investigated, though they might have been expected to contain the dialkyl derivative, i.e. dihexylbenzene.

Phenylcyclohexane—$C_6H_5C_6H_{11}$. A study of this hydrocarbon was carried out in order to determine the behavior of an aromatic hydrocarbon having as a substituent a large size radical linked through the tertiary hydrocarbon atom. The behavior of the radical itself was likewise of interest [13].

The properties of the synthesized hydrocarbon were: density = 0.9445 at 20 °C, boiling point = 238–240 °C.

The conversion experiment was conducted in a flask with reflux condenser, at a hydrocarbon-to-catalyst ratio of 1:0.9. The initial boiling point was 210 °C which decreased after 25 min to 126 °C and then remained unchanged. Examination of the products obtained showed:

benzene	12.0%
para-bicyclohexylbenzene	30.0%

The latter hydrocarbon was obtained partly in the form of crystals of 101–102°C melting point, which corresponds with data from the literature. The resulting benzene was of very low density, presumably owing to admixtures of non-aromatic compounds. To obtain more accurate results, the experiment was repeated under more drastic conditions, with heating for 2.5 hr. The experiment was terminated when the temperature of effluent vapors reached 140°C. Distillation yielded the following fractions:

Fraction (°C)	Yield (%)	Density	Refractive index
Below 76	10	0.8169	1.4640
76–78	10.8	0.8346	1.4723
78–81	7.6	0.8510	1.4850
81–235	0.1	—	—
235–245	25.8	0.9458	1.5280
245–350	7.7	—	—
210–212	13.6	0.9798	1.5430
212–212	5.0	0.9800	1.5432
212–248	3.8	—	1.5450
248–250	3.8	1.0020	1.5565
Above 250	9.1		
Losses	3.9		

None of the higher fractions was obtained in the crystalline state, though it may have been expected by analogy with the first experiment. The light fractions below 81°C were treated with sulfuric acid to remove benzene, whereby 4 g hydrocarbons of 0.7654 density and 1.4184 refractive index was recovered. The values for cyclohexane and methylcyclopentane should be

cyclohexane	density 0.7815, refractive index 1.4264
methylcyclohexane	density 0.7502, refractive index 1.4099

For a 50%-mixture of the two hydrocarbons, the values are calculated to be: density = 0.7658 and refractive index = 1.4181, which are very close to the properties of the hydrocarbons obtained.

If the light fraction is assumed to be a mixture of cyclohexane and methylcyclohexane, the molar proportions of the resulting products are

benzene	2.5
cyclohexane and methylcyclohexane	1.3
dicyclohexylbenzene	1.0

The liquid consistency of dicyclohexylbenzene obtained in the more protracted conversion reaction is probably due to complete or partial isomerization of the cyclohexane nucleus into methylcyclopentane. In such event, instead of dicyclohexylbenzene there may have been formed the methylcyclopentylcyclohexylbenzene or di-para-methylcyclohexylbenzene, which are liquids.

Tolylcyclohexane—$C_6H_{11}C_6H_5CH_3$. The principal trends of its conversion could be foreseen on the basis of the conversion of phenylcyclohexane or cyclohexylbenzene as examples. The synthesized tolylcyclohexane was heated together with the catalyst for 3–10 hr (in different experiments). The initial temperature of the mixture was 200–202°C, but it dropped rapidly to 152°C in the 10 hr experiment. The resulting mixture consisted of dicyclohexyltoluene, illustrating the great ease with which the tolyl radical can be displaced. In addition, a fraction of 80–85°C boiling point and 1.4452 refractive index was formed in negligible quantity. This fraction was not investigated, but it may be expected that cyclohexane as a contaminant or its conversion product was present therein. No significant amounts of trisubstituted hydrocarbons were found [12].

Ethylnaphthalene—$C_{10}H_7C_2H_5$. The synthesized ethylnaphthalene had the following properties: density at 20°C = 1.0037, refractive index at 20°C = 1.5916, boiling point at 2 mm Hg pressure = 98–100°C. Thermal catalysis was carried out in a flask with reflux condenser, at a hydrocarbon-to-catalyst ratio of 1:1, to give at a temperature of 230–240°C a conversion of about 34%. The same experiment in an autoclave showed a conversion factor reaching 80% for 9 hr heating time. The products obtained represented a complex mixture. Upon careful fractionation and elemental analysis, the following compounds were determined (in two experiments with a heating time of 9 hr at 300°C and 20 hr at 275°C):

	300°, 9 hr	275°, 20 hr
diethylbenzene	1.55	2.21
ethylbenzene	0.20	0.54
triethylbenzene	2.76	7.85
naphthalene	10.20	17.20
ethylnaphthalene	25.00	22.80
diethylnaphthalene	5.10	3.88
triethylnaphthalene	7.65	5.52
dinaphthyl	5.80	9.80
others and losses	31.74	30.20

The last-mentioned item includes resins and some not accurately determined compounds (tetrahydronaphthalene). In any case, the far-reaching conversion of ethylnaphthalene is evident because, besides the normal products of rearrangement of radicals, one of the naphthalene rings is split, probably via the tetrahydro derivative, to form mono-, di- and tri-ethylbenzene. In addition, the condensation of two naphthalene rings takes place to form dinaphthyl [16].

Sec.-*amylnaphthalene*—$C_{10}H_7C_5H_{11}$. The synthesized secondary amylnaphthalene had a boiling point of 128–135°C at 5 mm Hg pressure. B.G. Gavrilov and N. Kim conducted a thermocatalytic conversion experiment at atmospheric pressure and 260°C for 5 hr. Examination of the reaction products showed that about 1% pentane, 28% naphthalene and 10.4% dialkylnaphthalene were formed. The conversion factor reached 60%. Thus conversion occurred according to the general mechanism with partial splitting-off of the radical.

The catalyst and hydrocarbon were used in 1:0.5 ratio.

Sec.-*butylnaphthalene*—$C_{10}H_7C_4H_9$. The synthesized hydrocarbon had the following properties: density at 20°C = 0.9742, refractive index = 1.5701, and boiling point = 272–274°C. The conversion experiment was conducted in an autoclave at a hydrocarbon-to-catalyst ratio of 1:1 for 16 hr at 275°C.

The liquid conversion products were investigated by elemental analysis and other methods to obtain

diethylbenzene	10.5%
sec.-butylbenzene	43.5%
dibutylnaphthalene	35.0%
dinaphthyl	11.0%

B. G. Gavrilov and E. N. Nikitina reported also the presence of 9.5% octane of 117–119°C boiling point and 0.7199 refractive index at 20°C, and 6.1% tetrahydronaphthalene with a boiling point of 206–208°C, 0.9690 density at 20°C, and 1.5412 refractive index. In addition, naphthalene in the amount of 14.2% was found.

As in the instance of ethylnaphthalene, the conversion is accompanied by the formation of a considerable number of different products. The octane reported by the authors may have been formed as a result of splitting-off and condensation of butyl radicals [17].

Diphenylmethane—$C_6H_5CH_2C_6H_5$. Experiments relating to thermocatalysis of diphenylmethane were conducted in an autoclave at 200°C with activated Gumbrin in 1:1 ratio to the hydrocarbon. A total of three experiments were performed, the only difference being their duration which was 1 hr 45 min and 5 and 10 hr.

The conversion factor was computed on the basis of the benzene yield. The yield of benzene was

1 hr 45 min	20.1%
5 hr	21.7%
10 hr	21.8%

Thus, within a short period of time an equilibrium between the resulting products had been reached.

In addition to benzene, crystalline products of 86°C melting point and 245–250°C boiling point at 12 mm Hg were obtained. Analysis showed that they were di-para-benzylbenzene

$$C_6H_5CH_2C_6H_4CH_2C_6H_5.$$

Consequently, diphenylmethane is converted along the same lines as alkylbenzenes, and therefore diphenylmethane may be regarded as benzene linked to the benzyl radical $CH_2C_6H_5$.

In one of the experiments it was demonstrated that benzene and dibenzylbenzene in the presence of catalyst on heating, even at ordinary pressure, at a temperature in the range of 110–116°C, may yield diphenylmethane, which proves that an equilibrium exists in the reaction [18].

Diphenylethane—$C_6H_5CH_2CH_2C_6H_5$. Having a structure analogous to that of diphenylmethane, the diphenylethane theoretically should undergo conversion along similar lines, which has been proved by experiments. Diphenylethane was synthesized from dichloroethane and benzene in the presence of aluminum chloride. The perfectly pure hydrocarbon has a boiling point of 284 °C. Conversion was carried out in an iron vessel with the catalyst in 1:1 ratio, without distilling off the resulting products as soon as formed, at temperatures of 170°, 180° and 190 °C for 1–35 hr in the different experiments [19]. At 170° the equilibrium was reached after 30 hr, with 3.1% benzene being formed. At 180° the equilibrium was reached after 13 hr with a benzene yield of 4.6%, and at 190° after 15 hr with a benzene yield of 15%. Besides the benzene, a fraction boiling at 270–290 °C at 4 mm Hg pressure was recovered. Examination of this fraction in regard to molecular weight and elemental analysis, as well as by oxidation with permanganate, revealed that it was diphenylbenzene $C_6H_5CH_2CH_2C_6H_4CH_2CH_2C_6H_5$ as anticipated. Thus, in this instance, the conversion proceeds once more in accordance with the previously established rule.

Ditolylethane—$CH_3C_6H_4CH_2CH_2C_6H_4CH_3$. Synthesis of ditolylethane from dichloroethane and toluene over aluminum chloride gives a mixture of isomers (about 72% meta-ditolylethane and about 28% para-ditolylethane) as established by Yu. I. Kornilova [20]. The synthesized product had a density at 20 °C of 0.9677 and a refractive index at 20 °C of 1.5750.

For the conversion experiments under the usual conditions, 200 g catalyst and 100 g hydrocarbon were used. The mixture was heated with a reflux condenser to 200 °C, after which all of the resulting products were separated by distillation. They were

toluene	19.6%
toluene + xylene	2.1%
xylene	5.2%
trimethylbenzene	4.6%

In addition, higher molecular products were obtained which, by analogy with the previous items, may be expected to include a hydrocarbon having the structure

$$CH_3—C_6H_3—CH_2—CH_2—C_6H_4—CH_3$$
$$|$$
$$CH_2—C_6H_4—CH_3.$$

The possibility of both the toluene- and the xylene-type disintegration of ditolylethane thwarted any attempt to decipher the complex mixture of higher conversion products [19].

General trends of the conversion of aromatic hydrocarbons

The foregoing examples of the conversion of aromatic hydrocarbons permit the recognition of certain general relationships. Contrary to conversions over catalysts at temperatures of the order of 450–500 °C, those occurring at low temperatures proceed without any gas formation, i.e. without splitting-off of radicals. Instead of that, a rearrangement of radicals occurs in a manner such that one molecule loses a radical while another one acquires it, so that from a monosubstituted hydrocarbon a disubstituted one is formed in accordance with the equation

$$2C_6H_5X = C_6H_6 + C_6H_4X_2. \tag{1}$$

With a disubstituted hydrocarbon subjected to conversion, a monosubstituted and a trisubstituted derivative are formed

$$2C_6H_4X_2 = C_6H_5X + C_6HX_3. \tag{2}$$

Negligible amounts of tetrasubstituted compounds are formed from trisubstituted ones. When the reaction occurs according to eq. (1) so that a disubstituted hydrocarbon is formed, it may of course be followed by further conversion of the resulting disubstituted hydrocarbon into a trisubstituted one. Nevertheless, the first reaction always predominates and therefore, for example, in the conversion of toluene only small amounts of trisubstituted products are formed although the conversion of xylene yields a relatively large amount of trisubstituted hydrocarbons. The relative quantities of the products formed depend on the concentration of the hydrocarbons undergoing conversion and also on the structures of the theoretically expected products, and it is here that steric hindrances and the velocities of substitution reactions gain a high significance.

The first rule may thus be formulated as follows: *the thermocatalytic conversion of alkylbenzenes always yields alkylbenzenes of next lower and next higher degree of substitution.*

Experiments have shown that the conversion rate of monosubstituted benzenes, defined by the yield of the next lower and higher substitution products, depends on the size of the radical and its degree of isomerization or, more precisely, on the point of linkage of the nucleus with the radical. Methylsubstituted derivatives are converted with much difficulty, the conversion of homologs having an ethyl group is easier, and conversion of those with a propyl group is still easier. When the radicals are of equal length, displacement is facilitated if the linkage between the benzene nucleus and the radical is via a tertiary hydrocarbon and still further facilitated if it is via a quaternary carbon atom. Phenylcyclohexane is converted with greater ease than isopropylbenzene though both hydrocarbons possess a secondary bond between the radical and nucleus, but here the dominant importance lies with the mass of the radical, which is greater for cyclohexyl than for isopropyl.

The above relationship may be formulated as follows: *the thermocatalytic conversion of alkylbenzenes is accomplished the more easily, the larger the mass of the radical. The smaller the number of hydrogen atoms at the carbon atom linked with the benzene ring, the easier the conversion.*

The splitting-off of the radical in a benzene homolog is not a characteristic feature for conversion at low temperatures. However, it becomes progressively more appreciable with increase in the mass of the radical. Already in phenylcyclohexane a splitting-off of cyclohexyl or of its isomerization products is noted. This relationship is particularly evident in alkylnaphthalenes where the bond between the naphthalene nucleus and the radical is somewhat weaker in comparison with benzene homologs.

In the thermal catalysis of alkylaromatic hydrocarbons, the splitting-off of radicals depends on the size of the radical and becomes appreciable for C_5—C_6 radicals. This rule is highly significant in petroleum chemistry because it explains why crude oil does not contain any lower molecular-weight hydrocarbons of the aromatic series with radicals of greater chain length than butyl. Yet the above rule appears to contradict numerous conjectures about the presence of long-chain benzene homologs in higher molecular-weight fractions of petroleum. The nature of these hydrocarbons has not been definitely established.

The general mechanism of the conversion of aromatic hydrocarbons comprises in first place isomerization in which all of the elements of the molecule are retained, i.e. its transition into a more stable form. Then a displacement of radicals takes place. If these radicals are large, they are split off with the formation of nonaromatic hydrocarbons and aromatics of lower molecular weight

Simultaneously, aromatic hydrocarbons of higher molecular weight are formed by virtue of accumulation of migrant radicals in them. The latter in the course of further reactions undergo polycondensation to form complex aromatic hydrocarbons which ultimately are transformed into graphitic substances.

GENERAL MECHANISM FOR THE CONVERSION
OF AROMATIC HYDROCARBONS

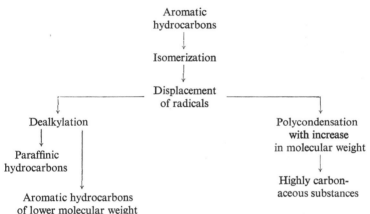

B. CYCLOPARAFFINIC HYDROCARBONS

Conversions of cyclohexane were studied by A. V. Frost and A. F. Nikolaeva [21] and also by other authors. Butylcyclohexane and isopropylcyclohexane were investigated by K. P. Lavrovskii, Yu. L. Fish and N. N. Naimushin [3]. The research, which was conducted at 450°C or temperatures close to it, demonstrated the capacity of cycloparaffinic hydrocarbons of the cyclohexane series for contracting their ring to a five-membered ring with ejection of one carbon atom in the form of an alkyl group. At the same time a more drastic course of conversion occurs, to form small fragments and aromatic hydrocarbons. Similar observations have been made in regard to decalin and tetralin. A number of papers are known which define an equilibrium of ring isomerization that has a close resemblance to the equilibrium in conversions over aluminum chloride. The analogy between the action of aluminum chloride and aluminosilicates has been noted by various authors.

G. N. Maslyanskii and T. S. Berlin [22] studied the catalytic action of aluminosilicates upon methylcyclopentane and cyclohexane at temperatures in the range of 515–560°C. At a lower temperature A. Ya. Larin [23] recovered in aluminosilicate catalysis about 26% of low boiling fractions, probably in the form of secondary products.

Significantly, in cycloparaffins a disproportionation of alkyl groups appears to be impossible though it takes place very easily in aromatic hydrocarbons. Therefore the thermocatalytic conversion of cycloparaffins of the substituted type occurs without accumulation of alkyl groups in the molecule.

Cyclohexane—C_6H_{12}. The cyclohexane used for conversion was free from aromatic hydrocarbons and had a density of 0.7778 at 20°C and a refractive index of 1.4265 at 20°C. Its boiling point was 80°C [24].

The experiments were conducted in an autoclave at a cyclohexane-to-catalyst ratio of 1:1, a temperature of 245–250°C, and a heating time of 21–60 hr. The pressure in the autoclave at these temperatures reached 34 atm.

The following results were obtained:

Reaction time (hr)	21	30	41	50	60
Yield (%)	87.7	87.2	88.15	92.6	87.15
Losses	12.3	12.8	11.85	7.4	12.25
Density d_0^{20}	0.7739	0.7708	0.7688	--	0.7661
Refractive index	1.4240	1.4220	1.4211	—	1.4199

Judging from the physical properties of the compounds obtained, the highest degree of conversion occurred in experiments with a heating time of 50 and 60 hr. Distillation of the product from the 50 hr heating experiment gave

Boiling range (°C)	69–74	74–77.5	77.5–81	Losses
Yield (%)	23.6	19.4	45.2	12.24
Refractive index	1.4122	1.4182	1.4245	

Redistillation of the 69–74°C fraction in a high capacity tower gave

Fractions (°C)	% of the initial material	Refractive index, 20°C
55–69	0.24	1.3939
69–71	0.12	1.4070
71–71.4	0.28	1.4098
71.4	8.24	1.4101

The last-mentioned fraction (at 71.4°) consisted of methylcyclopentane. Its density at 20 °C proved to be 0.7491 (the figure from the literature is d_4^{20} 0.7498). The refractive index at 20 °C was found to be 1.4101 which is the same as that given in literature.

The equilibrium between cyclohexane and methylcyclopentane at 250 °C corresponds to a methylcyclopentane content of 37–40% [25, 26]. According to Nenitzescu, in isomerization over aluminum chloride the equilibrium is noted also at a methylcyclopentane content of 37% [27]. In the lightest fractions the presence of paraffinic hydrocarbons appears probable.

Methylcyclohexane—$C_6H_{11}CH_3$. The properties of the compound used in the study were: boiling point = 100.5°C, density $(d^{20}) = 0.7685$, and refractive index at 20 °C = 1.4234. It contained about 0.5% aromatic hydrocarbons. The experiments were conducted in an autoclave at 245–250 °C for a period of 50–110 hr [28].

The results are cited below.

Reaction time (hr)	50	70	90	110
Product yield	90.83	90.19	89.6	91.4
Density d_4^{20}	0.7610	0.7600	0.7586	0.7594
Refractive index at 20°	1.4199	1.4186	1.4180	1.4185
Aromatic hydrocarbon content	0.7	1.11	not detd.	0.78

For the experiment with a heating time of 110 hr, distillation of the reaction product gave

Boiling range (°C)	Yield (%)	Refractive index, 20°C	Boiling range (°C)	Yield (%)	Refractive index, 20°C
48–87	4.44	1.3925	96–100	12.15	1.4187
87–93	22.46	1.4110	100–203	32.65	1.4220
93–96	2.81	1.4140	losses	11.72	

For the specially separated fraction, at 90.1–90.9 °C having the properties: density (d_4^{20}) = 0.7466 and refractive index at 20°C = 1.4105, a comparison with literature data showed that these properties are closest to those of the hydrocarbons 1,3-dimethylcyclopentane and 1,2-trans-dimethylcyclopentane:

	Density d_4^{20}	Refractive index, 20°C
1,3-dimethylcyclopentane	0.7456	1.4092 and 1.4076
1,2-trans-dimethylcyclopentane	0.7519	1.4120 and 1.4177

For final identification the Raman spectra of the products were determined, in which were found 6 lines specific to the first isomer, 5 lines specific to the second, and 6 lines common to both isomers. Thus the product is a mixture of the two isomers.

The light fractions from different experiments were combined to obtain, upon distillation:

Boiling range (°C)	Refractive index, 20°C
below 44	1.3580
40–58	1.3708
58–65	1.3790
65–70	1.3910
70–78	1.4060
78–82	1.4095

The first fraction almost corresponds to pentane, and the others represent paraffinic hydrocarbons apparently contaminated with naphthenic hydrocarbons.

Methylisopropylcyclohexane—$CH_3C_6H_{10}CH(CH_3)_2$. The synthesized hydrocarbon used in the thermocatalytic conversion study had the following properties: density = 0.8005, refractive index = 1.4414, and a boiling point of 170–171°C. The experiments were conducted by V. V. Tishchenko and A. D. Elizarova at 250°C with activated Gumbrin in an autoclave for 5, 10, and 15 hr. Cited here are the results of only one experiment (15 hr), after which it was found that the broad fraction contains about 6.5% aromatic hydrocarbons. The latter were removed. Thereafter, precise fractionation gave a number of fractions, among which by reference to physical and spectral data 1,2-dimethyl-3-isopropylcyclopentane was identified in the 161–163 °C fraction, having a density of 0.7914 and a refractive index of 1.4368. In addition, ethylcyclopentane was found in the fraction of about 103 °C. No gaseous products were noted.

General remarks on the problem of conversion of cycloparaffinic hydrocarbons

Unfortunately, the amount of existing information is insufficient for establishing the general picture for the conversion of cycloparaffinic hydrocarbons, yet the information available so far makes it possible to delineate certain rules.

One of the first consequences of the action of aluminosilicates upon naphthenes is their isomerization. It is known that a variety of catalysts and even simple heating will cause isomerization of six-membered naphthenes into five-membered ones and that in every instance the reaction is limited by an equilibrium which varies for the different hydrocarbons. The research on petroleums, more specifically their gasoline fractions, has shown long ago that five- and six-membered naphthenes are present in every gasoline and that highly modified crudes frequently contain a relatively large amount of five-membered naphthenes [29]. This fact was utilized by certain authors for calculating the geochemical age of crudes and the temperatures, to which the crude might have been subjected during the history of its genesis [30, 31]. Calculations of this sort, though correct in principle, fail to make allowance for the fact that the formation of five-membered naphthenes is not necessarily connected with the conversion of six-membered naphthenes having the same number of carbon atoms in the molecule. It may be that part of the five-membered naphthenes owe their origin not to isomerization but to the liberation of already existing five-membered rings from higher molecular-weight petroleum hydrocarbons. In such an event, a petroleum that for any reason has escaped catalytic conversion may contain an increased amount of five-membered naphthenes.

In any event, the isomerization of cycloparaffins over aluminosilicate catalysts, illustrated by a number of examples, permits the formulation of the first rule for the conversion of naphthenes, as follows:

Thermocatalytic conversion of cycloparaffinic hydrocarbons involves in first place the isomerization of six-membered systems into five-membered ones.

It may be assumed that condensed-ring hydroaromatics, such as decalin, are no exception to this rule. Experiments with aluminum chloride have shown that decalin indeed is destroyed via an isomerization stage, and as to the action of aluminosilicates, it creates a complex mixture of products that has not yet been separated.

In certain cases it was possible to note that catalytic conversion of cycloparaffins is accompanied by breakdown of part of the substance to paraffinic hydrocarbons. Perhaps this phenomenon is of general validity, especially for high molecular-weight cycloparaffins. Possibly also the breakdown may precede isomerization. The formation of paraffinic hydrocarbons in the case of relatively stable systems, such as cyclohexane and methylcyclohexane, does not appear to be a dominant reaction but this does not necessarily mean that specific structural features may not create more favorable conditions in certain cases. Hence, the second rule for the conversion of cycloparaffinic hydrocarbons may be stated as follows:

The thermocatalytic conversion of cycloparaffins may involve rupture of the ring or of one of the rings in condensed-ring cycloparaffinic hydrocarbons with the formation of paraffinic hydrocarbons.

In thermocatalytic conversions of monoalkylsubstituted derivatives of cyclohexane and cyclopentane, no disproportionation of alkyl radicals has been noted. Thus, for instance, no formation of dimethylcyclohexane or trimethylcyclopentane from methylcyclohexane, to give free cyclohexane, was noted. The possibility of such a reaction for benzene homologs is a specific feature of the aromatic structure.

The general mechanism of the conversion of cycloparaffinic hydrocarbons starts with isomerization processes, unless prevented by steric hindrances. Subsequently, partial decyclization and dealkylation reactions take place, resulting in the formation of paraffinic hydrocarbons and of moderate molecular-weight cycloparaffinic hydrocarbons, including bicyclic compounds. The latter, in turn, give monocyclic naphthenes which ultimately are converted to paraffinic hydrocarbons. At some of the stages, partial isomerization may occur, although this reaction is of no importance in principle.

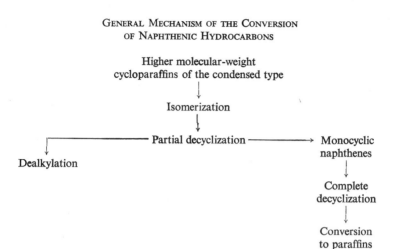

GENERAL MECHANISM OF THE CONVERSION
OF NAPHTHENIC HYDROCARBONS

Higher molecular-weight
cycloparaffins of the condensed type

↓

Isomerization

↓

Partial decyclization ⟶ Monocyclic naphthenes

Dealkylation

Complete
decyclization

↓

Conversion
to paraffins

C. PARAFFINIC HYDROCARBONS

Paraffinic hydrocarbons have been hardly studied at all in regard to thermocatalytic conversion. A few observations are available, for example, relating to the fact that heptane on being heated with activated clay at 250°C undergoes a very slight isomerization, as a consequence of which the initial boiling point of the heated hydrocarbon is somewhat lowered. Similar observations were made with 2,2,3-trimethylpentane. In any event, lower paraffinic hydrocarbons are characterized by high stability and therefore the ultimate conversions of all hydrocarbons lead to formation of the simplest members of the aliphatic series.

Higher molecular-weight paraffinic hydrocarbons such as paraffin wax and ceresin are less stable and upon thermocatalysis readily form lower molecular weight paraffinic hydrocarbons and aromatics but no cycloparaffins at all, though under experimental conversion conditions cyclohexane, cyclopentane, and even their closest homologs should be able to remain intact to a considerable extent.

For the conversion of paraffin wax and ceresin relatively large amounts of catalyst are required.

Paraffin and ceresin. The experiments were conducted with paraffin wax [32] of 52.0°C melting point, white color, density (d_4^{20}) of

0.8937, and refractive index of 1.4216 at 20°C (recalculated). The aniline point of the wax was 116.2°C.

Conversion over activated Gumbrin was carried out at 300°C for a period of 10 hr, to obtain:

Gas	1.2%		
Below 200°C	2.6%		
200–300°C	4.4%		
300–400°C	7.4%	melting point	33.5°C
400–450°C	50.9%	melting point	46°C
450–500°C	11.7%	melting point	55°C
Above 500°C	7.3%	melting point	60.2°C

Redistillation of the liquid fraction gave fractions having the following properties (Table 39 and 40):

TABLE 39. *Fractional and Group Composition of Fractions from the Conversion of Paraffin Wax*

Fractions (°C)	Yield based on wax (%)	Density	
		before removal of aromatic hydrocarbons	after removal of aromatic hydrocarbons
60–95	0.46	0.6709	0.6651
95–122	0.37	0.7053	0.6978
122–150	0.50	0.7299	0.7170
150–200	1.30	0.7634	0.7423
200–250	1.20	0.7804	0.7624
250–300	3.20	0.7941	0.7781

Taking the sum total of the last three columns of Table 40, we have

paraffins	80.9%
naphthenes	0.4%
aromatics	18.7%

Conversion of ceresin gives fractions in which the aromatic hydrocarbon content determined by the sulfonation method differs greatly from that determined by the aniline point method. Such variance is entirely negligible for fractions derived from paraffin wax and occurs only in the light fractions, the yield of which is low. Hence

TABLE 40. *Group Composition of Fractions from the Conversion of Paraffin Wax*

Fractions (°C)	Group Composition						
	Calcd. on the fraction (%)				Calcd. on wax (%)		
	A		N	P	P	N	A
	based on aniline point	sulfo- natable					
60–95	5.5	17.4	3.0	79.6	0.37	0.01	0.08
95–122	7.8	15.9	3.0	81.1	0.30	0.01	0.06
122–150	14.6	15.6	0.7	83.7	0.42	0.004	0.08
150–200	24.1	25.2	—	74.8	0.9	—	0.4
200–250	21.9	17.1	—	82.9	1.0	—	0.2
250–300	15.2	15.0	—	85.0	2.7	—	0.5

A = aromatics, N = naphthenes, P = paraffins.

the overall group composition of all fractions together corresponds to the actual figure. The negligible amount of naphthenes, which is below the limit of error in determination, has been confirmed again in these experiments. The content of aromatic hydrocarbons is high, but in the conversion of ceresin it is still higher. The high content of unsaturated hydrocarbons obtained in the conversion of ceresin is probably due to the presence of side chains in the ceresin, which are easily split off in thermocatalysis.

The origin of aromatic hydrocarbons is probably the same as in the conversion of ceresin, which will be discussed in some detail.

Another feature to be considered is the relatively high stability of paraffin wax. Presumably it survives the conversions of other components of petroleum and consequently there should be a build-up of it in the transformation of petroleum. This might explain why the presence of paraffin wax is characteristic for drastically modified paraffin-base crudes. However, such an assumption would, in turn, call for the supposition that a very substantial amount of the crude must disappear as such and be converted to gas. No data are available as yet at present for speculating about the quantitative proportions between oil and the gas which accompanies the latter. Probably, a substantial, if not the overwhelming, portion of petroleum wax is of a synthetic rather than relict origin.

13 PT

The thermocatalytic conversion of ceresin, carried out by G. Ya. Vorob'eva [32], was made with ceresin of 0.9021 density (d_4^{20}), 1.4330 refractive index as recalculated for 20°C, and a melting point of 71.5°C. The ceresin had an aniline point of 132.1°C. Conversion was effected over activated Gumbrin at 300°C for a period of 15 hr. The following product was obtained:

Gas	1.8%		
Below 200°C	7.4%		
200–300°C	12.2%		
300–400°C	9.3%	melting point	20°C
400–450°C	5.2%	melting point	39°C
450–500°C	6.1%	melting point	46°C
Above 500°C	28.3%	melting point	62.5°C

The losses and the residue on catalyst amounted to 29.7%.

The liquid fraction below 300°C was studied separately with regard to certain physical properties and group composition. The data were as follows (Table 41):

TABLE 41. *Yield and Density of Fractions Obtained in the Conversion of Ceresin*

Fractions (°C)	Yield (%)	Density	
		before removal of aromatic hydrocarbons	after removal of aromatic hydrocarbons
Gas	1.8	—	—
60–95	1.5	0.6749	0.6745
95–122	1.1	0.7048	0.7000
122–150	1.4	0.7321	0.7169
150–200	3.4	0.7490	0.7287
200–250	5.0	0.7762	0.7559
250–300	7.2	0.7970	0.7778

The group analysis of the fractions met with difficulties because the fractions proved to contain a substantial amount of unsaturated compounds, so that determination of aromatic hydrocarbons was impossible. Usually in group analysis the determination of the aromatic hydrocarbon content by the aniline point and by absorption with sulfuric acid gives values which do not differ much from one another, but in the investigation of fractions recovered by the conversion of ceresin the discrepancies proved to be appreciable. On the average, if it is assumed that the aniline points express the true content of aromatic hydrocarbons and that sulfuric acid dissolves aromatic and unsaturated hydrocarbons, then the difference may be used for evaluating the content of the latter. Thus it is established that, on the average, the portion removed by sulfuric acid consists of aromatic and unsaturated hydrocarbons roughly in the ratio of 1:1.

With these corrections, the group compositions of the fractions are expressed in the following terms (Table 42):

TABLE 42. *Conversion of Ceresin*

Fraction (°C)	Group composition						
	based on the fraction (%)				based on initial ceresin (%)		
	A		N	P	A	N	P
	based on aniline point	based on sulfonation					
60–95	27.9	48.4	1.6	50.0	0.75	0.05	0.7
95–122	29.4	54.4	—	45.6	0.5	—	0.6
122–150	27.6	49.2	—	50.8	0.7	—	0.7
150–200	30.8	53.4	—	46.6	1.6	—	1.8
200–250	26.9	59.8	2.4	37.8	1.9	0.1	3.0
250–300	22.2	44.5	—	55.5	4.0	—	3.2
Losses						1.8	

A = aromatics, N = naphthenes, P = paraffins.

Taken together, the fractions represent a mixture of

Paraffinic hydrocarbons	9.45	or	48.2%
naphthenic hydrocarbons	0.15	or	0.7%
aromatic hydrocarbons	5.1	or	26.0%
unsaturated hydrocarbons	4.9	or	25.1%

Every one of the fractions gave a strong reaction with formaldehyde and sulfuric acid for aromatic hydrocarbons. Their group composition is characterized by virtually complete absence of naphthenes, as formerly noted also for paraffin wax, but includes a much greater content of aromatic and unsaturated hydrocarbons than present in the wax. Research by N. D. Zelinskii on the action of aluminum chloride upon paraffin wax and ceresin likewise showed the formation of only insignificant amounts of naphthenes (about 3%). On repeating N. D. Zelinskii's experiments, V. Gorelova also failed to obtain naphthenic hydrocarbons although the total yield of aromatics was even higher than that noted by N. D. Zelinskii. All of these results are undoubtedly of great significance in the geochemistry of petroleum because they demonstrate that naphthenic hydrocarbons can not possibly be formed from non-naphthenic material.

The thermal conversion of solid paraffinic hydrocarbons is related to formation of unsaturated hydrocarbons which engage in secondary reactions of polymerization and hydrogen disproportionation, whereby saturated hydrocarbons and resinous substances as well as aromatic hydrocarbons are formed. In this particular sense the parallel between paraffinization of petroleum and its aromatization is a feature which deserves attention.

D. CONVERSIONS OF PETROLEUM OILS

The thermocatalytic conversions of petroleum are of special interest because they are the result of overall reactions between aluminosilicates and hydrocarbons not only of different series but also of different molecular weights. Though hydrocarbons of the same series all undergo the same type of changes as a result of conversion, their conversion rates are not alike. A comparison of toluene and ethylbenzene clearly indicates the effect of side chain length: the longer it is, the easier the conversion. When the chain is linked to the nucleus through a tertiary carbon atom, conversions occur at a much more rapid rate than in the event of linkage via a secondary carbon atom. Naphthenic hydrocarbons, if conversion is understood to mean merely ring contraction from six to five carbon atoms, present appreciably more difficulties to conversion than, for instance, the conversion of benzene homologs. The lowest tendency to conversions is noted in paraffinic hydrocarbons of normal structure and low molecular weight.

Petroleum comprises a mixture of hydrocarbons of different series and consequently it may be expected that under identical minimal conditions sufficient to ensure an appreciable conversion reaction, only a relatively limited group of hydrocarbons will participate in the process. As a first approach, such hydrocarbons would be the various homologs of aromatic hydrocarbons, which undergo conversion in such a way as to produce new hydrocarbons having more complex substituents as well as lower molecular-weight hydrocarbons such as the close homologs of benzene and naphthalene. By complete analogy therewith, complex cycloparaffinic hydrocarbons tend to form simpler cycloparaffins, though hardly any information is available as yet about the conversion rates of these two series of hydrocarbons. It may be assumed that in polycyclic cycloparaffinic hydrocarbons one of the rings is ruptured to form monocyclic naphthenes having several side chains, and since under the same conversion conditions some of the substituent aliphatic radicals may be split off, the conversion of cycloparaffinic hydrocarbons is accompanied by formation of low molecular-weight paraffinic hydrocarbons, i.e. the paraffinic portion of gasoline.

If this conclusion is considered in connection with the feasible formation of lower homologs of benzene from the high molecular-weight homologs, it may theoretically be supposed that the gasoline originating in the conversion of petroleum must, in first place, contain paraffinic and lower aromatic hydrocarbons, i.e. its constitution should correspond to that of gasoline present in paraffin-base crudes in which, as is known, the content of naphthenic hydrocarbons is frequently lower than the sum total of paraffins and aromatics. Secondly, in theory it should be expected that the converted crudes must not contain any appreciable amounts of aromatic hydrocarbons having substituents higher than butyl, which is indeed a well-known fact.

In the thermocatalytic conversion of higher paraffinic hydrocarbons, according to experimental data, no cycloparaffinic hydrocarbons of any kind are ever formed, so that practically the only source of hydrocarbons of the cyclohexane, cyclopentane and decalin series can be the higher polycyclic cycloparaffins present in petroleum.

Only a few papers are available which deal with the interesting subject relating to conversion of crude oil or fuel oil over aluminosilicate catalysts. These papers in the majority of cases do not specify the group composition of the products obtained and merely indicate the yield of certain commercial fractions. Such are the investigations of A. Ya. Larin [23]. Most of the authors conducted their studies at relatively high temperatures, which are of limited interest in the geochemistry of petroleum [33].

Experiments were carried out to verify the thermocatalytic conversion of petroleum by using some of its fractions, specifically kerosene, lubricating oils, and certain heavy petroleum fractions, as well as S-110 oil which is free from both paraffin wax and aromatic hydrocarbons.

In the experiments of this series the heating involved temperatures ranging from 150 to 300 °C (different experiments with different initial materials). The kerosene was heated in an autoclave so as to retain all constituents in the liquid phase, and the oils and higher petroleum fractions were heated in an iron vessel with reflux condenser, as in the case of higher aromatic hydrocarbons. During the heating, every effort was made to prevent heating of the vessel walls above the temperature chosen for the experiment. The catalyst was used in 1:1 proportion to oil. The conversion products obtained, including the products recovered from the catalyst, were subjected to fractional distillation and its group composition was determined. The initial material was likewise studied with respect to group composition.

EXPERIMENT WITH FRACTIONS FROM "PIRAUZ"
CRUDE OIL 400–450° AND 450–550°C

Composition of fraction 450–550°	prior to expt.	after expt.
paraffinic hydrocarbons	16.7	36.7
naphthenic hydrocarbons	74.2	50.2
aromatic hydrocarbons	9.1	13.1

The oil loss after the experiment was a mere 2.4%, so that the results before and after the experiment remain comparable with each other [34].

The composition of fractions proved to have undergone quite a change. Whereas the initial oil distilled mainly in the 450–550 °C range, the products recovered after heating with the catalyst at 250 °C for 32 hr had a wide boiling range as indicated in Table 43.

Included in this table are the group compositions of each of the fractions obtained, calculated both on the initial oil and on the fractions.

TABLE 43. *Group and fractional Composition of Oils after Experiment with the 450–550° C Fraction from Pirauz Crude*

Fraction (°C)	Yield (%)	Group composition (%)					
		Paraffinic		Naphthenic		Aromatic	
		on the fraction	on oil	on the fraction	on oil	on the fraction	on oil
158–200	2.5	—	0.2	—	1.5	—	0.8
200–300	8.4	9.4	0.8	59.6	5.0	31.0	2.6
300–350	4.9	19.5	1.0	55.5	2.7	25.0	1.2
350–400	13.0	38.5	5.0	45.4	5.9	16.1	2.1
400–450	41.0	40.5	16.6	50.6	20.8	8.9	3.6
450–500	24.6	44.6	10.9	47.0	11.6	8.4	2.1
500–550	3.2	40.8	1.3	47.9	1.5	11.3	0.4
Residue	2.4	—	—	—	—	—	—
Sum total			36.7		50.2		13.1

A conspicuous feature at first glance is the appearance of 69.8% of new fractions boiling below the boiling range of the initial oil, specifically the gasoline–kerosene fractions present in amounts greater than 10%. A number of intermediate fractions, which were absent in the initial material, also have appeared. The 450–550°C fraction itself has changed in composition to the extent that it could not be regarded as unconverted residue. Thus, for example, prior to the experiment this fraction contained

paraffinic hydrocarbons	16.7%
naphthenic hydrocarbons	74.2%
aromatic hydrocarbons	9.1%

The same fraction, when separated from the conversion products, was composed of

paraffinic hydrocarbons	44 wt.%
naphthenic hydrocarbons	47 wt.%
aromatic hydrocarbons	8.8 wt.%

In fractions boiling below 450 °C, the newly formed constituents were

paraffinic hydrocarbons	24.5 wt. %
naphthenic hydrocarbons	37.1 wt. %
aromatic hydrocarbons	10.6 wt. %
Total	72.2 wt. %

including a small amount (2.4%) of residue above 550 °C.

A notable feature is the decrease in concentration of aromatic hydrocarbons in the fractions with rise in their boiling range. The total content of aromatic hydrocarbons increased by 13.1—9.1 = 4%, but since the weight percentage of aromatic hydrocarbons present in the 450–550 °C fractions after the experiment amounts to 2.5%, it is evident that 10.6% of the final aromatic content was newly formed. The resulting impression is as though the large molecules of aromatic hydrocarbons had been split into smaller ones, which have gone over into the lower boiling fractions. This, however, is not the only source of aromatic hydrocarbons, since some formed both from paraffinic and naphthenic hydrocarbons.

Without pretensions for much accuracy, it may be interesting to calculate the concentrations of aromatic hydrocarbons in the 450–550 °C fraction before and after conversion. It is known that aromatic hydrocarbons in the aforementioned fractions are of the tricyclic type C_nH_{2n-18} with an average molecular weight of about 375. Hence, the formula for the aromatic hydrocarbons may be written as $C_{28}H_{38}$. The nucleus of the tricyclic hydrocarbon contains the phenanthrene structure $C_{14}H_{10}$. Consequently, this leaves for the side chains or cycloparaffinic radicals: carbon atoms $28 - 14 = 14$ and hydrogen atoms $38 - 10 = 28$, i.e. $C_{14}H_{28}$. In other words, 47.6% of the elements in the formula of the aromatic hydrocarbon are involved in the aromatic structure and 52.4% make up the non-aromatic portion. Cleavage of the complex aromatic nucleus is absolutely improbable, so that in the extreme case of complete stripping of the aromatic nucleus one may expect the formation of $(47.6 \times 9.1)/100 = 4.3\%$ aromatic hydrocarbons of lower molecular weight, which went into the newly formed fractions. Actually, $13.1 - 2.5 = 10.6\%$ aromatics, based on the whole crude, were obtained, i.e. more than twice as much. These aromatic hydrocarbons had not been formed from aromatic hydrocarbons, but from paraffinic or naphthenic hydrocarbons.

A similar computation for cycloparaffinic hydrocarbons in the initial oil fraction reveals that, by simply splitting off the radicals, the calculated amount of paraffinic hydrocarbons can never be more than 50%. The 72.2% of naphthenic hydrocarbons could yield only about 37% of paraffinic hydrocarbons and an equal amount of stripped naphthenes in the lower boiling fractions. Actually 13% more was obtained. Consequently, the mere stripping of a polycyclic naphthenic hydrocarbon is unlikely and consideration should be given to the possibility of partial cleavage of the nucleus to form paraffinic and other hydrocarbons.

Among the different components of the initial oil, the most mobile portion proved to be the polycyclic naphthenic hydrocarbons which serve as the reservoir from which paraffinic and aromatic hydrocarbons as well as monocyclic naphthenes originate.

It should be pointed out also that all of the fractions obtained are saturated and that no appreciable formation of gas has been noted.

G. Ya. Vorob'eva [35] carried out investigations with a 400–500°C fraction separated from two brands of SU oil. The results of the investigation confirmed the notion that the fundamental material for the formation of paraffinic hydrocarbons are polycyclic naphthenes and thus the higher the content of such hydrocarbons in the initial material, the greater the amount of paraffinic hydrocarbons obtained, and that the light fractions of the resulting products contain a substantial amount of aromatic hydrocarbons. The same fraction of the SU oil after complete dearomatization was subjected to conversion for 15 hr at 210°C, yielding about 32% newly formed lighter fractions with a content of 14.8% paraffinic, 12.5% naphthenic, and 4.3% aromatic hydrocarbons. In addition, up to 7.5% aromatic hydrocarbons were present in fractions above 400°C, though none had been present before the experiment.

Cylinder oil. The material used in the investigation was a fraction above 400°, separated from a cylinder oil [34]. This fraction was first studied in regard to group composition, with the following data being obtained (Table 44).

The experiments were conducted at ordinary pressure in an iron vessel for a period of 6 and 70 hr at a temperature of 250°C. The resulting product yield was 98.7% in the 6 hr test and 98.2% in the 70 hr test. The catalyst, activated Gumbrin, was employed in quantities equal to 75% of the oil. The resulting product was distilled to

13a PT

obtain fractions which were investigated in regard to group composition. It was found that no fractions below 200°C had been formed and consequently the experiments must be regarded as having been conducted under very mild conditions, causing formation of products of limited degree of conversion.

TABLE 44. *Fractional Composition of the Initial Fraction of Cylinder Oil*

Fraction (°C)	Yield (%)	Density at 20°C	Refractive index
400–450	27.0	0.9226	1.5085
450–500	41.3	0.9258	1.5106
500–550	30.9	0.9225	1.5106

	Group composition (%)					
Fraction	P		N		A	
400–450	29.2	14.70	54.5	7.85	16.3	4.40
450–500	41.6	17.20	31.4	13.00	27.0	11.15
500–550	51.8	16.0	21.8	6.75	26.4	8.15
Total fraction	48.3		27.8		23.9	

P = paraffins, N = naphthenes, A = aromatics.

Note. For each component group the first figure refers to component concentration in the fraction, and the second figure, in the entire oil.

Analytical data are cited in Table 45 in which the first figure in the columns for component groups denotes concentration based on the fraction and the second figure on the whole oil.

Short-time heating for 6 hr yielded only 6.1% of newly formed light fractions, whereas heating for 70 hr gave 29.5%, which may be used as a measure of conversion of oil as a function of time. Yet both experiments must be considered as merely the initial stages of conversion.

The data cited in Table 45 indicate that the aromatic hydrocarbon content in the initial oil diminished after 6 hr of heating from 23.9% to 19.7%, and after 70 hr to 18.0%.

Thus the initial aromatic hydrocarbons proved to be compounds of more stable nature. Through reduction of their molecular weight (owing to loss of side chains and other substituent groups) the aromatic hydrocarbons were shifted in to lower the boiling fractions and the greater the degree of conversion the lower the boiling range of the newly formed aromatics.

Heating for 6 hr did not cause any particular changes in the content of paraffinic hydrocarbons, for only 1.5% were newly formed, but after 70 hr the amount of low molecular-weight paraffinic hydrocarbons was over 8%. In addition, their maximum content had shifted from the 450–550°C fraction to a fraction boiling below that temperature.

TABLE 45. *Group Analysis of the Conversion Products of the Cylinder Oil Fraction*

Fraction (°C)	Yield (%)	Group composition (%)					
		Heated for 6 hr at 250°C					
		P		N		A	
200–350	1.7	37.4	0.61	21.5	0.40	41.1	0.70
350–400	4.4	21.1	0.91	51.7	2.31	27.2	1.20
400–450	20.3	19.7	4.00	62.3	12.65	18.0	3.65
450–500	41.0	24.2	9.90	59.1	24.35	16.7	6.85
500–550	25.6	42.9	11.00	33.7	8.65	23.4	6.00
based on oil, with allowance for losses		26.5		51.8		19.7	
		Heated for 70 hr at 250°C					
200–350	4.5	17.8	0.82	47.5	2.15	84.7	1.58
350–400	25.0	30.0	7.50	46.8	11.65	23.2	5.80
400–450	45.0	25.2	11.35	61.0	27.45	13.8	6.20
450–500	16.9	39.9	6.75	45.9	7.75	14.2	2.40
500–550	5.5	47.6	2.62	24.0	1.82	28.4	1.56
based on oil, with allowance for losses		30.2		51.8		18.0	

P = paraffins, N = naphthenes, A = aromatics.

The behavior of naphthenic hydrocarbons in the reported experiment was unusual: the total content of naphthenes, instead of diminishing, was almost doubled. Before the experiment, their content had been 27.8%, after 6 hr it rose to 51.8% and as much again after 70 hr. The only explanation for this may be that a major portion of the newly formed naphthenes owed their origin to splitting of existing naphthenic groups from aromatic hydrocarbons. Yet this source of naphthenes is not offset by the decrease in aromatics and consequently, there must be still some other source from which they were derived.

Kerosene. The experiments [36] were made with kerosene having the following properties:

$$\begin{array}{ll}
\text{boiling range} & 150\text{--}300\,°\text{C} \\
\text{density at } 20\,°\text{C} & 0.827
\end{array}$$

The fractional composition and the constituents in the fractions are cited in Table 46.

TABLE 46. *Fractional Composition of Initial Kerosene*

Fraction (°C)	Density	Yield (%)	Group composition (%)					
			Based on fraction			Based on initial kerosene		
			P	N	A	P	N	A
150–200	0.797	11.6	46.2	34.2	19.6	5.4	4.0	2.3
200–250	0.820	50.3	36.2	45.1	18.7	18.2	22.7	9.4
250–300	0.840	34.0	34.4	48.5	17.1	11.6	16.5	5.9
Above 300	0.851	4.1	—	—	—	—	—	—
Sum total	—	100	—	—	—	35.2	43.2	17.6

P = paraffins, N = naphthenes, A = aromatics.

The mixture of kerosene and activated Gumbrin, in equal quantities by weight, was heated in an autoclave for 30 hr at 250, 300, and 350 °C.

The usual examination of the products obtained gave the following results, which are indicated in Tables 47, 48 and 49.

From the data cited in the tables, it may be seen that there is little change in the quantity of aromatic hydrocarbons. However, this does not necessarily mean that no aromatic hydrocarbons are formed in the catalysis. A portion of the higher representatives of this series, without doubt, are simplified in regard to their composition through dealkylation so that aromatic hydrocarbons are shifted

TABLE 47. *Group Composition of the Products Obtained*

	Group composition of initial kerosene	Group composition of products for the different temperatures, %		
		250°	300°	350°
P	35.2	50.7	48.4	51.6
N	43.2	29.5	32.0	25.7
A	17.6	19.8	19.6	22.7

into the lower boiling fractions. On the other hand, a portion of the final aromatic hydrocarbons are newly formed. Furthermore, as a consequence of displacement of radicals when a monosubstituted aromatic hydrocarbon gives an unsubstituted and a disubstituted compound, there must be formed also a certain quantity of aromatic hydrocarbons boiling above the boiling range of the initial kerosene. Therefore the density of residues above 300 °C rapidly rises with temperature of the experiment, and instead of a density of 0.851

TABLE 48. *Yield and Properties of Fractions Obtained in the Catalytic Conversion of Kerosine*

Fractions	Yield (%) and density, at temperatures							
	Yield	Density	Yield	Density	Yield	Density	Yield	Density
	Initial		250°		300°		350°	
Gas	—	—	1	—	3.0	—	6.5	—
20–60	—	—	0.67	0.6626	0.7	0.6457	4.2	0.6513
60–95	—	—	0.41	0.7160	1.53	0.7116	2.8	0.7154
95–122	—	—	1.97	0.7600	2.70	0.7563	3.9	0.7410
122–150	—	—	2.80	0.7868	3.26	0.7805	5.5	0.7740
150–200	11.6	0.797	15.30	0.7990	17.7	0.7985	17.6	0.7964
200–250	50.3	0.820	44.44	0.8131	37.2	0.8135	30.8	0.8112
250–300	34.0	0.840	24.5	0.8330	22.3	0.8316	19.3	0.8302
Above 300	4.1	0.851	5.8	0.9215	5.5	0.9300	6.0	0.9486
Losses	—	—	1.0		3.0		1.0	
Resins	—	—	2.0		2.0		2.5	
Total	100.0	0.827	—	—	—			

TABLE 49. *Group Composition of Fractions Obtained in the Conversion of Kerosene at Various Temperatures*

Fractions	Group composition (%)					
	Based on fraction			Based on kerosene		
	P	N	A	P	N	A
		250°C				
Gas	100	—	—	—	—	—
20–60	100	—	—	0.67	—	—
60–95	50	50	—	0.21	0.21	—
95–122	29.3	49.0	21.7	0.60	0.96	0.42
122–150	38.0	33.8	28.2	1.06	0.94	0.80
150–200	47.6	27.1	25.3	7.28	4.1	3.9
200–250	52.9	29.1	18.0	23.5	12.94	8.0
250–300	50.5	30.6	18.9	12.4	7.5	4.6
Total	—	—	—	45.7	26.6	17.7
		300°C				
Gas	100	—	—	3.0	—	—
20–60	100	—	—	0.7	—	—
60–95	54.2	37.5	8.3	0.83	0.57	0.13
95–122	36.0	45.0	19.0	0.97	1.21	0.51
122–150	29.3	44.0	26.7	0.95	1.43	0.88
150–200	46.1	28.2	25.7	8.15	5.0	4.55
200–250	49.1	32.1	18.7	18.26	12.0	7.0
250–300	44.6	36.5	18.9	10.0	8.1	4.2
Total	—	—	—	42.8	28.3	17.3
		350°C				
Gas	100	—	—	6.5	—	—
20–60	100	—	—	4.2	—	—
60–95	61.4	31.2	7.4	1.7	0.9	0.4
95–122	38.8	45.0	16.2	1.5	1.7	0.6
122–150	22.0	50.0	28.0	1.2	2.7	1.6
150–200	41.0	25.7	33.3	7.2	4.5	5.9
200–250	47.9	28.7	23.4	14.8	8.8	7.2
250–300	47.9	25.3	26.8	10.1	4.9	5.2
Total	—	—	—	47.2	23.5	20.7

for the residue above 300° in the initial kerosene, we have for the residue above 250°C a rise in density to 0.9251, for the 300° residue a rise to 0.9300, and for the >350° residue a rise to 0.9486. Such high densities, of course, disclose the aromatic nature of the residue.

Thus the content of aromatic hydrocarbons is equal to the algebraic sum total of miscellaneous conversion processes of kerosene and, broadly of crude oil.

The rapid rise in the yield of light fractions below 150°C, which were not present in the initial kerosene, to reach 22.9% at 350°C, may be explained in first place by decomposition of naphthenes in the initial kerosene. Naphthenic hydrocarbons appear to be incapable of exchanging the radicals and shifting them about, but are liable to cast them off instead. Hence the higher naphthenes present in kerosene, on being deprived of radicals, form paraffinic hydrocarbons and lower naphthenes which, as it were, are relocated from the higher molecular-weight kerosene fractions to the lower boiling fractions. Though in first approximation the cyclic structure of naphthenes remains intact in the form of stripped rings, a study of individual naphthenes has shown the feasibility of breakdown of the naphthenic cyclic structure with the formation of paraffinic hydrocarbons. It goes without saying, that in such processes the six-membered naphthenes may be converted to five-membered ones, for example decalin into bicyclononane or bicyclooctane with the other carbon atoms detached in the form of side chains. The 39.2% naphthene content in the initial kerosene, upon recalculation into naphthenes boiling above 200°C, was equivalent to 20.4%, at 250° to 20.4%, at 300° to 20.1%, and at 350°C to only 13.7%.

The total content of paraffinic hydrocarbons rises from 35.2% to 51.6%, which is an increase of 47%, whereas the naphthene content decreases from 43.2% to 25.7%, i.e. a 41% decrease.

BIBLIOGRAPHY

1. MOLDAVSKII, B.L. and BEZDEL', L.S. *Zh. Obshchei Khimii*, **16**, No. 10, 1633 (1946).
2. OBOLENTSEV, R.D. and GRYAZNOV, N.N. *Dokl. Akad. Nauk SSSR*, **73**, No. 1, 121 (1950).
3. LAVROSVKII, K.P., FISH, YU.L. and NAIMUSHIN, N.N. *Trudy Inst. Nefti Akad. Nauk SSSR*, **2**, 101 (1952).
4. HIVEN, P. and HAMMICK, D.J. *Chem. Soc., Lond.* 1779 (1949).

5. SACHANEN, A.N., HANSFORD and MAYERS, *Ind. Eng. Chem.* **37**, No. 7, 671 (1945).
6. THOMAS, HEXTRA and PINKSTON, *J. Am. Chem. Soc.* **66**, 1694 (1944).
7. GREENSFELDER, WOOG and GOOD. *Ind. Eng. Chem.* **37**, No. 12, 1163 (1945).
8. NATANSON, G.A. and KOGAN, M.YA. *Zh. Obshchei Khimii*, **16**, 1639 (1946).
9. MAMEDALIEV, YU.G. *Izv. Akad. Nauk SSSR, Otdel. Khim. Nauk*, No. 2, 197 (1947).
10. DOBRYANSKII, A.F. and GAVRILOV, B.G. *Uchenye Zapiski LGU*, No. 155, 261 (1952).
11. DOBRYANSKII, A.F. and SAPRYKIN, F.YA. *Zh. Obshchei Khimii*, **9**, 1913 (1939).
12. RYBKINA, V.V. Author's own abstract of her thesis, Leningrad Technol. Inst., 1955.
13. DOBRYANSKII, A.F. *Zh. Obshchei Khimii* **23**, 1116 (1953).
14. GAVRILOV, B.G. and ZHGUN, O.I. *Uchenye Zapiski LGU*, No. 163 (1953).
15. DOBRYANSKII, A.F. and CAVRILOVA, E.K. *Zh. Obshchei Khimii*, **23**, 118 (1953).
16. GAVRILOV, B.G. and PUSHNOI, S.K. *Uchenye Zapiski LGU*, No. 169 (1953).
17. GAVRILOV, B.G. and NIKITINA, E.N. *Zh. Obshchei Khimii*, **24**, 303 (1953).
18. DOBRYANSKII, A.F. and KOLOMIITSEV, *Zh. Obshchei Khimii*, **24**, 1469 (1953).
19. DOBRYANSKII, A.F., PONOMAREV, L.A. and DYBKIN, L.D. *Zh. Obshchei Khimii*, **24**, 1632 (1953).
20. DOBRYANSKII, A.F. and KORNILOVA, YU.I. *Zh. Obshchei Khimii*, **23**, 325 (1953).
21. FROST, A.V. and NIKOLAEVA, A.F. *Zh. Obshchei Khimii*, **12**, Nos. 11-12 (1942).
22. MASLYANSKII, G.N. and BERLIN, T.S. *Zh. Obshchei Khimii*, **16**, No. 10 (1946).
23. LARIN, A.YA. *Izv. Akad. Nauk SSSR, Otdel. Tekh. Nauk*, Nos. 10-11 (1944).
24. TISHCHENKO, V.V. *Uchenye Zapiski LGU, Ser. Khim.* No. 211, 147 (1957).
25. GLASEBROOK, A. and LOWELL, W. *J. Am. Chem. Soc.* **61**, 1718 (1939).
26. BAZHULIN, P.A. *Izv. Akad. Nauk SSSR, Otdel. Khim. Nauk*, No. 1 (1946).
27. NENITZESCU and CANTUNIARI, C. *Ber.* **66**, 1097 (1933).
28. TISHCHENKO, V.V. and PETROVA, N.V. *Zh. Obshchei Khimii*, **24**, 1594 (1954).
29. DOBRYANSKII, A.F. *Geochemistry of Petroleum*, p. 159, 1948.
30. FROS T, A.V. and MIKHNOVSKAYA, A.A. *Dokl. Akad. Nauk, nov. ser.* **37**, Nos. 7-8 (1942).
31. OBRYADCHIKOV, S.N. *Neft. Khoz.*, Nos. 3-4, 36 (1946).
32. VOROB'EVA, G.YA. and DOBRYANSKII, A.F. *Izv. Akad. Nauk SSSR*, No. 3, 392 (1953).
33. ARESHIDZE, KH.I. *Zh. prikl. Khimii*, **18**, Nos. 4-5, 271 (1945); **21**, No. 3, 281 (1948); **22**, No. 2, 119 (1949); *Izv. Akad. Nauk SSSR, Otdel. Tekh. Nauk*, No. 2, 148 (1950).
34. DOBRYANSKII, A.F., BOGOMOLOVA, A.I. and SHKLYAR, I.V. *Zh. prikl. Khimii*, **22**, No. 10, 1124 (1949).
35. DOBRYANSKII, A.F. and VOROB'EVA, G.YA. *Zh. prikl. Khimii* (1953).
36. DOBRYANSKII, A.F., GAVRILOV, B.G. and GAVRILOVA, E.K. *Nauchn. Byull. LGU*, No. 23, 392 (1953).

CHAPTER IX

ORIGIN OF PETROLEUM HYDROCARBONS AND THE LAWS OF THEIR DISTRIBUTION IN THE FRACTIONS AND TYPES OF CRUDES

THE preceding chapters presented a discussion of thermodynamic principles and general relationships in the conversion of hydrocarbons of different series. However, the study has covered principally hydrocarbon mixtures and in particular the individual representatives. The kinetics of conversion has been left almost entirely unexplored by the investigations, so that at this time it can be merely stated that some hydrocarbons are converted with greater ease than others. When dealing with such a complex mixture as petroleum it is impossible to predict the quantitative results of the changes but there remains the possibility of defining the general outline of the processes, determining their trends and comparing the assumptions with actually observed relationships in petroleum chemistry. Some of the relationships in the chemical constitution of petroleum have been known for a long time, but as yet no working hypothesis has been proposed, the observed facts were not correlated into a single system and frequently were given an incorrect interpretation and fitted in the wrong places in the geochemical history of petroleum. This resulted in that the same phenomenon was regarded by some as the cause and by others as the consequence. Even such a phenomenon as sulfur in crude oil is considered by some authors as being an intrinsic phenomenon which is characteristic for the initial stages of petroleum genesis, so that in this particular case it becomes necessary to set up various unwieldy hypotheses about subsequent removal of sulfur in order to explain the existence of sulfur-free crudes. The understanding of resinous substances, heterogeneous compounds, etc. in petroleum is confused, too.

The present chapter does not pretend to shed light on problems of petroleum origin from organic matter. As is known, this problem was treated up to the present time by various hypotheses mainly from the viewpoint of the balance sheet, without taking into account the concrete chemical reactions which ultimately lead to formation of hydrocarbons. Thus we can understand the unanimous accord among many geologists who deny the actual existence of primordial petroleum and even the mere possibility of its existence. It also becomes clear why chemists cannot accept such a phenomenon as the origin of hydrocarbons directly from buried organic matter. Any organic matter contains in its decayed state up to 30% oxygen which must be eliminated if this matter is to be converted to hydrocarbons, even on the assumption that only a certain part of the matter rather than all of it participates in such conversion. The elimination of oxygen may take place only in a series of stages, via a number of intermediate products which contain successively smaller amounts of oxygen and other heterogeneous elements. Such processes, of course, will unavoidably be accompanied by various polymerization, condensation, etc., reactions. From the chemical viewpoint, any one of these intermediate products may be regarded as the primary petroleum, regardless of whether it is present in isolated condition or in solution in the hydrocarbon compounds formed. Thus it is not surprising that geologists no longer insist upon conversion of buried organic matter as the source of hydrocarbons, but concentrate their attention on the available hydrocarbons already present in the buried organic matter, which have been part of the living organisms. In this manner, the original source of hydrocarbons is shifted over into life's own laboratory, a procedure which extremely simplifies things but on the other hand calls for miscellaneous supplementary assumptions which have only a weak experimental backing at best. The problem of conversion of organic matter, or of its portion most liable to conversion, into hydrocarbons has not yet been solved and therefore the opinion is currently divided between two variants, in one of which the emphasis lies on already available hydrocarbons which actually exist and in the second on the as yet experimentally unproved ways of conversion of organic material into hydrocarbons. This complex problem is not treated in the present book because it comprises an entirely separate subject. The main point is the question of hydrocarbon conversions as a source of the formation of different types of petroleum, regardless of the nature of buried organic matter. Such a narrow approach sidesteps perhaps the most important problem in the geochemistry of carbon and specifically of petroleum, although this approach may be slightly expanded by commencing the study of petroleum history not with hydrocarbon mixtures but with the non-hydrocarbon substance which is the inevitable link that connects petroleum with its initial organic material.

Any buried organic matter of humus, sapropelite, or mixed origin still retains during the initial conversion stages certain component groups of living matter, for example, lignin, fats, waxes, humic substances or their conversion products. Besides, there are always present the mineral substances which undergo their own cycle of conversions.

The principal type of conversions of organic matter is the loss of oxygen in the form of water and carbon dioxide and possibly other water-soluble products. This loss leads to formation of products of lower oxygen content, so that the liberation of part of oxygen in the form of carbon dioxide causes an increase in relative content of hydrogen. In such conversion products the initial structures of the components must have completely broken down.

Thus the newly formed compounds are by no means related to the structure of original molecules. This, incidentally, means that petroleum types do not originate in organisms and V. I. Vernadskii's well known statement that petroleum originates in organisms must be understood to mean that the carbonaceous substance of petroleum originates in the organisms, in other words, organic matter is the source of petroleum. The structure of petroleum hydrocarbons does not reflect the properties of the original organic material, it reflects rather the chemical processes which ultimately produce the hydrocarbon mixture. The great diversity of organic compounds in the initial matter, which are converted at different rates into different intermediate products, entirely excludes the possibility that the whole mass be converted in a series of stages, thus giving the impression of continuous progressive change occurring in a single direction in an irreversible process.

Consequently, it would be futile to expect to find in nature certain specific formations which are more or less analogous to peat, lignite or coal, because the mobile consistency of the conversion products will always give rise to mixtures having transitory features. The concept of a hydrocarbon mixture has therefore an abstract connotation and to a limited extent corresponds to the entirely arbitrary stage when in the predominant element, though the mixture always contains remnants of the non-hydrocarbon substance. It is impossible to state on the basis of any kind of criteria except entirely arbitrary ones, that a particular mixture is already a crude oil and some other one is not yet oil. With some limitations, the resinous admixtures in crude oil may be considered as primordial petroleum, particularly if such admixtures are of a primary character; from this viewpoint, all crudes may be regarded as solutions of primary resinous substances in the body of hydrocarbons.

To draw any kind of boundary line between hydrocarbon crude oil and its mixtures with resinous substances would be as futile as trying to distinguish between sapropelite shales and sapropelite coals by specifying their mineral content; if coals are defined as substances containing less than 30% of mineral constituents, this is merely a non-scientific definition reflecting the current status of the technique of processing and utilization, without any real basis in fact.

The defenders of primordial petroleum have never assumed, at least from the chemistry viewpoint, that somewhere in nature there may be found some self-contained substances deposited separately from crude oil and isolated from the latter. There is no need to search for them, if only because they are present in varying percentage in any crude.

All of these remarks appear necessary in the course of further discussion of the questions of petroleum conversion which transforms it into various arbitrary series or types. Anyway, hydrocarbons are the predominant constituent part of most commercial crudes and it has been an established practice for some time to define the different crudes according to the hydrocarbon series present as major component.

In rather general terms it may be stated that paraffinic hydrocarbons are least liable to conversions and that all other hydrocarbons are converted to paraffins, if it be disregarded that a portion of carbon is changed into various carbonaceous substances. Yet even within the confines of the paraffinic series of hydrocarbons there may be individual compounds which are convertible with greater ease than, for example, naphthenic hydrocarbons. Therefore the content of paraffinic hydrocarbons in crude oil may, strictly speaking, only partially define the extent of petroleum conversion. The problem of genetic classification of petroleum would be substantially simplified if there were available some clear, determinable criterion for petroleum conversion. Meanwhile it is understood that neither the physical properties of petroleum, which vary under the action of external factors, or its chemical properties provide any definite criteria, so that the only frame of reference is the sum total of a number of petroleum properties contingent upon some dimensionless factor which includes all of the conversion factors. Taking advantage of this situation, it has been possible to plot diagrams representing the successive changes in petroleum. In its general form, such a diagram was proposed by the author [1] in 1948 and some time later by N. B. Vassoevich [2].

In Fig. 51 is shown a diagram of the geochemical conversions of petroleum, including some new features not indicated in the previous diagram.

The present diagram has not been drawn on the basis of qualitative relationships and merely represents their dynamics. Along the ordinate axis is plotted the conversion degree, arbitrarily divided into a number of stages identified by Roman numerals. Along the abscissa axis are plotted the percentages of the different component groups of petroleum. The diagram does not show the "waste products" of conversion, i.e. water, carbon dioxide etc. substances. The items shown in the diagram are as follows.

1. Initial, already highly deoxygenated, organic matter in sedimentary rocks. It corresponds to the concept of ooze material, sapropel substance, and the like.

2. Primary resinous substances not yet of hydrocarbon character, which are the connecting link between the modified material and petroleum hydrocarbons. Conversion of this matter results in formation of hydrocarbons and organic waste products of the process, precipitated in the form of insoluble residues from the system. This group of waste products possibly includes a substantial amount of humic substances.

3. Secondary resinous substances arising in the stage involving the advent of hydrocarbons and their conversions. Here belong also the condensation products of heterogeneous compounds, though generally these resinous substances must not contain oxygen be-

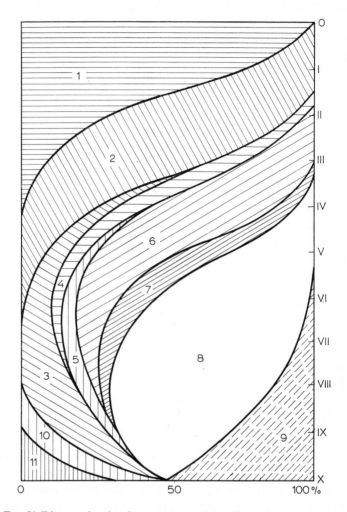

FIG. 51. Diagram showing the group composition of petroleum as a function of degree of conversion. *1* deoxygenated initial petroleum substance; *2* primary resinous substances; *3* secondary resinous substances; *4* polycyclic aromatic hydrocarbons; *5* monocyclic aromatic hydrocarbons; *6* polycyclic naphthenes; *7* monocyclic naphthenes; *8* paraffinic hydrocarbons; *9* natural gas; *10* highly carbonaceous compounds; *11* graphitic compounds.

cause they are derived from hydrocarbons. In practice, the secondary and primary resinous substances are combined under the name of petroleum resins during their analytical determination.

4. Aromatic compounds of high molecular weight and predominantly hybrid type, i.e. containing one or more cycloparaffinic rings joined with the aromatic ring proper.

5. Simple monocyclic and bicyclic aromatic hydrocarbons.

8. Polycyclic cycloparaffinic hydrocarbons. This is the least stable portion of petroleum, which readily undergoes conversion in different directions, including a partial disintegration of the rings. The radicals split from substances of this type, together with those split from the lower and higher aromatic hydrocarbons, form the first increments of low molecular hydrocarbons of the paraffinic series and predominantly branched-chain structure.

7. Monocyclic and bicyclic cycloparaffins. They are the result of conversions of higher cycloparaffinic hydrocarbons and partly of various hybrid hydrocarbons.

8. Paraffinic hydrocarbons as the final object of all conversions.

9. Natural gases of the paraffinic type. The two conversion stages 8 and 9 have been separated in the diagram for formal reasons in order to indicate the dynamics of the emergence of gas from hydrocarbons of the different types. The diagram shows that appreciable gas formation is limited to later stages of conversion.

10. Highly carbonaceous compounds of high molecular weight and cyclic structure; a typical secondary product which has not yet lost its solubility in organic solvents and which is a connecting link between graphitic substances and the hydrocarbon portion of petroleum.

11. Graphitic bodies, into which the petroleum or a portion of it is converted at the conclusion of its conversions.

Division of the diagram into sections identified by Roman numerals allows us to correlate these sections with a certain degree of conversion. Thus, for example, the substance in section II corresponds to a high-resin crude containing as yet a limited amount of hydrocarbons and occurring in nature at depths which exclude the possibility that the increased resin content is due to evaporation of crude oil. Sections IV and V correspond to a petroleum rich in cycloparaffinic hydrocarbons, this being the so-called naphthene base crude oil. Finally, sections VII and VIII depict the composition of typical paraffin-base oils accompanied by substantial quantities of gas.

The diagram permits forecasting the existence in nature of petroleums in which cycloparaffinic hydrocarbons are of no consequence at all and which consist solely of paraffinic hydrocarbons mostly of moderate molecular weight, paraffin wax, and lower aromatic hydrocarbons. Minusinsk crude oil belongs to this type. Since paraffinic hydrocarbons facilitate the precipitation of resinous substances, petroleums of this type should be practically free from resins. Figure diagram allows us also to predict the existence of highly resinous crude oils which form unsaturated hydrocarbons on distillation. Such crudes ought to have only a very low gasoline content.

The transition of heterogeneous compounds into hydrocarbons of different series at the expense of internal energy of the heterogeneous compounds is, as previously shown, in accordance with thermodynamic requirements. The question is concerned merely with the type of initial hydrocarbons, and the response to it is based on the previously noted direct relationship between the age of crude with respect to its conversion and its paraffinization. From this it follows that primary petroleum must be, firstly, of the polycyclic type and, secondly, must contain relict, modified forms of heterogeneous compounds in relatively larger quantities than do paraffin-base crudes. In this connection, the constant content of oxygen in higher aromatic petroleum hydrocarbons is a matter of special significance. The absence of direct analyses precludes extending a similar conclusion to cover the cycloparaffinic hydrocarbons in higher fractions of petroleum.

Thus, in discussing the origin of petroleum hydrocarbons in general, their principal source should be identified as polycyclic hydrocarbons of mixed naphthenic-aromatic type or heterogeneous compounds of related structure. Several ways may be suggested for the origin of hydrocarbons from polycyclic hydrocarbons.

In the first place, it may occur through splitting-off of side chains, the length or position of which in the molecule does not insure sufficient stability of their bond with the polycyclic nucleus or its close heterogeneous analog. Experimental data indicate that the structure of the nucleus is incapable of retaining side chains longer than the amyl or hexyl radical. At low temperatures the length of this chain may be greater. A linked or fused radical of cyclic structure is likewise easily detached.

Fused aromatic rings cannot be split up. Thus, in petroleum, the source of simpler hydrocarbons may be either the linked or coupled cyclic hydrocarbons or their alkylated homologs. Theoretically, the fused-ring hydrocarbons may likewise serve as a source of simpler hydrocarbons, but only if one of the rings is completely saturated with hydrogen. In such event, depending on the general structure, a simplification of the molecule is feasible via splitting-off of side chains or via scission of one of the saturated rings. In both cases the formation of paraffinic as well as cycloparaffinic hydrocarbons (at the expense of fused-ring naphthenic-aromatic hydrocarbons) is possible.

Based on the concept of polycyclic structure of initial petroleum hydrocarbons, the mildly converted crudes should contain a limited amount of light fractions and substantial amounts of polycyclic hydrocarbons in the higher boiling petroleum fractions.

Petroleum conversions involve not only the splitting-off of alkyl radicals from polycyclic structures but also hydrocarbon disproportionation reactions, as for example in aromatics. Here the situation involves, as previously shown, an interaction of two molecules, one of which loses a radical and the other picks it up. As a consequence a hydrocarbon of lower molecular weight and simultaneously a hydrocarbon of higher molecular weight are formed. Disproportionation of radicals causes the conversion of a hydrocarbon having a boiling point at a certain temperature into other hydrocarbons boiling within a lower and a higher range, respectively. In other words, disproportionation may give both lighter and heavier petroleum fractions. Thus heavy fractions of petroleum may contain both the initial high boiling hydrocarbons as well as newly formed hydrocarbons. The combined processes of breakdown and disproportionation may go on in parallel directions and thus highly complicate the history of higher fractions of petroleum.

Polycyclization of aromatic rings into still more complex systems is the only possible process for the conversion of aromatic hydrocarbons because only some powerful factor, such as hydrogenation with external hydrogen, could change its direction by reducing the polycyclic aromatic hydrocarbons into more or less hydrogenated forms capable of having their structure simplified through cleavage, but aromatic nuclei are never destroyed.

The polycyclization process is apparently accelerated with rise in the number of rings in the initial system. Benzene and its homologs at low temperatures up to 300 °C are hardly capable of forming diphenyl. However, from naphthanene homologs under these conditions the formation of substantial amounts of dinaphthyl is noted, and of dianthryl from anthracene homologs. Possible further condensation into the di-ortho position might explain why still more highly condensed systems are found. Thus, once started, the polycyclization process goes on and on toward highly complex systems consisting of a multiplicity of rings which carry only peripheral atoms of hydrogen.

Therefore higher aromatic petroleum hydrocarbons cannot be regarded as merely the residual structures of the initial petroleum substance: they may also include new systems that originated through petroleum conversions. It is evident also that with progressively further conversions of petroleum the quantity of initial polycyclic structures must continuously diminish down to a limit corresponding to the quantity of aromatic nuclei present in the initial system. The quantity of newly formed structures increases, which in the most generalized form corresponds to transfer of hydrogen to a portion of the crude oil and ultimately into methane, and transfer of carbon to another portion comprising highly carbonaceous materials and ultimately graphite.

The presence of an aromatic nucleus in the molecule of a hydrocarbon confers special properties to the molecule, practically without regard to the presence of radicals as side chains or saturation of one of the rings in the polycyclic aromatic hydrocarbon with hydrogen. Among these properties are the reaction with sulfuric acid, extraction with selective solvents and, finally, adsorption properties. In any of these cases the aromatic nucleus gives a specific manifestation, which is normally utilized in analyzing the group composition of petroleum. Yet there are reasons for doubt in determining the structure of aromatic hydrocarbons. Elemental analysis serves as a means for determining the homologous series of the aromatic hydrocarbon separated from the petroleum. For strictly aromatic hydrocarbons free from hydrogenated rings, elemental analysis provides the means for defining the series according to the formula C_nH_{2n-x}, where x is equal to 6 for the benzene series, 12 for the naphthalene series, and 18 for the anthracene series. Whenever x is not a multiple of six, the possibility always exists that non-aromatic rings are present in the molecule, provided that the hydrocarbon under study is an individual chemical compound or a mixture of those belonging to the same series. Since aromatic hydrocarbons recovered from petroleum have hardly ever a value of x equal to a multiple of six, it is reasonable to expect that they are a mixture of aromatic hydrocarbons of different homologous series or that incompletely hydrogenated hydrocarbons are present. The choice between these two possibilities may be made in the majority of cases by studying the pyrolysis products of such hydrocarbons. As it turns out, the yield of the lowest members of the anthracene or phenanthrene series is far below expectations based on the proposition implying that polycyclic aromatic hydrocarbons are very easily stripped of radicals.

From this it may be concluded that tricyclic aromatic hydrocarbons are not of much importance in petroleum fractions. On the other hand, the presence of large amounts of naphthalene suggests that bicyclic aromatic hydrocarbons are quite abundant in petroleum. Thus, among the two alternatives, preference should be given to complex aromatic structures containing a hydrogenated ring.

In all high specific gravity crude oils the aromatic hydrocarbons are concentrated predominantly in the higher fractions, whereas in the modified, paraffinic crudes of low specific gravity the bulk of aromatic hydrocarbons is present in the light fractions [3]. This distribution should be correlated with that particular degree of petroleum conversion in which, among other things, the strictly aromatic polycyclic structure is transferred from the higher fractions to intermediate and partly to the lower fractions. Let us assume the hydrocarbon $C_{16}H_{14}$ to consist of a naphthalene nucleus fused with two cycloparaffinic rings and substituted with different radicals. This hydrocarbon belongs to the C_nH_{2n-18} series and thus should be formally classified as a member of the anthracene or phenanthrene series. If in this hydrocarbon the splitting of a cycloparaffinic ring is accompanied by the liberation of part of the radicals in the form of paraffinic hydrocarbons, the result would be a hydrocarbon of the C_nH_{2n-12} series and of lower molecular weight, i.e. the aromatic grouping is shifted, as it were, from the higher fractions into the lower ones. On the same basis, tetralin homologs should produce the simplest aromatic hydrocarbons. Yet this is a totally impossible process as far as application to polycyclic homologs of the aromatic series is concerned, because a system of purely aromatic rings thermodynamically does not permit simplification via decrease in number of rings. The higher tricyclic hydrocarbons, whose presence was indicated in petroleum by elemental analysis, are most probably nothing of this sort, and the high value of x in the formula C_nH_{2n-x} is explained by the presence of not more than two aromatic rings linked with complex cycloparaffinic rings as previously shown. This might explain the inability of hydrocarbons of this type to give picrates and compounds with triphenylmethane, the anomalies noted in their oxidation products, etc.

The formation of benzene homologs in thermocatalytic conversion of naphthenes up to 300°C is merely of secondary importance unless certain specific catalysts are used. The principal trend of conversion is toward contraction of the ring when direct dehydrogenation to benzene homologs is extremely hindered or requires special conditions. Lower molecular-weight aromatic hydrocarbons are totally uncommon in naphthene-base petroleums and, conversely, are characteristic for paraffin-base crudes. The conversions of paraffin wax and ceresin, as previously indicated, do not produce any cycloparaffins at all. The latter were not formed from initial materials of this type in the presence of aluminum chloride. Hence arises the supposition that paraffinic hydrocarbons may be capable of cyclization to form aromatic, but not naphthenic, rings.

However, information is available that the catalysis of certain isomers of paraffinic hydrocarbons yields cycloparaffinic hydrocarbons (for example, 1,1-dimethylcyclohexane has been obtained from 3,3-dimethylhexane). This reaction was carried out with a platinum catalyst. It has been demonstrated also that in the formation of aromatic hydrocarbons from paraffinic hydrocarbons, the absence of naphthenes may be due to the fact that the dehydrogenation velocity of naphthenes to aromatic hydrocarbons is 100 times greater than the cyclization velocity of the paraffinic chain to form a cycloparaffinic ring. All reactions of this sort require special conditions, which are impossible in an oil-bearing formation, and their probability in thermochemical conversion over aluminosilicates may be accepted at this time merely as a supposition.

The point is that if velocity of the dehydrogenation of naphthenes is really so high, then substantial aromatization ought to be expected in the thermocatalysis of individual naphthenes. Yet this reaction is entirely of secondary importance. In the catalysis of lower naphthenes the yield of aromatic hydrocarbons is even smaller than from paraffin wax. In any event, even with a platinum catalyst, normal paraffinic hydrocarbons may be converted to aromatics without formation of appreciable amounts of naphthenes as an intermediate phase. This problem as a whole has been insufficiently studied as yet, and there is hardly any explanation for the fact that cycloparaffinic hydrocarbons are formed in the catalytic conversion of saturated and unsaturated fatty acids over aluminosilicate catalysts.

The decided predominance of benzene homologs in paraffin-base petroleums and their negligible content in naphthene-base petroleums lend emphasis to the rule that conversion of petroleums occurs in the direction from polycyclic, via crudes of medium cyclic type, to paraffin-base crudes. In this context, a high content of benzene homologs in the light fractions of petroleum attests that the crude has undergone drastic conversion.

The history of cycloparaffinic hydrocarbons has been insufficiently studied. In organic chemistry no simple reactions are known, which would lead to formation of hydrocarbons of this series. An additional difficulty is that the scarce experimental material available tends to create the impression that aromatic hydrocarbons are a later product, compared with naphthenic hydrocarbons. As a consequence, conversion by way of hydrogenation of the aromatic ring to a cycloparaffinic one appears hardly probable, particularly because such a reaction requires hydrogen from an external source. It may be assumed, of course, that hydrogen disproportionation reactions occur between unsaturated cycloparaffinic rings, but we do not know anything about the role of such hydrocarbons under conditions of petroleum genesis.

More probable by far is the assumption that the less complex cycloparaffinic rings originate from more complex ones as a result of breakdown of one of the cycloparaffinic rings in the molecule. From the experimental viewpoint such origin of monocyclic naphthenes is well documented: polycyclic naphthenic oils certainly yield substantial amounts of monocyclic naphthenes over aluminosilicate catalysts, and therefore the latter should be regarded as a product which forms later with respect to polycyclic naphthenes. It appears probable also that monocyclic and polycyclic naphthenes may be formed from cyclic non-hydrocarbon material, although a more definite characterization of this substance presents difficulties.

The formation of naphthenes in the polymerization of olefins appears quite probable to many chemists. For instance, it is known that the dehydration of ethyl alcohol over aluminum oxide gives, besides ethylene, also a certain amount of liquid hydrocarbons including cycloparaffins, but the reaction mechanism is obscure. Polymerization of olefins over aluminum chloride may yield complex cycloparaffinic hydrocarbons along with representatives of other series, among which the higher aromatic hydrocarbons are especially notable. The analogy between the action of aluminosilicates and aluminum chloride suggests that synthesis of naphthenes from olefins may be possible to some extent. For a number of reasons it may be assumed that decomposition of paraffinic hydrocarbons over aluminosilicates proceeds via the stage of unsaturated hydrocarbons, because if during decomposition the resulting products be withdrawn from the reaction vessel, they are found to contain olefins, though none of the latter are present when all of the products formed are returned to the reaction with aluminosilicates. If naphthenes are converted to aromatic hydrocarbons much more rapidly than they are formed, then obviously no formation of naphthenes is to be expected. Such an explanation is good enough for interpreting the composition of the catalysis products but it does not contribute anything to the notions about the initial formation of naphthenes at the stage in which petroleum is close to its primordial source, i.e. to notions about the origin of naphthene-base crude oil.

Thus the most probable source of lower naphthenes appear to be the higher cycloparaffinic hydrocarbons or the naphthenic-aromatic hydrocarbons, directly related genetically with similar heterocompounds.

The transition from higher to lower forms of cycloparaffins is due to the high reactivity of cycloparaffins of complex cyclic structure. The monocyclic naphthene stage is considerably more stable, so that all petroleums contain lower naphthenic hydrocarbons as a principal component part.

The origin of paraffinic hydrocarbons is intimately linked with the splitting of radicals from cyclic compounds. The bulk of paraffinic hydrocarbons appears in the crude when the higher fractions are significantly simplifying their composition. Besides, the paraffinic hydrocarbons present in petroleum are represented largely by relatively simple, low molecular-weight compounds. The body of petroleum is thus capable of shifting in composition from high molecular-weight compounds into low molecular-weight paraffinic hydrocarbons. This process is comparable with the similar transformation of polycyclic naphthenic hydrocarbons. It is rather unlikely that the processes involving loss of radicals and ring rupture occur synchronously along the entire course of petroleum transformation. The initial quantities of paraffinic hydrocarbons are formed, though in insignificant amount, at the beginning of the history of petroleum. Probably at this stage the least stable isoparaffinic radicals are split off. Thereafter the petroleum transformation process slows down and involves the conversion of more resistant systems. At this stage are formed the major amounts of lower molecular-weight naphthenic hydrocarbons which constitute the characteristic naphthenic gasolines wherein the paraffinic components are of secondary importance. The next stage witnesses the partial rupture of complex ring structures with simultaneous formation of paraffinic hydrocarbons which ultimately are present in quantities far greater than the hydrocarbons of other series.

The reaction of stripping off the radicals furnishes a satisfactory explanation for the generally rather low molecular weight of paraffinic hydrocarbons in petroleum; their content always decreases with rise in boiling point of the fraction, and only within the highest boiling fractions of some crudes do increasing amounts of high molecular-weight paraffinic hydrocarbons, chiefly of normal structure, appear again. However, information about the composition of higher fractions is very limited. Certainly, an important constituent in these fractions are isoparaffinic hydrocarbons which, because of their low solidifying temperatures, cannot be separated for analysis from polycyclic naphthenic hydrocarbons. The actual significance of these isoparaffinic hydrocarbons may be considerably greater than current notions would indicate, so that the present picture of actual distribution of paraffinic hydrocarbons in progressively higher petroleum fractions will have to be substantially revised.

Available circumstantial evidence definitely indicates that the content of isoparaffinic hydrocarbons is indeed considerably higher than, and that, perhaps, they may even sharply predominate over, normal paraffins. If so, then the low molecular-weight paraffinic hydrocarbons may be regarded as being fragments of much larger molecules of the paraffinic series. This is the starting point of still another idea about the source of paraffinic hydrocarbons.

In this connection it may be of interest to recall the observation

[4] that slightly modified crudes, more particularly the naphthene-base crudes which are low in paraffinic constituents, contain in their gasoline fractions a preponderant amount of isoparaffinic hydrocarbons, whereas the drastically converted crudes of paraffin base contain in their gasoline fractions a preponderant amount of normal isomers. If slightly modified petroleums contain isoparaffins (ceresin) instead of normal paraffin wax in the higher fractions, then obviously it may be expected that the initial forms of lower molecular-weight paraffinic hydrocarbons will be predominantly of branched-chain structure, as actually observed. Highly modified petroleums contain largely normal paraffin wax and therefore its fragments must consist principally of low molecular-weight paraffinic hydrocarbons. Here, as on many other occasions in geochemical thinking, the researcher is often obliged to consider ideal, isolated processes although he well knows that in actual conditions a number of processes overlap one another, affecting the ideal course of reactions, etc.

One of such assumptions relates to the formation of paraffin wax, which occurs in crudes at the intermediate and severe stages of petroleum transformation. Such formation may be considered as being the result of synthesis reactions such as condensation of lower molecular-weight fragments at the instant of their stripping in the form of radicals. Paraffin wax in accordance with these concepts is regarded as a secondary product but the mechanism of its formation remains obscure. The fact that its accumulation in the crude coincides with the formation of a large amount of lower molecular-weight paraffinic hydrocarbons and with the disappearance of such hydrocarbons in intermediate fractions tends to suggest a possible genetic connection between them. Heating heptane with alumino-silicate catalyst causes only negligible changes, whereas under the same conditions paraffin wax and ceresin are quite extensively decomposed, so that higher paraffinic hydrocarbons appear to be less stable than the lower paraffins.

Greensfelder and Woog have demonstrated that though the relative stability of paraffinic hydrocarbons decreases with increase in number of carbon atoms in the molecule, it still is higher for all of their representatives as compared with naphthenes or substituted aromatic hydrocarbons. The authors established that for paraffinic hydrocarbons from C_3 to C_{24} the rupture of the bond between carbon atoms does take place and that the reaction is accompanied by various secondary processes. The authors found also that branch-ed-chain hydrocarbons are less resistant than normal compounds. E. K. Mankash and other authors [5] carried out the cracking of synthetic paraffin wax over aluminosilicate and obtained up to 28 % gasoline, the yield of which diminished with rise in reaction temperature.

These papers have been cited in order to show that the notion about the synthetic nature of paraffin wax can hardly be reconciled with available information on the stability of paraffinic hydro-carbons. Thus another idea about the relict origin of paraffin wax arises, i.e. about its connection with molecules of fats, waxes, and other materials related to it. All paraffin-base crudes contain paraf-fin wax and if it is accepted as a relict, then the naphthene-base crudes, having been converted to a lesser extent, should contain this prospective paraffin wax in its potential form, i.e. in the form of the above-mentioned fats and waxes or as fatty acids of the correspond-ing molecular weight. Yet no such material is present in naphthene-base petroleum, or, if so, it is definitely present in negligible con-centration. This contradiction could be overcome by assuming that paraffin-base petroleums originated from some special material other than that from which the naphthene-base crudes were derived, i.e. it would be necessary to turn back to the old ideas about the specific role of the initial petroleum material which is responsible for the future type of the crude. Yet this, in turn, would be contrary to the concept of a single initial material for all petroleums and would necessarily presuppose the selection of such material, which is difficult to imagine.

A. V. Frost [6] and A. A. Mikhnovskaya [7], A. F. Nikolaeva and A. V. Frost, G. N. Maslyanskii and M. V. Veltistova [8–11] noticed that catalytic action of aluminosilicates upon olefins partially gives saturated hydrocarbons of the same molecular weight as a result of hydrogen disproportionation and simultaneous formation of re-sinous substances which function as hydrogen donors. All of these papers are concerned with low molecular-weight paraffinic hydro-carbons and it is not certain that the observations made are appli-cable to the case involving higher representatives.

Thus the material source for paraffin wax of normal structure must be sought in petroleum hydrocarbons. In this connection, it seems to be a fertile idea that normal hydrocarbons are obtained from higher molecular-weight hydrocarbons through the breaking away of radicals from the straight chain of carbon atoms. For example, if 5-butyl-docosane ($C_{26}H_{54}$) of 20.6 °C melting point would lose its butyl group, the remaining normal docosane $C_{22}H_{46}$ will have a melting point of 44 °C. Likewise, 11-(3-pentyl)-uneicosane which solidifies at –40°C would be converted, upon loss of its radical, to uneicosane which has a melting point of +40.6 °C. The usual petroleum paraffin waxes of normal structure contain up to 35 carbon atoms, possibly even as many as 40 atoms, which correspond to melting points of up to 80 °C, but in every instance we deal with mixtures which have a lower melting range. Since ceresins contain up to 55–65 carbon atoms, they could be considered to be a source of normal paraffins of lower molecular weight, particularly in the event that the extensive branching of such ceresins caused them to have low melting points or even have a liquid consistency at ordinary temperatures. Unfortunately, scattered information available on the structure of ceresins does not confirm the assumptions about its being of the branched-chain type, and their rather high melting point is an additional argument against it.

Entirely new ideas arise in connection with the research by N. I. Chernozhukov and L. P. Kazakova [12] who demonstrated that not only ceresins, but also certain paraffin waxes which were formerly considered as having a normal structure and belonging to the aliphatic series, have a cyclic structure, i.e. they contain cycloparaffinic and aromatic rings which carry a substantial proportion of carbon atoms in the form of side chains. If this really is the case, then the problem of the origin of normal paraffins is, strictly speaking, settled at once because, under such considerations, their existence in petroleum is denied or at least greatly limited. At the same time the prospective role of isoparaffinic hydrocarbons is likewise minimized. From the viewpoint of the hypothesis about the transformation of petroleum, the new proposition offered by N. I. Chernozhukov certainly does not change matters and even confirms the basic features of this hypothesis because if such cyclic paraffin ever were present in petroleums, they should be very unstable with respect to conversion into lower molecular-weight products of paraffinic and cyclic structure.

The term "regularities in the properties of petroleum" is understood to mean those properties that are present in all crude oils, or at least in an overwhelming majority of them, and are mutually interrelated so that any one property is to a considerable extent defined when another is known. As long as the problem of the chemical composition of petroleum remained insoluble by known analytical methods, the regularities in the composition of petroleum were limited largely to two items: decrease in density with depth and the paraffinic character of crudes produced from greater depths. At the present time the number of such regularities has increased. In the following discussion, the most important of them are set forth and an attempt is made to interpret them from the standpoint of the petroleum transformation hypothesis.

1. *Specific gravity of crude oil decreases with depth of the oil-bearing formation.* The specific gravity of crude depends on the content of low molecular-weight components present in it, the type of hydrocarbons, and the presence of resinous substances. With rise in molecular weight or boiling point of the hydrocarbons the difference in their specific gravities tends to become minimized. Resinous impurities have a specific gravity close to one. Hence the decisive factor is the content of low boiling fractions and the content of resinous substances are only of secondary significance. The reality of this regularity has been revealed in one of the early chapters of this book where it was substantiated by numerical data. Geologically old petroleums, which have gone through a considerable amount of conversion, are characterized by large amounts of light fractions rich in paraffinic hydrocarbons. In certain cases even a relatively high content of resinous substances may not completely hide the reduction in specific gravity. The conversion of petroleum, specifically its paraffinization, appears to be an adequate and general cause of the afore-mentioned regularity. The converse relationship, i.e. a rise in specific gravity with depth, is not generally valid and applies principally rather to slightly converted naphthene-base crudes. Some geologists admit that gravity separation of crudes may be possible. The majority of geologists at this time acknowledge that specific gravity of crude does decrease with depth, but not all of them agree with the explanation of this effect. For instance, hypotheses have been put forward about a secondary rise in the specific gravity of crude in zones at or near the ground surface as a result of microbiological action on the crude in a hypergenic zone. This presents some difficulties in application to platform crudes, where the concept of original subsidence and subsequent uplift of oil-bearing horizons is not justified by the situation.

2. *The content of hetero compounds in the crude oil diminishes*

with depth of burial. This statement might have been extended to include also the primary resinous substances if there were a possibility of analytically separating the primary and the secondary resins. Since at the present time such separation is not feasible, the above regularity covers oxygenated and nitrogenous compounds only. The same applies also to the optical activity of crudes, though it is caused by the hydocarbon components.

Naphthenic acids are often regarded as products of superficial oxidation of petroleum [13]. Yet it is known that the specific structure of naphthenic acids does not permit regarding them as being the oxidation products of cycloparaffinic hydrocarbons unless there occurs a selective oxidation of only such structures as are capable of giving naphthenic acids, which from the chemical viewpoint is rather implausible. An assumption of this sort is clearly far-fetched. L. G. Gurvich [14] has his doubts about the formation of naphthenic acids by oxidation of naphthenes and explains that naphthenic acids are associated strictly with naphthene-base crudes because "the conditions under which the cycloparaffins were formed in petroleum had been favorable also for the conversion of fatty acids into naphthenic acids".

The content of naphthenic acids in petroleums exhibits a certain relationship with the content of resinous substances and is of the positive kind, i.e. it increases with increase in resins. This relationship cannot be defined more precisely at present because the analytical determination of naphthenic acids in petroleum is not too accurate, whereas the acid numbers do not show the suspected parallel relationship with naphthenic acid content. Furthermore, it is known that in the distillation of petroleum the acid content in the sum total of its distillates is higher than that in original crude oil.

Consequently, it may be supposed that the acids in petroleum are present partially in the form of anhydrides and esters, which undergo hydrolysis in the steam distillation of crude oil. Whereas Kaluga crude contains 0.8% naphthenic acids and about 20% resins, Dossor crude also contains 0.8% acids but less than 2% resins. Binagady and Shorsu crudes contain approximately the same amount of resins, namely 12.5% and 14.6%, yet the naphthenic acid content is 1.61% in the former and only 0.1% in the latter. If these figures are correct, it is obviously futile to try to establish any broad relationship. Nevertheless, it has long been known that paraffin-base crudes contain far less naphthenic acids than do naphthene-base crudes, although here again no accurate numerical data can be given. Offhand, the best way out in the matter of naphthenic acids is to acknowledge that they originate from some high molecular substances as a result of natural processes which lead to their liberation, not unlike the facts known in regard to nitrogen and sulfur compounds which are largely of secondary origin and are present in crudes partly in the same state as after thermal treatment in distillation. As to the origin of the naphthenic acids, it has been previously examined and will not be discussed here in detail [15]. The feasibility of producing them by artificial oxidation with air has been disproved by Kharichkov's experiments, who oxidized kerosene at an elevated temperature and in some experiments even in the presence of alkali. The resulting acidic products were termed asphaltogenic acids by the author. They are different from naphthenic acids, as demonstrated by Tyutyunnikov.

The formation of new hetero compounds in crude oil and its optical activity have not been experimentally proved, and the question about the positive role of microbiological processes along these lines remains open.

3. *The content of normal paraffinic hydrocarbons as related to their branched-chain isomers increases with decreasing specific gravity of crudes because of paraffinization of the crude as a result of its conversion.* Previously [16] it has been shown that normal paraffinic hydrocarbons predominate over other isomers, especially in the case of paraffin-base, i.e. modified crudes, but the problem could not be studied in detail owing to lack of sufficient data. At this time the situation has changed in that a number of complete individual hydrocarbon analyses of gasolines have been published [4], so that the entire problem can be put forth within a much broader scope. Therefore this regularity will be discussed here in more detail than the others.

To begin with, the previously stated assumption that after normal hydrocarbons the next most abundant are di- and trisubstituted derivatives has been clarified or rather confirmed. Isomers having a quaternary carbon atom are as a rule very infrequent and have not even been found in a number of crudes. The isomers containing a large number of radicals are also rarely encountered.

In Table 50 are quoted some of the published analyses of gasolines to illustrate the relative proportions between normal paraffinic hydrocarbons and their isomers.

Only the isomers of hexane and heptane are included in the table, since similar values for the pentane isomers might be somewhat distorted owing to their low boiling points. In addition to the figures for absolute content, calculated on gasoline, there is shown

TABLE 50. *Relative Proportions of Normal Hydrocarbons and their Isomers for Certain Petroleums*

Petroleum	Sp. Gr.	Hexanes			Heptanes		
		Normal*	Sum total of isomers*	% of normal hydrocarbons in the total	Normal*	Sum total of isomers*	% of normal hydrocarbons in the total
Michigan (Grindell)	0.81–0.82	12.11	2.77	81	4.19	2.74	60
Oklahoma (Ponca)	0.84–0.85	5.98	2.76	68	7.55	4.98	60
Karachukhur	0.85	3.17	2.00	63	4.26	3.77	53
Tuimazy (Devonian)	0.85	8.43	5.63	60	9.74	5.90	63
No. 2	—	2.60	2.01	57	—	—	—
Surakhany (rich in lubricating oil)	0.88	3.82	3.64	51	6.40	5.78	52
Texas (East Texas)		5.34	5.35	50	5.14	6.21	45
Pennsylvania (Bradford)	0.82	6.31	6.58	49	7.71	6.59	55
Texas (Conroy)		2.48	3.23	43	5.47	3.37	62
Surakhany (ordinary)	0.87	0.69	2.14	25	0.33	2.97	10
California (Midway)	0.95	1.04	3.67	22	1.28	3.47	24
Texas (Winkler)	0.92	1.19	7.15	14	1.34	9.44	12
Koschagyl	0.91	0.70	4.55	14	—	3.58	0
No. 3	—	0.62	3.66	14	+	7.44	0

* As percent by weight of the gasoline fraction

also the percentage of isomers of each hydrocarbon, calculated on their sum total. Certain authors do not indicate the exact characteristic of the crude from which the gasoline originated. In such cases we were compelled to pick up the information about the average specific gravities of the crudes from various handbooks.

The data cited in the table indicate that in low-gravity crudes the normal isomers predominate, whereas in naphthene-base crudes of high specific gravity branched-chain isomers are almost always the predominant variety. In other words, highly modified crudes are rich in normal isomers, thus accounting for the low octane number of their gasolines despite the increased content of aromatic hydrocarbons in the gasolines. A.I.Bogomolov was the first to express the idea that even the distribution of isomers according to their types is subject to certain regularities, though the available quantitative data are as yet insufficient for making final conclusions.

In discussing the reasons which prescribe specific regularities in the distribution of hydrocarbon isomers, it is necessary first of all to point out that in modified crudes the gasoline content is always higher than in the slightly modified, naphthene-base crudes. If the bulk of the crude during conversion, or rather during average conversion, undergoes relatively little change (limited for the most part to gas formation), it is reasonable to expect that the low molecular-weight isoparaffinic hydrocarbons formed at some stage will be changed only to a limited extent throughout the further history of petroleum and that their concentration in the gasoline fraction will decrease mainly because of the massive appearance of normal isomers which are thus of secondary origin with respect to isoparaffins.

In connection therewith it may also be assumed that the primary isoparaffinic hydrocarbons originate from polycyclic hydrocarbons and their radicals. The normal hydrocarbons are then produced through stripping of the side chains from isoparaffinic hydrocarbons of higher molecular weight, perhaps even from ceresin. Consequently, the amount of normal paraffinic hydrocarbons decreases with rise in molecular weight, so that in naphthene-base crudes both heptane and octane may be entirely absent although their isomers are present in appreciable amounts.

A.I.Bogomolov noted also the fact that naphthenic kerosenes are generally free from normal paraffinic hydrocarbons removable in the form of complexes with urea, but may contain many representatives of isoparaffins.

4. *The substantial increase of gasoline content in petroleums is related to the appearance of large amounts of paraffinic hydrocarbons in gasoline, as simultaneously simple aromatic hydrocarbons appear in the gasoline.* In petroleums of high gasoline content the bulk of the latter consists of paraffinic hydrocarbons, whereas crudes

low in gasoline are distinguished by their largely naphthenic gasoline composition. If the naphthenic hydrocarbon content in gasoline up to 150°C is computed as per cent of the crude, the average figure obtained for typical naphthene-base crudes is about 6.7% and for paraffin-base crudes about 5%, in other words the spread between the two figures is small and anyway they are of the same order of magnitude.

A similar computation made for paraffinic hydrocarbons (Table 51) gives for naphthene-base crudes on the average about 4% (from 2.5 to 6.5%) and for paraffin-base crudes about 10%, or a differential ranging from 7 to 16%.

TABLE 51. *Content of Paraffinic and Naphthenic Hydrocarbons in Gasolines Boiling up to 150°C from Paraffin-base and Naphthene-base Crudes*

Crude	Sp. Gr.	Gasoline yield (%)	P	N	A	P/N	$\dfrac{A}{P+N}$
Balakhany	0.876	7.3	2.4	4.7	0.21	0.51	0.027
Surakhany	0.848	12.0	4.0	7.6	0.39	0.53	0.033
Nebitdag	0.880	8.7	3.1	5.0	0.61	0.63	0.075
Okha	0.871	15.1	5.7	8.1	1.31	0.70	0.095
Bibi-Eibat	0.865	15.0	6.2	8.1	0.70	0.70	0.048
Grozny paraffin-base	0.887	13.9	7.0	5.6	1.22	1.25	0.095
KIM	0.853	14.7	7.8	5.7	1.19	1.38	0.083
Changyrtash	0.868	12.8	7.7	4.1	1.13	1.81	0.096
Kulsary	0.815	17.0	9.9	6.1	1.00	1.60	0.062
Iskine	0.802	24.8	16.4	6.3	2.12	2.69	0.093
Grozny paraffin-base	0.844	14.5	10.2	3.7	0.64	2.79	0.047
Tuimazy	0.852	15.8	11.4	3.4	1.03	3.32	0.070

P = paraffins, N = naphthenes, A = aromatics.

These figures imply that the bulk of paraffinic hydrocarbons in gasoline from paraffin-base crudes originate primarily from sources other than naphthenic hydrocarbons. The conversion of the original naphthenes to paraffinic hydrocarbons, if it occurs at all, apparently takes place towards the end of the complete conversion of the petroleum, i.e. at a time when theoretically they are to disappear in general.

The ratio of paraffinic to naphthenic hydrocarbons is a significant factor, too. For naphthene-base crudes it is always less than unity, ranging from 0.5 to 0.7, whereas for paraffin-base crudes it ranges from 1.25 to 3.3. The ratio of aromatic hydrocarbons to the sum total of paraffinic and naphthenic hydrocarbons is on the average about 0.05 for naphthene-base crudes and about 0.08 for paraffin-base crudes. Paraffinization of crude is associated with the formation of aromatic hydrocarbons in the low boiling petroleum fractions, and such hydrocarbons may be regarded as resulting from simplification of the molecules of hybrid higher molecular-weight hydrocarbons and partly from cyclization of paraffinic hydrocarbons. Gasolines from paraffin-base crudes very frequently contain a relatively large amount of aromatic hydrocarbons, although this cannot be regarded as a definite regularity. It has been pointed out previously that paraffinic hydrocarbons are formed through stripping of radicals from higher paraffinic hydrocarbons and through rupture of cycloparaffinic rings. Ultimately, with the progressive conversion of petroleum, there should be produced an increasing amount of gasoline consisting largely of paraffinic hydrocarbons, but simultaneously the amount of naphthenic hydrocarbons will diminish, whereas the more resistant aromatics will gradually accumulate in gasoline fractions.

Thus, on the threshold of complete gasification of crude, as understood to mean its conversion into a methane-rich gas, the crude or at least its light fractions should contain almost exclusively paraffinic and simple aromatic hydrocarbons.

5. *In light petroleum fractions, the quantity of benzene homologs increases along with their molecular weight.* This regularity is clearly manifested in all crudes. It signifies that no such crude exists in which the benzene content would be higher than the toluene content, or a toluene content higher than that of xylene. The ratio between homologs is not constant, so that it can be stated rather roughly that there is 1.5 times as much toluene as benzene, and twice as much xylene as toluene. Another relationship, though not too clearly defined, depends on the type of crude: in naphthene-base crudes which as a rule contain a small amount of low molecular-weight hydrocarbons, the toluene is present in a somewhat higher than the 1.5:1 ratio to benzene.

These proportions may be readily explained by conversion of higher into lower homologs, i.e. benzene is a secondary product with

14a PT

respect to toluene. Moreover, the disproportionation of radicals, leading ultimately to formation of benzene and its multisubstituted derivatives, takes place the more readily the longer the radical and the more numerous they are, so that the formation of benzene should generally occur with more difficulty. Since, from the standpoint of thermodynamics, the benzene homologs having long side chains are unstable compounds, there should exist some threshold, beyond which the substituted benzene molecule becomes unstable. Experiments have shown that in conditions of thermocatalysis over aluminosilicates the existence of butylbenzene becomes problematical, consequently there is little likelihood that benzene and particularly its closest homologs could be present in paraffinized crudes. This is in good agreement with the fact that crude oils may contain, for example, trisubstituted hydrocarbons with short-chain but not with long-chain radicals, even if there is only a single radical.

At this point another interesting characteristic of aromatic hydrocarbons should be mentioned: in pyrogenesis products the xylene fraction contains insignificant amounts of ethylbenzene whereas in petroleum xylenes the ethylbenzene content at times reaches 15–20%, based on the total weight of xylenes. Furthermore, though the meta-xylene content is higher than that of other isomers, it does not reach the values noted in products of pyrogenetic origin. It might not be worth while to discuss here ethylbenzene and its role in crude oil, except for occasional ideas expressed about the high temperature origin of petroleum, when the proportions would have been entirely different. All properties of lower aromatic petroleum hydrocarbons as well as their quantitative proportions clearly contradict the assumption that high temperatures have been operative in the formation or conversion of petroleum.

6. *In high specific gravity crudes most of the aromatic hydrocarbon components are concentrated in the higher fractions and therefore the distribution of such hydrocarbons among the petroleum fractions is non-uniform. Conversely, in crudes of low specific gravity the aromatic hydrocarbons are uniformly distributed among all of the fractions and sometimes their content even increases in the lighter fractions.* The aromatic hydrocarbon content usually increases with transition from light fractions to heavy fractions, but this rule is only approximate and may be explained by the more frequent occurrence of the heavy crudes in nature. However, there are a number of crudes in which the distribution of aromatic hydrocarbons is

considerably more uniform, with occasionally even a certain reduction of their content in the heavier fractions. Such are crudes of moderate molecular weight ranging from 0.810 (or lower) to 0.850.

In discussing petroleums from the standpoint of aromatic hydrocarbon content, they may be compared with one another either in regard to the concentration of such hydrocarbons in the fraction, regardless of the quantity of this fraction in the crude, or in regard to the concentration of aromatic hydrocarbons in the fraction with allowance for the quantity of this fraction. Both computation methods are of value. The first method of calculating the concentrations of aromatic hydrocarbons in the fraction characterizes the fraction as such and gives a clear indication of how this concentration varies along with the conversion of the oil. The second method of calculating the yield of hydrocarbons according to the fractions, based on the petroleum or its distillate portion, gives a clear picture of the dynamics as the highly cyclic structures of hybrid aromatic hydrocarbons are simplified, owing to decrease in the molecular weight of hydrocarbons being transferred from higher to lower boiling fractions progressively with conversion of the crude. Since the aromatic nucleus is indestructible, it may be stated that the specific significance of the aromatic structure proper grows with increasing simplification of the molecular weight of aromatic hydrocarbons.

In Fig. 52 is presented a comparison of a number of crudes having different specific gravities, with the concentrations of aromatic hydrocarbons plotted as ordinates and the boiling points of fractions plotted along the abscissa axis.

It shows at once that in heavy crudes such as Baichunas (0.937), Nordvik (0.930), Tyulegen (0.928) and Makat (0.90) the aromatic hydrocarbon concentration in the 350–550°C fractions lies within the range from 25 to 35%. In low density crudes having specific gravities of up to 0.85, for example, Kulsary (0.815), Grozny paraffin-base (0.849), and Iskine (0.84 and 0.78), the concentration on the average is within the range of 5–12%. There are a large number of crudes of 0.85–0.90 average specific gravity which contain aromatic hydrocarbons in intermediate concentrations from 12 to 25%. To such intermediate type crudes partly belongs also the Makat crude, as evidenced by its specific gravity. In the region of low boiling petroleum fractions, i.e. below 350°C, the foregoing

difference tends to vanish because in such fractions which are greatly diluted by non-aromatic hydrocarbons, the aromatic hydrocarbon concentrations can not reach high values.

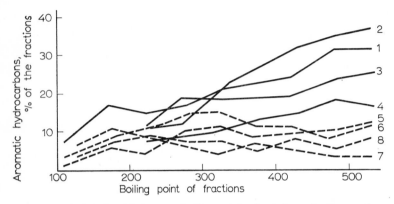

FIG. 52. Relationship between boiling points of petroleum fractions and
the content of aromatic hydrocarbons therein for crudes of different
specific gravities. *1* Baichunas 0.937; *2* Nordvik 0.930; *3* Tyulegen 0.928;
4 Makat 0.901; *5* Kulsary 0.815; *6* Grozny paraffin-base 0.849; *7* Iskine
0.785; *8* Iskine 0.842.

In Figs. 53 and 54 are indicated the aromatic hydrocarbon concentrations in weight percent of the distillate portion of the crude,
for the different fractions. If the quantitative yields of fractions in
every one of the crudes were identical, then for each crude the same
relationship would have been noted as for the aromatic hydrocarbon
concentration in the fractions. But this will never occur because the
amount of corresponding fractions in different crudes is never the
same. Nevertheless, both graphs indicate that aromatic hydrocarbons are indeed concentrated in the high boiling fractions of
heavy crudes and are much more uniformly distributed among all
of the fractions in low specific gravity crudes. For certain crudes the
aromatic hydrocarbon content even tends to decrease in the higher
fractions. As a very rough approximation, without allowance for
other sources of aromatic hydrocarbons, it appears possible to
estimate the portion lost by the hybrid hydrocarbons of the higher
petroleum fractions as they simplify their structure and are shifted
into the intermediate and lower fractions in the form of aromatic
hydrocarbons in which the nucleus is a relatively more important

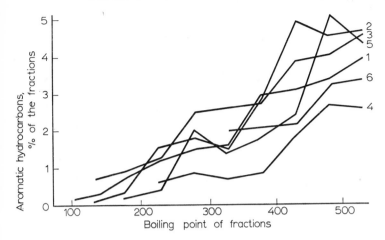

FIG. 53. Relationship between the boiling points of fractions of some heavy crudes and the content of aromatic hydrocarbons therein, calculated on the entire crude. *1* Nordvik 0.937; *2* Okha 0.930; *3* Okha 0.901; *4* Makat 0.901; *5* Baichunas 0.937; *6* Tyulegen 0.928.

part of the molecule. A comparison of the area occupied in the graph by aromatic hydrocarbons in fractions above 350 °C from heavy crudes with the area occupied by aromatic hydrocarbon 350°C from low specific gravity crudes reveals that the hybrid higher molecular-weight hydrocarbons lose through simplification of their structure

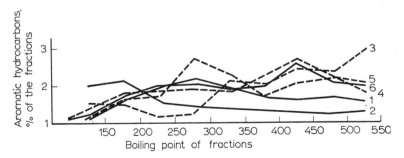

FIG. 54. Relationship between the boiling points of fractions of some light crudes and the content of aromatic hydrocarbons therein, calculated on the entire crude. *1* Surakhany 0.848; *2* Iskine 0.840; *3* Sagiz 0.861; *4* Grozny paraffin base 0.849; *5* Kulsary 0.815; *6* Dossor 0.840.

about one-half of their weight, i.e. about one-half of their weight is converted to paraffinic and naphthenic hydrocarbons. On p. 392 an analogous calculation was quoted for a petroleum fraction, which demonstrated a similar relationship.

The nature of this relationship in the aromatic hydrocarbon portion of petroleum indicates that the complex hybrid compounds constitute the primary form and that the simpler aromatic hydrocarbons such as benzene, naphthalene and their homologs are secondary products of conversion. From the viewpoint of the microbial hypothesis such a distribution of aromatic hydrocarbons would be difficult to explain.

7. *In corresponding dearomatized fractions, the ring content diminishes with decrease in specific gravity of the crude.* After the dearomatization of a petroleum fraction, a mixture of paraffinic and cycloparaffinic hydrocarbons is obtained which cannot be separated by current methods of analysis. Thus the actual content of cycloparaffinic hydrocarbons in fractions boiling above 300°C remains unknown. The ring content of the fraction, i.e. the content of cyclic hydrocarbons in the mixture, may be determined by physical methods, for example, by the refractive index or density. Both of these values for cycloparaffinic hydrocarbons are much higher than for paraffins. On the other hand, for each temperature range the average value of these constants for paraffinic hydrocarbons may be determined from the constants of synthetic paraffinic hydrocarbons, many individual compounds of which are known. As a rule, not a single one of the dearomatized fractions boiling above 300°C has a molecular weight corresponding to the average molecular weight of paraffinic hydrocarbons. The molecular weight of the former varies within a very broad range, clearly indicating extremely large variations in the content of both components in the fraction. With increase in ring content of the cycloparaffinic hydrocarbons their density increases. If it were certain that paraffinic hydrocarbons are absent, this relationship could serve to some extent as a guide, but unfortunately no such certainty can ever exist. Thus the reasons for variations in density of dearomatized fractions are: (1) variable amounts of paraffinic hydrocarbons present therein; (2) ring content of cycloparaffinic hydrocarbons; or (3) a combination of the two reasons, which is probably the most general case.

On comparison of the specific gravities of dearomatized fractions above 300 °C for different crudes it may be noted that variations in the specific gravities follow a special rule: the higher the specific gravity of a petroleum, the higher the specific gravity of the dearomatized fractions. These relationships for a series of Soviet crudes are presented in Fig. 55. For crudes of 0.80–0.85 specific gravity, the specific gravity of the dearomatized fraction of 400–450 °C boiling range varies from 0.82 to 0.85, respectively, and for crudes of 0.90 to 0.95 specific gravity it varies from 0.87 to 0.90. Whatever the reason for this relationship, it is clear that in the case of heavy crudes the dearomatized residue contains either more cyclized cycloparaffinic hydrocarbons or a smaller quantity of paraffinic hydrocarbons and,

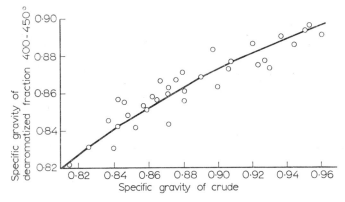

Fig. 55. Relationship between specific gravity of the dearomatized 400–450 °C fraction and the specific gravity of crude oil from which this fraction was recovered.

conversely, in the case of low specific gravity crudes it should be assumed that either the ring content is lower or the paraffinic hydrocarbon content is higher. From the viewpoint of crude oil conversion such relationships appear logical since the conversion consists as a matter of fact in that either one of the rings is split off from the complex cycloparaffinic nucleus or is ruptured to form paraffinic radicals or even paraffinic hydrocarbons. Strictly speaking, the relationship discussed here appears to be merely a specific item of the general decrease in the specific gravity of crudes in the course of progressive conversion toward paraffinization.

This regularity is highly significant because it permits us, in many cases, to disregard the rise in specific gravity of crude through evaporation of light fractions as well as through their supposed oxidation. Evaporation of crude oil and its oxidation are two different processes which may or may not be related with one another. When crude evaporates on reaching the ground surface or locations very close thereto, it loses its light volatile components and its specific gravity, of course, rises. The residue formed thereby gives kir† deposits and, perhaps, asphaltic substances. This process is perfectly obvious and does not need further explanations, at least as far as kir formation is concerned. However, evaporation may take place in deeper zones of the petroleum deposit, where evaporation into the atmosphere is excluded by virtue of the sum total of geological conditions, and in such case merely a displacement of the more volatile portion of the crude occurs. A stratification of the crude takes place, as it were, into a lighter and a heavier portion. This is a purely physical process which in many cases may be indistinguishable from adsorptive filtration of crude oil. There is no doubt but that processes of this sort may be noted in nature and they can be easily deduced by an analysis of the crude, for example, by comparing the specific gravity of the corresponding fractions, which should be the same for such "segregated" crudes. It seems also that the quantitative content of each of the corresponding fractions in such natural separated crudes should show substantial differences.

In any event, without accurate consideration of the characteristics of petroleum fractions, no judgment can be made about the evaporation of crude, the latter term being understood to mean the segregation of the light portion of the crude into the atmosphere or into other horizons. A considerable number of available observations clearly indicate that evaporation is by no means always the only cause of an increase in the specific gravity of crude oil.

These data are cited in Table 52 which clearly shows that the higher specific gravity of Lok-Batan crude from horizon VIII and Balakhany crude from horizon XI cannot be explained by evaporation, because the kerosene fractions have different specific gravities although their yield is pretty much the same. Particularly sharp is the difference in character, but not in the fractional composition of Maikop and Malgobek crudes which yield the same amount of kerosene fraction having entirely different specific gravities and consequently a different group analysis. It is absolutely clear that

† See footnote on p. 223 [Transl. Ed.]

TABLE 52. *Properties of Some Heavy and Light Crudes
from the Same Deposit*

Crude	Sp. Gr.	Wax content %	Kerosene	
			sp. gr.	yield (%)
Lok-Batan VIII	0.897	3	0.840	28.3
	0.902	1	0.848	28.1
	0.926	0.6	0.852	23.6
Balakhany XI	0.867	1	0.830	34.6
	0.919	0.5	0.857	20.3
Malgobek	0.846	7.4	0.812	16.5
	0.922	3.1	0.856	15.4
Voznesenskaya	0.903	2.6	0.842	25.8
	0.921	1.2	0.853	25.3
Maikop	0.828	—	0.837	32.2
	0.893	1.6	0.858	31.4

evaporation alone could not have caused a difference in the group composition of the crude.

As to the problem of asphalt or kir formation, it should be borne in mind that geologically slightly modified crudes of the naphthene-base type rarely contain any wax and therefore at points of emergence of such crudes on the surface of the ground the formation of asphalts, which are free from wax, takes place as expected. Apparently, similar considerations apply to their evaporation at various depths. However, in the evaporation of more drastically modified crudes which normally contain a large amount of wax, it would be reasonable to expect that predominantly kir products are formed, which contain wax. At times such expectations prove to be justified, but by far not in every case, so that the problem of asphalt formation cannot be regarded as having been solved from the chemical standpoint, even if allowance is made for the conjectural action of bacteria.

8. *The content of solid paraffinic hydrocarbons of straight-chain structure increases with progressive paraffinicity of the crude.* This regularity is one of the earliest discovered features relating to petroleum composition. It is associated with the appearance of masses of solid paraffin wax at a definite stage of petroleum evolution. Mildly modified crudes contain principally isoparaffins or ceresin,

but always in amounts far below the potential content of straight-chain paraffin wax. In certain crudes, for example in crude from Gora-Gorskaya and Benoi, the rapid rise of wax content even tends to pinch out the other group components, as evidenced in a previously published diagram [17]. This growth in wax content has no relation with concentration processes of any kind, because it occurs parallel to a profound regeneration of the entire body of crude. For instance, the dearomatized 300–350°C fraction from Gora-Gorskaya crude has a specific gravity of 0.808, i.e. lower than the corresponding fraction of the lowest specific gravity crudes.

The prospective mechanism of wax formation has been described in the preceding pages which included a critical discussion of the current views relating to this problem, and it was shown that none of the hypotheses is capable of providing a completely satisfactory interpretation of the observed relationships. Therefore this regularity is cited in the present chapter as a fact for which no satisfactory explanation is available as yet.

9 *The content of resinous substances in petroleums increases with rise in the content of high molecular-weight aromatic hydrocarbons in higher boiling petroleum fractions.* The resinous substances are the least known component part of petroleum. Such substances are determined either by adsorption on silica gel or by the so-called excise† method. The data obtained by these two methods do not show any consistent relationships, presumably because in the excise method a part or all of the aromatic hydrocarbons are entrained together with the resins [18].

Table 53 demonstrates the existence of a direct correlation between the content of aromatic hydrocarbons and of silica gel-adsorbable resinous substances in crude oil and, since a relationship has been previously shown to exist between specific gravity and aromatic hydrocarbon content in petroleum, it may be stated in general terms that a relationship exists between the resins in petroleum and its specific gravity. However, this relationship includes a large enough number of exceptions that should not be overlooked. The higher aromatic hydrocarbons recovered from crude oil nearly always contain oxygen and sulfur in amounts such that they cannot be explained away as impurities. The elemental analysis of aromatic hydrocarbons and of petroleum resins (neutral varieties), expressed in the form of empirical formulae, fre-

† "Excise" tars are defined in the footnote on p. 65. [Transl. Ed.]

quently gives almost identical values. Thus it may be assumed that a genetic relation exists between resins and aromatic hydrocarbons, with the resins being a connecting link between petroleum and the initial material [19]. Still, a problem exists in that along with incompletely converted resins the crude may contain also secondary substances which are by-products of hydrogen disproportionation.

TABLE 53. *Correlation between the Resinous Substances in Petroleum and Aromatic Hydrocarbon Content in Higher Fractions*

Crude	Sp. gr. at 20°C	Silica-gel resins	Excise resins	Aromatic hydro- carbons
Kulsary	0.778	about 2	2.6	4.5
Iskine	0.786	about 2	2	4.8
Dzhaksymai	0.843	about 3	5	6.5
Dossor	0.866	1.6	9	9.9
Grozny paraffin-base	0.841	7.3	12	10.3
Surakahany	0.848	4	8	10.7
Balakhany	0.876	5	13.6	13.9
Bibi-Eibat	0.865	9.3	18	15.8
Ishimbaevo	0.880	13.8	30	19.7
Tyulegen	0.930	19	38	20.0
Okha (Sakhalin)	0.929	18.8	45	21.5
Uch-Kyzyl	0.962	38.7	92	about 40
Chusovaya	0.954	23.4	54	36

A diagnosis of the primary and secondary resinous substances is not possible at the present time, and yet it is one of the important problems in the geochemistry of petroleum. Perhaps an explanation of the exceptions to the relationship discussed here may be that the primary resinous substances which have not yet completed the conversion cycle are camouflaged by secondary resins, a factor which, of course, would be reflected in their quantitative proportions.

The correlation between the resinous substances present in petroleum, the aromatic hydrocarbons, and the specific gravity of the petroleum in this particular case indicates that the rise or drop in resin content is associated with far-reaching changes in the group composition of the crude, which cannot be interpreted through such elementary concepts as evaporation of petroleum, its oxidation in the earth, and similar suppositions. At the same time the hypothesis about the transformation of petroleum easily consolidates these properties into a single system.

The sulfur content in petroleum varies within a fairly broad range even within the confines of the same oil field. Wherever the sulfur content is generally low, such as for instance in Baku, it may vary by 100% or more from one horizon to the other, without any clear correlation with the depth of the oil-bearing horizon. In the event of high sulfur content, such variations are much smaller and the sulfur content thus becomes a consistent characteristic throughout the entire region (Second Baku). There are cases on record where petroleums throughout an entire region have an insignificant sulfur content though some individual crudes are high in sulfur. For instance, in the Western Ukraine all of the crudes are low in sulfur (about 5% 0.4–0.5%), but the crude from Sodovaya Vishnya contains as much as sulfur. N. B. Vassoevich reports a decrease of the sulfur content with greater depth and explains this fact through enrichment with sulfur in the hypergene zone by microbiological factors. A similar relationship might prevail also in the Grozny region, but it is by no means generally valid for other oil-bearing regions where frequently a diversified picture of changes in sulfur content with depth is observed. It is quite possible that the petroleum transformation processes cause a destruction of part of sulfur compounds by converting the sulfur to hydrogen sulfide, but this process should occur in conformance with the structure and type of the sulfur compound.

Very frequently an increase in the content of resinous substances in the petroleum is associated with a rise in sulfur content, but this relationship is due to causes other than evaporation. For instance, in the Baku region very frequently the sulfur content of resinous crudes of high specific gravity are twice that of lighter crudes, whereas some low specific gravity Lok-Batan crudes contain the same amount of sulfur as the high specific gravity Baku petroleums. Finally, very heavy and resinous crudes are known, which are by no means exceptional with respect to their sulfur content. The relation between sulfur and the type of reservoir rocks is not quite clear, but anyway it is not as obvious as commonly thought.

In discussing the presence of sulfur in petroleums, it should be noted that the major part of the sulfur is contained in the non-volatile petroleum fractions, i.e. in the resinous substances. Nevertheless, even if such resinous substances be regarded as being of primary origin, there are no sufficient reasons to regard the sulfur compounds as being of primary origin too, because subsequent introduction of sulfur into the crude would have caused, from the standpoint of chemistry, the formation of various resin-like products of secondary character. Thus there is no reason to regard the sulfurized state of petroleum as one of the stages of its genesis, whatever be the origin of such sulfur.

There also is no relation between the type of crude and the sulfur content. The Second Baku crudes belong to the paraffinic-naphthenic type and are high in sulfur, but so are the Mexican crudes which are of the naphthene-base type. Yet it must be admitted that in many cases the high-sulfur crudes do belong to the paraffin-base type, and this fact gave rise to various hypotheses about a causal connection between the sulfur and the paraffinicity of petroleum, for example, the hypothesis about the dehydrogenation of naphthenic hydrocarbons by sulfur, about the primary forms of the sulfur, etc.

Upon considering the different opinions about the origin of sulfur in petroleums and about the vague relationships, it may be assumed that the sulfurization of crude oil is a secondary process and that the sulfur is not related with the origin of petroleum. Sulfur may be introduced into the crude oil in cases where the conditions prevailing in the particular location or area ensure secondary sulfurization and, possibly, in connection with an increased content of sulfates in the water bodies in which deposition of the initial petroleum material occurred (e.g. the mud deposits in the bay of Kara-Bogaz). It may be possible also that sulfurization of crude oil is a sign of bacterial activity, and in such an event the sulfurization of crude must be regarded as the single essential result of this biological process. However, the real microbiological situation in sulfur-bearing crudes has not been investigated as yet. Thus at the present time it would be difficult to define any clear correlations between sulfur and the other properties of petroleum.

The present chapter does not include a discussion of many other relationships, particularly those which are specific for the individual oil-bearing regions. Further investigation of certain group components in petroleum should provide an opportunity to establish certain conclusions about the mutual relation between petroleum components. Thus, for example, a detailed study of cycloparaffinic hydrocarbons would provide a more definite basis for assuming the same number of rings in aromatic and cycloparaffinic hydrocarbons [20], for the relationship between cyclohexane homologs with respect to their isomers, the association between nitrogen and sulfur content in petroleum, the relationship between the primary and secondary resinous substances and the type of crude, etc. Still more important would be to establish a correlation between liquid oil and gas for crudes of different geological age.

The regularities in petroleum composition and its other properties represent a special case of a certain general regularity which is consistent with the idea that substances having a lower reserve of free energy are formed in petroleum. If the petroleum is regarded as a closed system exposed to the action of internal energy potentialities with or without the participation of physical factors only, then all of the changes in the crude have to be treated as a certain directional process. When the crude loses, for example, a portion of the cycloparaffinic hydrocarbons, they are replaced by other hydrocarbons, for example, paraffins. This causes a decrease in specific gravity of the crude, the appearance of aromatic hydrocarbons, decrease in the number of rings in the crude, etc. phenomena which have been previously described as regularities in petroleum composition. It is easy to visualize that all of these relationships are merely details of a single, overall rule which is common for all crudes, namely the decrease in the size of its molecules and increasing paraffinicity. None of the relationships is an accidental one that is unrelated to the other relationships; this is the convincing aspect of the general theory of transformation of petroleum.

An entirely different picture is presented by the conversion of petroleum under the action of external factors such as oxidation, sulfurization, bacterial action, etc. All of these factors are not intrinsic in the petroleum itself, they are not of the compulsory type, they merely reflect the influence of conditions external to the system, and in any event may change the oil in a way which is not necessarily consistent with the general trend of transformation. In spite of their broad distribution, such petroleums cannot be regarded as typical and are not discussed in the present chapter because it is not possible to generalize random phenomena.

The significance of regularities in petroleum properties lies in that such regularities prove useful in discussing the problem of petroleum origin, they may be helpful in treating problems relating to correlation of oil-bearing horizons, and in many cases allow us to predict the properties of crude oil on the basis of its geological environment. This, however, requires the existence of some kind of a hypothesis which would not only interpret such regularities but also unify them. It would be absolutely incorrect to give an interpretation of certain problems of petroleum origin merely on the basis of some particular regularity chosen at random from the entire list of such generalizations. A hypothesis is fruitful only if it takes into account all of the regularities. A disregard for this requirement is the reason for the failure of many propositions about the formation of various petroleum types and, perhaps, also of its origin.

Most of the hypotheses about petroleum origin differ from one another merely in details relating to the original source substance, whereas in the broad scope of the problem it might be that determination specifically of this original substance is not too important after all, because of the ubiquity or organic matter in nature. Therefore it may be stated with equal probability that petroleum is of vegetable or of animal origin, or a combined hypothesis may be established. The point is that petroleum is not formed directly from living matter or from the products originating after the death of the organism, but is formed from products which are relatively distant from living matter and which have lost the functional groups that are characteristic for animal or vegetable material. The important point is that in such material a definite association already exists between carbon and hydrogen atoms, since the creation of such an association between free atoms of these elements in the form of relatively complex compounds is hardly probable within the confines of the biosphere. There is no possibility at all for discussing the role of the initial substance of petroleum, as far as it belongs to the animal or vegetable kingdom, in order to interpret the different types of crude oils, nor by far the role of the various kinds of plants. The substances which are the precursor of petroleum have been altered to such an extent and have undergone so many conversions that the typical properties of living matter are no longer present, except for a few components of quantitatively little significance in the balance of petroleum components (porphyrins, waxes, etc.).

The most widely recognized hypothesis relates to the origin of petroleum from mud deposits in bodies of water. These products may be termed sapropel or something else, whatever it may be. Such substances presumably may ultimately form petroleum as a principal product of their conversion or as a material which is quantitatively of secondary importance.

The differences in opinion between the supporters of the various hypotheses of petroleum origin concern in principle not the initial material, but the condition of this material and the underlying causes of its conversion. Thus, for instance, some of the supporters are in favor of concentrated forms of buried organic substance and some in favor of dispersed forms. From the viewpoint of chemistry this question is of no significance in principle and certainly does not have the high significance attributed to it by certain researchers. The importance lies only in the conditions relating to the existence and subsequent fate of this substance because the environment determines the direction of its change. In this question, an objective approach to the evaluation of possible conversions is a tremendously important factor.

Very frequently preference is given to the dispersed forms of organic matter which are distributed everywhere but are not always a source of petroleum, and such dispersed organic matter is quite often assigned the role of petroleum precursor merely because there are no other possible petroleum sources in the neighborhood. In so doing, the possibility is frequently overlooked that the dispersed organic matter might have undergone a change in a direction which, obviously, can no longer lead to transformation into petroleum, i.e. if it had been subjected to the action of such factors as oxidation, humification, etc.

Some are of the opinion that the hydrocarbon substance of petroleum has been inherited from the organisms and that hydrocarbons do not represent some stage in the conversion of the entire mass of buried organic matter but are derived from that portion of it, which is best adapted for hydrocarbon conversion. This serves as a basis for conjectures that petroleum has originated from waxes, from the bitumen present in coal, from resinous substances, and similar particulate material.

There are also adherents of the overall transformation of buried organic matter into hydrocarbons. Such concentrated forms include, for example, sapropelitic and even humic kinds of coal, liptobiolithic coals, and the kerogen of bituminous shales.

Perhaps the really correct viewpoint is that the buried matter may undergo a change in different directions depending on external conditions. If the conversion occurred towards formation of coal, it would be futile to expect conversion to petroleum, but if under special conditions the alteration turned towards reduction processes, it may be expected that conversion of the initial substance into petroleum will occur.

It has been also suggested that bituminous shales of the sapropelite type represent a final development no longer capable of yielding petroleum, whereas the initial shale substance, i.e. the sapropelite material itself, might have yielded petroleum under suitable circumstances.

The last-mentioned example is a good illustration that the differences in opinion about the problem of petroleum origin are basically not concerned with the initial material itself but with the course of its transformation depending on external conditions. That is the very reason why the seemingly important question of the concentration of organic material in rocks has in reality not much significance from the standpoint of chemistry. It arises chiefly because complete conversion runs up against a lack of hydrogen, so that one is puzzled about the absence of the mass of carboniferous material which supposedly was separated out during the formation of such a hydrogen-rich material as petroleum. The same objection, of course, may be cited also against the dispersed forms of organic substance, when the "waste products" of the reduction process are visualized to consist of various forms of dispersed nonhydrocarbon materials in spite of the fact that it most frequently is of humic character. The supposition arises that only a negligible portion of the buried organic matter is converted to petroleum or only an insignificant portion of the already formed hydrocarbons is segregated from the buried organic matter. Furthermore, various calculations usually are made to show that these hydrocarbons are present in the earth's crust, i.e. in its organic component, in quantities so large that the reserves of such potential baffle the imagination. The only thing that needs to be done is the segregation and accumulation of such dispersed petroleum, and with this objective in mind some purely speculative assumptions are called upon to save the situation.

A further point of disagreement between geologists and chemists involves the characteristics of the hydrocarbon substance evolved from the organic matter in which it is present in preformed state or in which it is formed. V. A. Uspenskii, a chemist, believes that the primary hydrocarbons are principally paraffinic hydrocarbons, perhaps in the form of the higher members of this series. Other researchers find that the initial hydrocarbons possess the polycyclic structure of the hybrid aromatic series and that these hydrocarbons are not segregated in a preformed state but are formed from the buried organic matter or a portion thereof, certainly via a series of stages including various as yet non-hydrocarbonaceous compounds. In other words, the primary form of petroleum consists of hetero compounds which perhaps are generally free from hydrocarbons and which are transformed into hydrocarbons through loss of hetero atoms, chiefly oxygen in the form of water and carbon dioxide. An interpretation of this sort makes it absolutely necessary to presuppose the existence of primary crude oil, whereas the backers of the segregation of preformed hydrocarbons do not see any need for the existence of such a substance. The supporters of preformed hydrocarbons are unquestionably on the winning side because the chemical mechanism of hydrocarbon formation has been shifted into the mysterious laboratory of the organism. The emphasis is no longer on preformed hydrocarbons which sometimes are naturally present in peat and coal in the form of scarce, purely local minerals having no significance in the economics of nature or occur in various, principally vegetable organisms. The supporters of this hypothesis must operate with tremendous oil-producing areas, whereas those favoring the conversion of buried organic matter attach no significance to dispersed preformed hydrocarbons and derive the petroleum from limited oil-producing areas. To express these ideas in a somewhat vulgar manner, we can say that the supporters of the former hypothesis are gathering up the highly dispersed hydrocarbons in the finished state, and the supporters of the latter hypothesis make petroleum from a corresponding non-hydrocarbon material.

Still another hypothesis about the origin of petroleum exists, which was proposed by N. B. Vassoevich. This hypothesis has been evolved by borrowing certain features from V. A. Uspenskii's hypothesis (primary formation of hydrocarbons in organisms and in products of their modification) and the hypothesis of one of the authors of the present book (hypothesis about the conversion of hydrocarbons by thermocatalytic means). These features were then combined into a single composite hypothesis which lacks individuality to such an extent that it is difficult to find therein any factors capable of guiding scientific thinking along novel paths. The essential idea in the hypothesis of Uspenskii and Vassoevich is the participation of the biological factor which, in the opinion of its authors, introduces substantial changes in the group composition of the crude, the latter being, of course, a point not to be overlooked in any hypothesis. The participation of the microbiological factor, in their opinion, is almost the fundamental element governing the type of crude formed.

An additional factor operative in the conversion of initial hydrocarbons is said to be the oxidation reactions in the aeration zone, and this zone has been shifted down to such depths, at which no geologist ever found any trace of oxygen. Nobody argues about the fact that crude oil on the surface of the ground is capable of reacting with the atmosphere, but such reaction is limited to loss of volatile constituents of the oil and formation of residual asphaltic substances in which the oxygen content does not exceed the value formerly present in the resinous substances of the petroleum, so that the question of oxidation does not arise. Since oxidation of petroleum at subsurface depths is a debatable process, the hypothesis of conjugated oxidation by sulfate-reducing microorganisms was set up instead. Nobody disputes the existence of such reducing organisms in nature, but in application to buried hydrocarbons in this hypothesis the only really correct thing is that whenever one substance is oxidized, some other one must undergo reduction, and vice versa, but the courses and results of such oxidation may vary greatly.

More probable from the energy viewpoint appears to be the oxidation to water and carbon dioxide and in such an event, if the microorganisms are really a factor, the net result is the destruction of crude oil rather than modification of its component hydrocarbons, all the more since nobody ever succeeded in isolating and determining the intermediate products of the supposed oxidation. Notwithstanding, the Uspenskii–Vassoevich hypothesis attributes precisely to these organisms the appearance of optical activity, of nitrogen compounds including the porphyrins, etc. Vassoevich believes that the hydrocarbon mass of the petroleum as it separates from the buried organic matter with progressive subsidence into the region of elevated temperatures in the catagenic zone, is converted to paraffinic hydrocarbons or mixtures rich in such hydrocarbons. Thereafter, upon transfer into the hypergenic zone, these hydrocarbons are subjected to varying microbiological treatment and it is here that all of the diverse types of petroleums originate. Theoretically, the possibilities of such a process are improbable from the chemistry standpoint, and the pertinent experimental proof is nil. To sum up, according to this hypothesis, the crude oil at progressively greater depth is characterized by an increasing content of paraffinic hydrocarbons.†

Thus the paraffinic type of crude is not an acquired but a relict feature whereas the naphthenic type is not a relict but an acquired feature, i.e. everything proceeds in a way exactly opposite to that demanded by chemistry and thermodynamics. Nevertheless, the Vassoevich hypothesis discussed here must be regarded as the most complete and coherent production of this kind despite a multiplicity of debatable points; but as to its conformity to real facts, matters do not look too good. In attempting to combine two mutually contradictory hypotheses, Vassoevich sacrificed the logic of each hypothesis. The combined hypothesis lost the intrinsic meaning which its primary sources had possessed and, naturally, it acquired all of the defects inherent in these primary sources. All of the inherent defects of the hypotheses of Uspenskii and A. F. Dobryanskii were concentrated in the new scheme, with the result that a rather hybrid scheme was obtained in which defects were brought more clearly into focus.

As a matter of fact, many of the aspects in the fundamental hypotheses may be considered from diametrically opposite points of view, and examples of such interpretations will be presented herein below. This is not the place for developing in detail any hypotheses about the origin of petroleum because the subject of the present book is to discuss the problems of transformation of petroleum. Nevertheless, it seems worthwhile to examine in some detail the circumstances and relationships that are liable to be explained from different points of view and, of course, with a varying degree of the scientific probability of such explanations.

The decrease in optical activity of crude oil with depth of the oil-bearing horizon and with increasing paraffinicity of the petro-

† The assumption about the subsidence of a crude oil deposit to a certain depth and subsequent rise of the oil from the catagenic zone into the hypergenic zone is understood to be not only a real migration but also a consequence of erosion of the overburden of sedimentary rocks, so that the oil-bearing beds approach closer to the surface of the ground, where the various processes of microbial and oxidative character supposedly take place.

leum may be explained by the disappearance of the asymmetrical carbon atom. For instance, even a mere heating reduces the optical activity. Naturally, a decline in the optical activity of petroleum may be expected when many of its molecules have been reorganized into more stable systems of lower molecular weight. On the other hand, it is proposed that optical activity is the result of microbiological processes occurring in the hypergenic zone, whereby the initial optically barren crude becomes active. An experiment can prove the disappearance of optical activity, but the possibility of its appearance has as yet never been experimentally proved.

Naphthenic acids, according to Vassoevich and other authors, are a product of petroleum oxidation, but according to different opinions these acids are a typical relict product. Therefore it naturally may be expected that paraffin-base crudes should have a low content of naphthenic acids as well as of other hetero compounds and, conversely, there should be an abundance of them in the more recent naphthene-base crudes. Thus, according to some opinions the paraffin-base petroleums have already lost the acids and according to others they have not yet gained any. But nobody as yet has been able to prepare naphthenic acids by the oxidation of petroleum in any manner. Consequently, though the supporters of microbiological processes rely upon naphthenic acids by dragging them into their armory, nevertheless the use of this weapon does not bring victory any closer for the adherents of microbiological or oxidative conversions of petroleum.

The regular association of aromatic hydrocarbons with higher fractions of naphthene-base crudes and with resinous substances is understood to be a genetic system with sequential relationship of its components. The complex molecules of aromatic hydrocarbons are converted to simpler ones, and it is difficult to draw a sharp distinction between certain resin fractions and aromatic hydrocarbons. The adherents of microbiological and oxidation processes think, on the contrary, that the hybrid higher molecular-weight aromatic hydrocarbons are newly formed products rather than relict forms. Whereas experimental evidence clearly proves the conversion of higher into lower molecular-weight molecules, there is not a shred of evidence in favor of a real increase in the molecular weight of hydrocarbons that had been brought about by any kind of oxidation except when the molecules are being freely shifted about on paper.

The abundant formation of gasoline in the paraffinization of petroleum is a direct result of thermocatalytic conversion and has been proved by dozens of experiments.

Vassoevich had his reasons for including the afore-mentioned process into the scheme proposed by him. Thermocatalytic reactions prove that in geologically young naphthene-base crudes the gasoline has not yet formed, whereas the supporters of biogenic and oxidative conversion of petroleum maintain that the gasoline which had been formed in the catagenic zone was subsequently upon transportation of the crude into the hypergenic zone either evaporated or dissolved, or eaten up by bacteria; in short, it disappeared somewhere, although all of these mysterious processes can be forced only with the greatest difficulty into various far-fetched hypotheses. Here, again, experimental evidence is confronted with schemes which ladle out the arguments from an inexhaustible pot of speculative stuff.

Vanadium in crudes is known to be associated with resinous substances and the destruction of the latter, of course, liberates this element so that it is transferred from the petroleum system into a medium which is external with respect to the crude oil. Hence it is plain that vanadium is present in larger amount wherever the quantity of resinous substances is larger. The backers of microbiological processes of petroleum transformation reckon that vanadium is introduced into the petroleum in the hypergenic zone and consequently, of course, the microorganisms are considered to be the cause of this process. Porphyrins, too, are introduced into the petroleum by the same processes. Hence is deduced the association of vanadium with naphthene-base crudes. This example, as do others, gives a very good illustration of how the adherents of microbiological transformation of petroleum are striving to summon to their assistance any fact and any consistent relationship in the composition of crude oil, without being at all embarrassed that in doing this they have to turn the facts upside down and put the cart before the horse.

The question of paraffin wax is commonly known to be one of the most difficult to solve. Paraffin wax occurs characteristically only in highly modified crudes and is from the thermocatalysis standpoint a typical secondary product. Uspenskii considers the paraffinic wax to be an inherited substance, and hence the initial crude must be rich in this component. Vassoevich has shown in regard to this item some independence by not insisting upon the paraffinic nature of the initial crude oil and assuming that paraffin wax is formed in the catagenic zone, which is generally quite correct. However, he supposes that in the migration of crude upwardly into the hypergenic zone the paraffin wax disappears as a consequence of microbiological activity. Thus regardless of whether the paraffin wax existed in the initial crude during its subsidence into the cata- genic zone or has merely been formed in that zone, its fate is sealed anyway because it must disappear in the hypergenic zone. Now an explanation is due about the disappearance of lower hydrocarbons of all types, which accompany the catalytically converted crude. Here again it becomes necessary to marshal the familiar arguments such as evaporation, leaching out, consumption by bacteria, etc., although every one of these processes is difficult to accept because such hydrocarbons as the benzene homologs (and there are more than enough of them present in the gasoline portion of crudes upon emergence from the catagenic zone) may serve as nutrition for aerobic bacteria only. Evaporation does not much help matters because the gases associated with naphthene-base crudes, i.e. crudes that underwent treatment in the hypergenic zone, are distinguished by a negligible gasoline content in contrast to paraffin-base crudes, though everything is supposed to be exactly the opposite, i.e. the gases with naphthene-base crudes are supposed to contain a lot of gasoline.

The sulfur in crudes, according to the biogeochemists, is con- sidered to be caused by reduction of sulfates and therefore this manifestation must be or may be characteristic for the hypergenic zone where the type of crude is supposedly defined. Yet it has al- ready been demonstrated that sulfur in crude oils is frequently not related with the type of crude: this manifestation may or may not occur with any crude, and therefore one might think that in some cases there have not been any bacteria or any sulfates at hand.

The examples cited above are sufficient to make it evident that the same fact may be given a completely different interpretation, and therefore only an experimental verification of the fundamental propositions can provide an escape from the blind alley. Unfortu- nately the adherents of microbiological and oxidative processes have had so far nothing to brag about in this respect.

One of the defects in many hypotheses about the origin of petro- leum is the illusory completeness of the picture. In such hypotheses everything appears to fit in the proper place and the unresolved questions, if any, seemingly pertain to details which do not require close attention. In addition, chemists as a rule pay little attention to geological problems, while the geologists reckon that if the chemists really try, they will develop reliable chemical grounds for eliminating various chemical discrepancies. Such a formal orderly state usually hides a number of important problems and frequently, instead of their solution, various more or less fantastic conjectures are presented which at times strike the imagination and make an undeservedly serious impression on the reader. Such are, for instance, the notions about the tremendous reserves of ready-made hydrocarbons in sedimentary rocks, the outstanding role of fatty acids or fats as the parent material for petroleum, the creative role of bacteria, etc. Perhaps here belong also the different suppositions about migration of dispersed crude oil into commercial reservoir rocks. It is hardly possible to cite any mechanical accumulation process which would not have been regarded, at some or other stage of the science, as a fundamental cause of the accumulation of oil.

Currently, the phenomenon of crude oil solubility in gas has attracted general attention. Of course one should not renounce a new method of perceiving nature, but considering the eagerness with which this new method of observation is being accepted into general usage to displace the former observation methods that quite recently were considered fully conclusive, this repudiation of previous concepts appears at times excessively hasty and does not signify that all is well as far as the problem of accumulation of dispersed crude oil is concerned, since it tends to remind one about the drowning man who will grasp at a straw. Some years ago Krejci-Graf made the interesting statement that we often tend to overlook an elephant but study a mosquito under the microscope. One-quarter of a century had elapsed before the realization came that petroleum bacteria are active in destroying the oil rather than creating it, though even at the present time there are a few geologists and chemists who have great expectations for the bacteria. Nobody has any doubt about the ability of bacteria to reduce sulfates, but the role of petroleum in this process remains undefined and, in any event, it has by no means been proved that the changes in crude oil proceed exactly as stated on paper. Yet specifically in this item are hidden a large number of details relating to chemistry, which are simply ignored.

It is possible also that the illusory completeness of the different hypotheses about the origin of oil merely tends to inhibit the development of scientific ideas relating to this problem, because it diverts attention in a different direction without stimulating exploratory thinking. When setting forth some or other hypotheses, it is desirable that the author at once points out the unfinished portions thereof and he should not be excessively self-confident so as not to overlook such defects. On the other hand, whatever is considered firmly established must be proved experimentally to account for all of the aspects of the phenomenon, otherwise a blunder might happen as it did some years ago to Engler who obtained in the distillation of blubber some hydrocarbonaceous liquid which he stated to be kerosene because it would burn in a lamp. Such experimental data must be required as a basis for establishing a specific hypothesis about the origin of oil.

BIBLIOGRAPHY

1. DOBRYANSKII, A. F. *Geochemistry of Petroleum*, 1948, p. 468.
2. VASSOEVICH, N. B. *Geolog. Sbornik*, **2**, 16 (1953).
3. DOBRYANSKII, A. F. *loc. cit.*, 193.
4. KAZANKII, B. A. and PLATE, A. F. *Trudy Vsesoyuzn.Soveshch. po Khimii Nefti. Baku*, **32**, (1953).
5. MANKASH, E. K., BORISOVA, G. P., OROCHKO, D. I. and FROST, A. V. *Neft. Khoz.* Nos. 6–7, 26 (1946).
6. FROST, A. V. *Zhur. prikl. Khimii*, Nos. 9–10 (1940); *Zh. Fiz. Khimii*, **14**, Nos. 9–10, (1940); *Dokl. Akad. Nauk SSSR*, **37**, 255 (1942); *Izv. Akad. Nauk SSSR, Otdel. Tekh. Nauk*, No. 10 (1942); *Uchenye Zapuski MGU*, No. 86, Kn. 1 (1964); *Vestnik MGU*, No. 5 (1947).
7. FROST, A. V. and MIKHNOVSKAYA, A. A. *Dokl. Akad. Nauk SSSR*, **37**, Nos. 7–8 (1942).
8. FROST, A. V. and NIKOLAEVA, A. F. *Zh. Obshch. Khimii*, Nos. 9–10 (1943).
9. MASLYANSKII, G. N. and VELTISTOVA, M. V. *Zh. Obshchei Khimii*, **16**, No. 12, 2132 (1946).
10. FROST, A. V. and PETROV, A. D. *Dokl. Akad. Nauk SSSR*, No. 6, 851 (1949).
11. TOPCHIEVA, K. V. and PANCHENKOV, G. M. *Dokl. Akad. Nauk SSSR*, **55**, No. 6, 509 (1947).
12. CHERNOZHUKOV, N. I. and KAZAKOVA, L. P. *Khimiya i Tekhnologiya Topliv i Masel*, No. 1 (1957).
13. VASSOEVICH, N. B. *loc. cit.*, *32*.
14. GURVICH, L. G. *Scientific Principles of Petroleum Processing*, 1940, p. 100.
15. DOBRYANSKII, A. F. *loc. cit.*, 230.
16. DOBRYANSKII, A. F. *loc. cit.*, 56.
17. DOBRYANSKII, A. F. *loc. cit.*, 52.
18. DOBRYANSKII, A. F. *loc. cit.*, 293.
19. DOBRYANSKII, A. F. *loc. cit.*, 303.
20. DOBRYANSKII, A. F. *loc. cit.*, 451.

INDEX

451

OTHER TITLES IN THE SERIES IN
EARTH SCIENCES

Printed in Great Britain